[signature] K. Hancock

Dept. Forest Science

Utah State Univ.

1971 — November

Forest
Recreation

Forest
Recreation

ROBERT W. DOUGLASS
ASSISTANT PROFESSOR OF FORESTRY
THE PENNSYLVANIA STATE UNIVERSITY

PERGAMON PRESS

OXFORD · LONDON · EDINBURGH · NEW YORK

TORONTO · SYDNEY · PARIS · BRAUNSCHWEIG

Pergamon Press Ltd., Headington Hill Hall, Oxford
4 & 5 Fitzroy Square, London W. 1
Pergamon Press (Scotland) Ltd., 2 & 3 Teviot Place, Edinburgh 1
Pergamon Press Inc., 44-01 21st Street, Long Island City, New York 11101
Pergamon of Canada Ltd., 207 Queen's Quay West, Toronto 1
Pergamon Press (Aust.) Pty. Ltd., 19a Boundary Street, Rushcutters Bay,
N.S.W. 2011, Australia
Pergamon Press S.A.R.L., 24 rue des Écoles, Paris 5ᵉ
Vieweg & Sohn GmbH, Burgplatz 1, Braunschweig

First edition 1969

Library of Congress Catalog Card No. 68-8530

08 012827 0

Contents

Contents

Contents

Contents

Preface

WITHIN the last few years, forest recreation has become an important part of forest management. Large increases in demands for forest-oriented recreation have made land managers sharply aware of their responsibilities to meet those demands. Forest recreation is a new and driving influence in the management of forest lands within the United States. It is beset by many uncertainties that need solution. Research has just begun to give land managers and technicians the answers that they need to cope with recreational needs of the American public. The specific research findings on how to plan, to develop, and to administer forest recreation areas are scattered throughout hundreds of pamphlets and newsletters. This book strives to consolidate the scattered findings of many researchers, the problems that confront forest recreation administrators, and the desires of the using public into one publication.

The research completed to date just scratches the surface of the problem that faces the land managers. Many recreation management decisions must be based on the seat-of-the-pants management or intuitive reasoning that comes with experience until more concepts of management can be developed by researchers.

This book has been written to provide the forest land manager with a broad background in the generalities of forest recreation needs and in forest recreation planning. Also, it provides the reader with specific recommendations on how to do the job at the technician level. Land managers, forest technicians, professional foresters, park technicians, and private landowners can use the information assembled here to aid in planning, developing, and administering forest recreation areas.

Acknowledgements

THE author greatly appreciates the support and the encouragement that he received from Henry H. Chisman and Peter W. Fletcher of The Pennsylvania State University. Elizabeth Thomas, librarian, deserves much of the credit for getting the author over the rough spots near the beginning of this project. Special mention should be made of the works done by Wayne Brigadier in drawing many of the illustrations contained within the text.

Part I

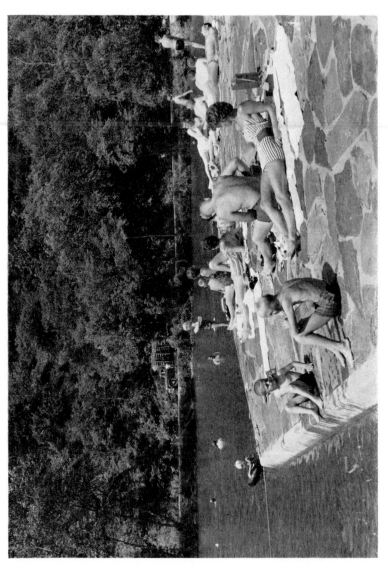

A favorite forest recreation area resulted from the site rehabilitation work completed at Blue Bend on the Monongahela National Forest in West Virginia. Here, recreation, watershed management, and timber production exist with each other without any great conflict.

CHAPTER 1

Introduction

FORESTS were once thought of as areas to be cleared or to be utilized and their products put to use for the good of the nation. The production of timber was the dominant reason for forest management except in local areas where mining or grazing was strong enough to infringe on this domain. During the early 1900's, timber began to give up its role as king of the forests to a newcomer called water. Water became important because local areas slowly ran out of it or suddenly had too much of it. Water was found to be the key to economies throughout the United States as it had been the foundation of civilizations throughout history. Forested areas were set aside to protect headwaters of major waterways. Large areas of denuded land were planted to stop the erosion of the land and the silting in of reservoirs and watercourses.

As the economy of the United States developed after World War II, the force of recreation was felt upon the forests. However, the pressures of forest recreation were slow to show themselves to land managers who misunderstood and mistrusted their impact. Forest recreation was discussed and given lipservice, but the problems it posed were never faced. In 1960, recreation finally became recognized for its real value at all levels. Recreation is no longer a poor sister to other forest products; but rather, it is recognized as being a major part of the forest resources. In some areas of heavy public use, recreation is the most valuable use of the forest. Certain influential foresters feel that the U.S. Forest Service should declare recreation as the most important resource of the national forests of the Northeastern United States. Federal and state agencies are falling over one another in their bids to meet the needs of the recreation demand that has been so well outlined by the Outdoor Recreation Resource Review Commission in 1962. Private capital is beginning to flow into developing all forms of recreation. The demand for forest recreation facilities is being made by the American population. In order to cope with this enlarging demand, technically trained people must be schooled to plan, to develop, and to administer recreation areas.

The public has turned to the forested areas of the United States to satisfy much of its recreation needs. The forests provide a natural and logical direction for the pressure to force itself. The forest areas are generally large enough to provide solitude of the varying degrees that different recreation interests desire. By definition, a forest is a collection of trees and associated vegetation that creates its own climate or environment. Space, solitude, inspiration, habitat for wildlife, and above all an opportunity for a person to practice a slight degree of self-reliance can be found in the forests for those who seek it. Some campers and hikers come to the forest because they prefer to pursue their recreation interests in the atmosphere created by the forest. Many come because of other reasons. Social status, group pressures, economics, and even the desire for companionship, may bring visitors to the forests. Whether the attraction is being John Muir or David Douglas, Daniel Boone or Nathaniel Bumpo for a short period of time, or whether it is just to escape to the cool, quiet climate of the mountain woodlands, people usually enjoy being out in the woods. Perhaps people are not even certain as to why they participate in forest-oriented outdoor recreation. Many people spend large sums of money in order to bring the conveniences of the modern home into the forest environment. Often, the woods support a secondary feature that is the attraction that the public seeks. Rivers, streams, and lakes provide millions with water-oriented activities. The cover and habitat provided for wildlife attracts additional people to the forests for hunting, nature study, and sightseeing. The forest provides the backdrop for these activities; but it does not make them exclusively forest recreation activities.

Outdoor recreation is becoming a major influence on our modern society. Areas that had not been able to develop a stable economy in recent decades suddenly have become centers for the new flood of outdoor recreationists. The sudden and overwhelming demand for outdoor recreation has caused many realignments in policies concerning land management.

Professional forest land managers always have considered recreation in their management planning. However, in the past, forests primarily have served the more pressing demands of timber, grazing, and water. Now that the recreation needs of the public must be satisfied, qualified personnel must be trained in the field of outdoor recreation. Professional foresters, forest technicians, conservationists, landscape architects, and others that are involved in forest land management require training that will enable them to cope with the various facets of the recreation demand.

Part I of this book treats outdoor, and more specifically, forest recreation from the planning standpoint. It presents a general background of the problems connected with forest recreation and the "whys" of the solutions. Outdoor recreation's history, its impact, and its future are important in planning and developing forest recreation.

CHAPTER 2

Outdoor Recreation

INTRODUCTION AND HISTORY

Outdoor recreation has a complexity of meanings and includes a variety of disciplines such as landscape architecture, forestry, physical education, conservation, and civil engineering. The problems concerning definitions and responsibilities are those problems associated with a new and dynamic discipline.[16] Outdoor recreation, as treated by this textbook, is that wholesome recreation that is done without the confines of a building. It covers a broad field of topics from a backyard barbecue to a Boy Scout Jamboree. It can mean recess on the paved playground of a downtown grade school or a two-week pack trip into the Bob Marshall Wilderness area in Montana. But whatever its form, it is part of an entity known as *recreation* and this word must be explained before such terms as outdoor recreation, forest recreation, and water-oriented recreation can be understood.

Any action that refreshes the mental attitude of an individual is recreation. Recreation is a wholesome activity that is engaged in for pleasure, therefore it is play. The man who works long hard days in a foundry or a coal mine may consider the working of crossword puzzles or the reading of short magazine articles the answer to his daily recreational needs. Mental activity in the evening balances, to an extent, the physical work load of the day. Since this worker pursues these activities for pleasure, he considers them a form of play and thereby recreation. The housewife who spends her long day taking care of domestic chores, administering to the needs of three youngsters from sunrise to after bed time does not want to play

6

horseshoes in her own backyard, she wants a change of environment. What she actually does is not necessarily important so long as it is different from her daily pattern and away from the everpresent surroundings of the home. A quick trip to the nearby lake might be a hectic evening's experience; but it makes the trip back into the house a pleasure.

Recreation may take various routes; however, the results are the same. Recreation revitalizes the spirit. It restores a person's vitality, initiative, and perspective of life; thereby preparing the individual to return to his toil.

Today, people not only hope for recreation, they demand it as part of their life. The interest in various types of recreation has varied as the population's way of living has varied. Conditions affecting leisure time and its use have changed quickly during the last 50 years. In 1910, the United States operated on a rural economy that had 90 percent of its population living in rural areas.[5] Transportation was slow and limited. The population had not achieved the mobility nor the freedom from sustenance requirements that would give the time and the means for recreation.

Most recreation researchers today speak of the surging recreation demands that have become a major factor in our present-day economy. Government publications tend to treat all recreation in their present-day terms and thereby ignore the recreation activities of fifty years ago. True, the conditions affecting leisure time and its use have changed; however, at that time, the people were active in outdoor recreation. It was during this period that the large railroad excursion picnics took place. People would use their limited leisure time to its best advantage by attending parks developed along railroad lines by private companies or by the railroads to promote business. They would use the community commons for picnics, for parties, or just for walking.

Rural living then, as today, provided a closer contact with the natural environment. The people were not beset by the problems of social frictions that develop as people become crowded together. Outdoor living and contact with nature was part of everyday living. With this relatively immobile and largely rural population busy fulfilling its existence and subsistence requirements, the United States Government had no policy on recreation. In the isolated areas where urbanization had taken place, a local need for recreation was recognized. New York's Central Park was designed in 1850 and Philadelphia, Chicago, and Boston established municipal parks within the next fifty years. These city parks were local attempts to provide open areas for outdoor recreation within the city. No popular pressure existed for parks or other forms of recreation areas at the national level. Even the establishment of the Yellowstone area as a 3000 square mile federal park by President Grant was brought about by the efforts of individuals who did not represent the thinking of the majority of Americans. Men such as John Muir, David Douglas, and Gifford Pinchot could see the value in holding in public trust areas of special beauty for future enjoyment.

Because Judge Cornelius Hedges held out for the public ownership of Yellowstone at the time the land was practically valueless and lost in the distance from civilization, he was able to win his fight in 1872.[19] His victory and that of John Muir for a National Park at Yosemite were the results of individual fights and conservation-minded presidents. They were harbingers of future demands; but not a reflection of national policy.

Although government actions concerning recreation were scattered and dealt with specific situations, they became more common and more inclusive as time passed. The Antiquities Act of 1906 provided the authority for the federal government to establish historic, scientific, or cultural sites as national monuments. A need for a general policy was recognized in 1916 by the establishment of the National Park Service within the United States Department of the Interior. Today, the National Park Service is one of five bureaus within the Department of the Interior that is concerned with outdoor recreation. The departments of the Interior, Agriculture, and Defense are all in today's outdoor recreation business. More than thirty federal agencies have recreation programs. [4] The Bureau of Outdoor Recreation has been created within the United States Department of the Interior to correlate the recreation efforts of all the other interested bureaus.

With the exception of New York and California, the state governments did not enter the outdoor recreation field until they received a big federal push in the 1930's. Many state parks in the eastern states are on lands that were turned over to state governments at the end of the Federal Submarginal Land Program. [9] Many of the structures and established conservation measures that serve as the foundations for many of today's parks were built by the Civilian Conservation Corps in the 1930's.

The industrialization of our agrarian society placed people out of touch with outdoor living. Hunting, fishing, or even picnicking were not convenient activities. At the turn of the century, a work week was 60 hours long and the people were being swept up by the new rush towards urbanization. Pay scales varied with forms of work and manual labor was looked upon as activity for the lower class. Therefore, manual activity gradually fell into disrepute. As a result of its unfavorable view of manual activity, the United States public placed little emphasis on physical fitness. Poor physical fitness became the vogue. This misguided attitude goes beyond driving cars or using labor-saving devices. Presently, three out of seven American youths who are at the peak of their physical career flunk the Army physical examination. But one does not need to turn to the U.S. Army for examples. Any man over twenty-five caught playing touch football is viewed with distrust in many neighborhoods. The problem reached such proportions that President Kennedy thought it necessary to establish a committee on physical fitness. This Council on Youth Fitness received wide publicity and made thousands of Americans conscious of their physical conditioning. As people turn to outdoor recreation in greater numbers, they are finding the opportunity to enjoy exercise as part of their recreation. In some cases, good conditioning is a prerequisite for outdoor recreation. Many skiers are injured each year because of the lack of the simple physical toughness that is required in preparation for taking to the slopes.

Outdoor recreation has become a major factor in modern living. Federal, state, and local governments are forming policies to guide outdoor recreation development. Private interests are aiding in the rush to recreation by providing facilities for public use and by entering the recreation field with manufactured products for the recreationist.

The Eighty-fifth Congress of the United States passed a law establishing a bipartisan Outdoor Recreation Resources Review Commission. This committee was charged with studying the present and future needs for outdoor recreation and with determining the available and future supply of outdoor recreation resources. In 1962, this commission made its report to the President and the Congress. The Outdoor Recreation Resources Review Commission Report covers twenty-seven volumes of study reports on outdoor recreation. The findings are summarized in *Outdoor Recreation for America* which is available from the Superintendent of Documents in Washington, D.C.[9] This ORRRC report has stimulated much activity in the field of outdoor recreation at all levels of government and in private industry. The findings of this report are questioned by some researchers on the basis of the sampling techniques that were used; however, the federal government employees using the information included in the ORRRC report claim that it is holding up under use. Regardless of the accuracy of the data contained in it, the report has done more for outdoor recreation in the United States than any other piece of research in that field.

Over 70 percent of our population now lives in approximately 200 cities.[5] Every state except Vermont and Wyoming now has at least one major metropolitan area. The federal interstate highway system has made us the most mobile population in history. Travel from the cities to outdoor recreation sites is no longer the limiting factor that it was twenty years ago because people can get into the family car and travel hundreds of miles for a short vacation. More than 25 percent of vacation trips are longer than 1000 miles. [9]

As more and more research produces more involved and longer publications concerning the recreational use of leisure time, the difference between outdoor recreation and forest recreation becomes more indistinguishable. Forest recreation is any form of outdoor recreation that takes place in forested areas whether or not the forest provides the primary purpose for the activity. This is an oversimplified definition because of many confounding issues, but it is generally true. Sightseeing can be outdoor recreation on Fisherman's Wharf in San Francisco but it becomes forest recreation when done at Franconia Notch in the White Mountains of New Hampshire.

Whether the activity requires the direct use of the forest for consumption or indirectly as a background setting, that activity is included as forest recreation. If managing and altering of the forests would have an impact on the activity, it should be considered as forest recreation management.

BASIC FACTORS INFLUENCING OUTDOOR RECREATION

Americans prefer the simple, more convenient, and less expensive forms of outdoor recreation that do not require great expenditures of money or time. Driving for pleasure, walking, and sightseeing are the most popular forms of outdoor recreation. [9] Many factors influence the participation in outdoor recreation and by their very nature tend to confound one another. People, money, time, communications, and supply are five basic factors contributing to the recreation demand. Each of these five basic factors have subdivisions that have a great influence on participation.

The nature of the three most popular forms of outdoor recreation gives some hints as to the nature of the factors involved. Obviously, money and time are factors since the most popular activities are also the least expensive and the most convenient forms of outdoor recreation. The supply of available facilities is also important in that people tend to use the facilities

11

available to them. Sightseeing is something that can be enjoyed by all age groups; but it is generally associated with people living in cities and away from forest or rural scenery. The influence of people, money, time, and communications on recreation is discussed in this chapter. Supply covers such extensive material that it is discussed singly in Chapter 3.

TABLE 2.1
BASIC FACTORS INFLUENCING OUTDOOR RECREATION

People	Population size
	Living areas—urban, suburban, exurban, regional
	Age
	Education
Money	Disposable income
	Affluence
Time	Occupation
	Mobility
Communication	Mass media—social status, advertising, enlightenment
	Personal—convenience
Supply	Availability
	Accessibility

People

POPULATION SIZE. People are the fundamental factor influencing recreation use. Since all recreation usage and values are based upon use by people, the number of people in existence or population becomes important. If the population increases while all other factors remain static, it will cause an increase in recreation area usage. Any changes in the other factors influencing participation in outdoor recreation that are coupled with a population change will be accelerated and multiplied by the population change. The 15 percent population change from 1951 to 1959 would have given a corresponding increase to recreation if everything else had remained the same.[9] However, a 15 percent increase in disposable income *per capita* occurred during the same period. This means that a

12

15 percent larger population had a corresponding increase in disposable income because of the larger population. In addition, the *per capita* disposable income has increased by 15 percent so that the total effect when compounded is a 32.2 percent increase over the total disposable income available in 1951. This shows that the increase is not a simple addition of percentage changes; but rather the changes multiply one another. The increase in family funds will change the standards of living and thereby change the participation pattern which will act along with many other factors to confound attempts to make accurate predictions about outdoor recreation. The assumption has been made that the future world political situation will continue along the same line that it has been following. Any great upheaval in politics or the economy would alter the outdoor recreation demand that is discussed here.

The population growth of the United States has brought a change in our entire social and economic structure. The population of the United States increased from 76 million in 1900 to 180 million in 1962.[5] By the year 2000, we can expect a net increase of approximately 200 million people.[15,12] A predicted population of over 380 million people by 2000 A.D. will be seeking ways of spending its leisure time and money. The demand for outdoor recreation will be many times greater than existing facilities can handle by the year 2000.

It is apparent to today's user that the intensive-use outdoor recreation facilities are inadequate for the existing demand. Beaches are jammed or closed to the general public. Campers are advised to be on hand at dawn to get a spot in the developed campgrounds. Picnickers waiting in line for tables create scenes reminiscent of postwar restaurant lobbies.

Although the demand for forest recreation opportunities will increase with the rising population, this demand may not parallel the exact population rise. As crowding occurs, satisfaction might drop off for some users. When the satisfaction level drops to a certain point, people will begin to turn to other activities which offer better returns for their investments of time, money, and energy. Recreation researchers refer to this switch in activities as "substitution". At what level of satisfaction does substitution occur for each activity? What are the primary influences that cause substitution? Problems related to substitution are discussed in Chapter 15. The answers to these questions will help the land managers plan to provide the increasing population with the best possible recreation opportunities.

LIVING AREA. As the population grew, it caused a concentration of industrial, political, and commercial activities to take place around the cities. This concentration of activities and services caused the flow into the cities to increase. Economic opportunities were better in the city where the better jobs were to be found. Also, the technological advances in agriculture had reduced the demand for farm labor. By 1962, nearly three-quarters of our population lived in metropolitan areas where the people are subjected to social friction and denied daily contact with the relaxing powers of outdoor recreation. Many individual irritations and even mass riots are rooted in problems caused by congestion or the rapid pace and grating existence of big city living. Although the lack of both indoor and outdoor recreation can not be considered as the sole cause for the riots that have swept the large cities in recent summers, it is being investigated as a major contributor to the upheavals. The federal government is interested in a proposal to study the affect of recreational opportunities on the community behavior in the Watts Community of Los Angeles, California.

The cities themselves have changed character since the early 1900's. Before individual automobiles were available, the cities were compacted into a high density of inhabitants per square mile. The lack of mobility and communications forced the compact situation even though the railroad provided access to corridors reaching out from the city.[5] Because travel to the core of the city or to the railroad was limited by the capabilities of horse-drawn means, there was a distinct edge to the city. The transition from urban to rural was abrupt and the people lived either in the city or in the rural areas.

14

The suburbs did not exist beyond what was referred to as the "outskirts of town".

With the introduction of the automobile and its attendant highway system, a backwash of people occurred in the flood toward urbanization. The 1950's brought on the great expansion of the densely settled cities into the great suburban development. Suburbia, U.S.A., reached its romantic peak by 1960. The dispersal of people and their increased mobility around the metropolitan areas has encouraged industry to follow the pattern. The horizontal growth of the growing cities is no longer considered in terms of suburban developments; rather, it has become urban sprawl. This urban sprawl consumes thousands of acres per year and shows signs of conttinuing to spread. Aside from the area it occupies, urban sprawl removes much more land from use for certain outdoor recreational uses. Hunting, shooting, field trials and other extensive outdoor recreation activities are especially vulnerable to the pressure of urban sprawl. As people who are unfamiliar with the sporting use of firearms move into a previously rural area, they intrude upon lands where the use of firearms has been a historic fact. Concern for home and family prompt the homeowners of urban sprawl to press for elimination of the danger. The noise of the hunter's firearms indicates a danger to the housewife. Even if the danger is imagined, the annoyance is still real. Unfortunately there are enough thoughtless hunters and shooters to justify regulation of the use of firearms in heavily populated areas.

Living patterns of people affect the choice of recreational pursuits. Sightseeing and swimming are the common activities of the city dweller. The suburbanite is much more active in outdoor recreation in that he is involved in more forms of outdoor recreation. He participates mostly in sightseeing, camping, hiking, and swimming. We must realize that the adage "access promotes usage" generally holds true in this field. However, it is the urban area dweller who is causing much of the increase in outdoor recreation demand. He wants to get away from the confines and the irritations of the city for a short period. He wants to participate in some outdoor recreation such as skiing, hunting, fishing, or just relaxing in the forest environment. Many city dwellers are elated at witnessing or participating in what their rural cousins consider daily routine. The success of recreation farms in the Mid-Atlantic states area indicates that urban dwellers are quite willing to pay for the privilege of participating in farm activities for a vacation. Since the land manager has spent much of his professional life in a rural or forested area, he may have difficulty in understanding the high, but intangible, value that the urbanite places on a sightseeing visit to the forest. The farmer participates in outdoor recreation much less than men engaged in city-oriented activity. The major exception here is in hunting where access again promotes use.

Regional differences are evident in the preference of people toward forms of outdoor recreation. The differing land forms, climate, water availability, and social status symbols that occur throughout the country have a bearing on the people's choice of activity. Table 2.2 shows how the preferences for outdoor recreation vary from one geographic region to another.

TABLE 2.2
REGIONAL PREFERENCES FOR OUTDOOR RECREATION
ACTIVITIES AS SHOWN IN THE ORRRC REPORT OF 1962[a]

Region	Activities preferred		
Northeast	winter sports	swimming	hiking
North Central	boating	fishing	hunting
South		fishing	hunting
West	outdoor living in general		

[a] ORRRC, *Outdoor Recreation for America.*

AGE. Age makes a difference in the form of recreation in which an individual will participate. It is to be expected that younger people will participate more in the strenuous sports such as horseback riding and skiing. The only activity that shows an exception to less participation as age increases is walking.[9] Walking for recreation increases in popularity with increasing age. Walking is a very flexible term to express participation in outdoor recreation. Because it is very inclusive in its meaning, walking for pleasure is recorded under most circumstances by nearly everyone. Walking is convenient, healthful, relaxing, and enjoyable. Time available seldom precludes going for a walk; it just controls the length of participation. Walking for pleasure can be done anyplace where walking is possible. Beaches, boardwalks, city streets, open fields, and forest trails all provide the settings for pleasure walks. Since walking can be done on a short-time basis of a stroll around the block or a circuit through the local park, it is the ideal outdoor activity for people with small pieces of leisure time. Also the physical act of walking is not too strenuous for many older persons who have been forced to limit participation in more active fields. Therefore, it provides the older person with the opportunity for some outdoor recreation activity.

Camping, sightseeing, and picnicking are three major forest recreation activities. They maintain their popularity among adults as age increases. Because of their popularity among people of parental age, these three activities, along with hiking and swimming, are the core attractions in the forest recreation demand. Although outdoor recreation can be treated by gathering information on individuals, it is most often a result of group or family participation. Family units or organizations are responsible for most of recreational camping and picnicking done in the U.S. Participation in one activity often leads to participation in others. Swimming areas attract family picnickers who may also be classed as sightseers. Many private campground owners have learned that water for swimming or boating is necessary for a successful campground.

EDUCATION. Generally, those persons who have the higher salaries also tend to have the greatest education. Their influence on the demand for outdoor recreation, however, seems based on their affluence, not on their intellectual background.

17

Therefore, this is discussed under the basic influence title of *Money*.

Money

Many people dream of horseback trips into wilderness areas of the Rockies, of skiing down the slopes of the White Mountains, or of sightseeing through the Yosemite and Crater Lake National Parks. Millions do these things every year and many millions more just dream about them. For most people, a trip to a nearby state park or lake is possible on a weekend; but any long trip or specialized recreation is limited because of its cost. Activities such as boating or skiing require high initial investments. Continued participation in these activities requires funds that are not needed for more essential uses. Even the uncomplicated sightseeing trip requires the costs of transportation, meals, and sometimes lodging. This cost can be prohibitive to a large family that is working on a tight budget.

Available money is a factor that restricts or encourages outdoor recreation. With changing social values and rising affluence diverting more money into outdoor recreation, many families of modest means are beginning to participate in the more costly forms of recreation. The general pressure on forest recreation resources comes in two forms. The people who flee the concrete and asphalt labyrinths of their work-a-day world for an afternoon in the forest are generally associated with certain types of activities. Sightseeing, picnicking, and swimming fit the needs and finances of this group. Funds available often determine that a family will go for a picnic at the nearby lake rather than go water skiing at the seashore. The second form of pressure on the recreation facilities comes from the group that has vacation time and is doing some family camping. The camping itself is an enjoyable activity; but is also a means of allowing many families to be mobilized sightseers. Foresters and wilderness enthusiasts should not be too critical of the windshield hiker.

In spite of what many article writers and hiking enthusiasts might claim, leisure camping and back country trips are expensive. Perhaps the costs are not evident at first; but they are there. Time itself is equal to money. Time away from the job or time when house and car payments are running due while camping and travel fees are mounting make the average wage owner head for home. Many families with young children have realized the pleasures of family camping and hiking. The majority of young families must be able to drive to an attraction if they are to visit it at all.

Most people can drive to a National Park to enjoy the scenic attractions available; but only a relatively few people can take long periods of time from work, hire a guide and pack animals, and arrange a wilderness trip into the back country. Although wilderness and back country areas fill an important position in the supply of recreation facilities, they may be more important for their historical or ecological value than for their recreational values so far as the majority of Americans are concerned today. Research has shown that most wilderness or back country users earn more than $10,000 per year. In one study, 63 percent of the visitors to the Glacier National Park back country were in this upper bracket.[8]

As our population has gained in affluence, it has put more of its wealth into recreation. The Outdoor Recreation Resources Review Commission Report supports the theory that available money is a basic factor in outdoor recreation participation. The people who hold the higher salaried jobs form the groups that participate the most. The increasing family income is providing the incentive for many families to become involved in outdoor recreation. In 1959, 14 percent of American families had an income that was greater than $10,000. Persons in this group averaged near 50 days participation whereas families with an annual income of $3000 to $6000 averaged below 34 days per person each year. Participation in outdoor recreation is directly proportional to income.[9] As the family income increases, its participation increases accordingly. By 1976, 40 percent of the families will be earning more than 10,000 constant 1959 dollars per year. This figure shows a relative increase of more than 300 percent over 1959.

19

This great increase in the affluence of the population portends a huge increase in participation and might indicate a greater use in the more costly forms of recreation.

TABLE 2.3

PREDICTED RELATIVE AFFLUENCY OF AMERICAN FAMILIES[a]

(based on constant 1959 dollars)

Year	Families with annual income greater than $10,000
1959	14%
1976	40%
2000	60%

[a] ORRRC Report 1962.

At the present, most forest recreation planning is based upon the assumption that the least expensive activities will remain the most popular. Camping is expected to retain its popularity since many families use camping as a means to an end. Camping becomes a way of minimizing the costs of food and lodging while travelling. Picnicking requires only planning and transportation in addition to regular food expenses. The combined costs usually are lower than a meal at a mediocre restaurant.

Presently, personal income strongly controls participation in outdoor recreation and influences the form and the intensity that the participation will take. With the changes in values that are taking place in our society, it is possible that participation and income may not remain so well correlated.

Time

Time is listed as a basic factor influencing participation in outdoor recreation. Available time or the lack of it has an obvious effect on what people will do. Time as it is considered here has two facets of which the first is available or leisure time. The second facet of time is mobility which is a person's relative ability to move easily from one point to another. Some of the travel can be considered as driving for pleasure or sight-

Fɪɢ. 2.1. Some of the most popular forms of outdoor recreation are sightseeing, swimming, and walking. Here a group of sightseers have hiked to the top of Seneca Rocks near the Monongehela National Forest, West Virginia. (USFS photo.)

seeing. However, up to a certain point, travel consumes leisure time.

Leisure time is the period in which a person is free to choose his own activity. Leisure time can be thought of as one of three blocks of time available to an individual. [3] Marion Clawson describes these three blocks as existence time, subsistence time, and leisure time. Any person must devote a certain amount of the day's time to existing. He must sleep, eat, and perform personal maintenance operations. After the basic existence requirements are met, the individual must take some time for meeting his subsistence needs. He must obtain food, clothing, housing, and transportation. Any time remaining after the existence and subsistence requirements have been fulfilled belongs to the individual as his leisure time.

It is the occurrence of this leisure time that has much to do with the types of recreation that people engage in. The increase of leisure time and the increasing means to do something with it are causing tremendous upsurges in recreation activity. Leisure time is available in daily, weekend, vacation, and retirement forms. It is how these pieces or forms of leisure time occur that influences the way they are used. Small pieces of leisure time occur throughout the day or evening between or following the existence and subsistence needs of hygiene, working, household chores, and other daily regimen. These doses of daily leisure are often too short for engagement in forest recreation. These are the times spent at backyard barbecues, reading, or watching television. Physical relaxation is usually the rule when using daily leisure because this time is insufficient to prepare for, equip, and make an outing further than to the local bowling alley or movie theater.

Weekends provide a longer block of leisure time that has always been appreciated by school children. Weekends provide sufficient time to escape from the frictions of city dwelling for a short outing or for an overnight campground visit. Shortening work weeks will continue to enlarge the blocks of time available for recreation in each day and at weekends.

Vacation and retirment time provide the recreationist with leisure time that he requires to participate in outdoor recreation in depth. Vacations permit travel to distant points of interest. People with vacation or retirement time become users of recreational resources for the enjoyment of the activity. Vacationers camp and make investments in camping equipment because they enjoy camping as an end in itself or a means to obtaining an end such as travel. This is quite different from the sightseer who is temporarily fleeing the steel and concrete cliffs for a quick, refreshing glimpse of the out-of-doors. Vacation leisure doubled in the fifty years from 1900 to 1950 and doubled again in the ten years from 1950 to 1960.[3] Predictions made in 1963 called for a fivefold increase during the last half of the twentieth century. These predictions already appear to be too conservative in the light of changing philosophies of government and business toward national prosperity.

Union–management labor negotiations have begun to show an attempt to spread prosperity to all members of society by including longer vacations and a form of sabatical leave in contracts. Coupled with the efforts of state and federal governments to keep the economy on the upswing, this increase in leisure time appears to be headed toward a great upswing within the next decade and it will be reflected in the increasing participation in outdoor recreation.

OCCUPATION. With the advance in technology, there has been an increase in professional and skilled workers. These are the people that show interest and have the time and the financial means to participate in outdoor recreation. As their numbers multiply, so does the recreational demand. The length of the average work week has gradually decreased to less than 39 hours. By 1976, it will be approximately 36 hours. Unless a four-day work week is adopted, any reduction in working hours will be dissipated into daily uses. It is the increasing length of paid vacations and annual salaries for skilled workers that has provided a major boost in the amount of time spent in outdoor recreation. Today, more than half of the working population of the United States receives a paid vacation of three or more weeks. The extended vacation plan that was negotiated in 1963 between the United Steel Workers and the basic steel industry provides for thirteen-week vacations for 10 percent of the senior half of the workers each year.[2] This policy of prolonged vacations and the advent of semi-retirements have enabled thousands of families to engage in recreation activities. In 1964, the first year of the contract, over 30,000 senior steel workers took advantage of the thirteen-week vacations. No doubt this number is going to increase as time passes. In addition, federal efforts to stop the imbalance of payments with other nations have stepped up a "See-America-First" program that has encouraged people with large blocks of leisure time to travel throughout the United States rather than overseas. Generally, this "See-America-First" approach encourages forest recreation and the use of native recreation pursuits.

MOBILITY. Time is used in travel to and home from outdoor or forest recreation activities. This travel time becomes more critical as the distance increases or the mode of travel becomes more primitive.The railroad excursions of the early nineteen-hundreds were all-day affairs that had to be planned well in advance and according to the railroad's schedule. A trip to the seashore by a Philadelphia resident took approximately 2 hours in 1950 if the traffic was not heavy. A total four-hour traveling time for the 140 mile round trip meant a long, hot effort to live for five or six hours on the beach. However, the individual's automobile presented him with the choice of going or not going. It allowed him to set his own travel schedule to meet his particular needs or desires. The family car has provided mobility. Commercial transportation, on the other hand, has improved in some fields and deteriorated in others. The most notable improvement in commercial travel has been the universal use of the jet airliner. Now, it is possible to fly from coast to coast in less than four and a half hours.

The jetliner has increased mobility to the point where distance is now measured in time not in miles. This concept of distance equaling time more adequately fits into the overall recreation picture than does the mileage concept. Interstate highway systems are nearing completion throughout the country. Uninterrupted controlled access driving is available for thousands of miles on this system. Pennsylvanians can camp in the Thousand Island camping areas in Canada and New York by following the Interstate Route 81 for approximately 7 hours. The tedious and always dangerous trip across the Sierras on U.S. Route 40 has been made into a rapid and comfortable tour by the construction of a 4 lane interstate highway through the beautiful Donner pass. The smooth trip across this once forbidding wall of mountains is a far cry from the grisly adventure that faced the hapless Donner Party in 1847.

This relatively new mobility on a national scale brings the population into contact with the recreation attractions that exist in all parts of the country. It causes the public to demand even more recreation opportunities.

Automobile sales have been averaging approximately 8 million new cars per year. From 1950 to 1959, the passenger miles traveled in private cars in the United States increased 49 percent and air travel tripled.[18] This increase in travel parallels the increase in recreational visits during the same period. By 1976, Americans will own 100 million cars and will be traveling a completed interstate system that will provide uninterrupted travel from coast to coast and into any part of the country.[6]

Because sightseeing is the most prevalent outdoor recreation pursuit, scenic drives have been recommended for construction by the federal government.[13] This is a logical move for the government to take because such a costly undertaking is beyond the means of any other organization. The development of a system of scenic highways comparable to the Skyline Drive of Virginia will be undertaken to satisfy the sightseer. This scenic highway building venture will increase forest recreation activities such as hiking, camping, picnicking, as well as providing general enjoyment of the forest vistas.

24

Communication

Why do people want to participate in outdoor recreation? Relaxation, self-gratification, escape, and travel have already been mentioned as motives. Certainly enjoyment is the immediate goal of recreation. But beyond the motivating forces lies the fact that people must know outdoor recreation exists, that it is available to them, and that they could and would enjoy it. Communication provides the media to transmit these messages to the public. Mass and personal communication have continued to make technologic advancements to the point that now live television broadcasts can be transmitted around the world by an orbiting satellite system, overnight mail delivery is available in most metropolitan districts, and inexpensive long distance telephone calls can be made by direct dialing. This case of long distance and mass communication creates an illusion of smallness for all of the United States.

Through communication people learn about outdoor recreation. They can compare themselves with others engaged in outdoor or more specifically forest recreation. Although the comparison might be real or illustrative, it makes the people understand that they might also enjoy it. Mass communication media such as newspapers and television do more than expose the public to recreation ideas. They create an obligation to travel, picnic, camp, and to partake in other outdoor activities for social status as well as for personal gratification. Advertisements for products that are completely unrelated to forest recreation use mountain scenery or a forest recreation activity for a backdrop. This motivation technique ties the product to the status or the enjoyment associated with wilderness trail riding, mountain stream fishing, or some other forest recreation activity. Besides the desired effect that it has concerning the product, the advertisement exposes the readers to the supposed or real pleasures of the forest and its environment.

Manufacturers of equipment associated with forest recreation are producing better and more elaborate gear to meet any demand. Besides making forest recreation easier for the devotee, new and better equipment stirs interests in non-participants. The advertising that is needed to present the equipment to the public eye also encourages the increase in the demand for the equipment and thereby an increase in forest recreation participation.

ECONOMIC ASPECTS

Outdoor recreation is big business. It is no longer an adjunct to our economy. It has become a major influence in that it generated approximately 3.3 percent of the Gross National Product in 1964. Visits to recreational facilities have tripled in the last twenty years and will probably increase tenfold between 1960 and 2000. Approximately 20 billion dollars worth of business is generated each year by outdoor recreation in this country.[15] As outdoor recreation continues to grow, its contribution to the Gross National Product will become more and more significant. Some areas now hold recreation as one of the dominant factors influencing prosperity.

All levels of government have become involved in recreation through efforts to satisfy the voting public. Millions are being alloted to recreation each year. The Land and Water Conservation Fund Act alone contributes approximately 180 million dollars of federal funds per year to recreation. A dozen or more states have instigated their own multimillion dollar recreation programs.

A National Recreation Advisory Council was established by President John F. Kennedy to study the needs of the country for recreation and to make recommendations to the President. The make-up of this Council was a striking demonstration of the impact that recreation has had on our society and its economy. Its members were the Secretaries of the Interior, Agriculture, Defense, Commerce, and the Secretary of Health, Education, and Welfare along with the Administrator of Housing and Home Finance. Policy guidelines that have been laid down by this group give recreation a leading place in our economy. They have stated that, "Recreation is to be recognized on an equal basis with other beneficial water uses in management policies and programs." [14] This one statement opens the way for tremendous expansion of water-oriented recreation in the Tennessee Valley Authority and the Corps of Engineer impoundments where summer draw-down for low stream augmentation seriously hampers lake shore development. This statement places recreation in competition with industrial and municipal users of water. It means that pollution control is being justified as part of a national recreation policy as well as part of conservation and health programs. President Lyndon B. Johnson replaced the National Recreation Advisory Council with the Council on Recreation and Natural Beauty. This was done by Executive Order 11278 of May 4, 1966.

The government interest in water-oriented recreation is, in part, a reflection of the fact that freshwater boating is the largest generator of recreation dollars. More than eight million families own boats. [11] Boating requires large initial investments and substantial sums for upkeep of the equipment. More than two billion dollars is spent on retail purchases of boats each year. [9] Supporting facilities such as docks, marinas, and restaurants are needed to meet the demand brought on by the increase in recreational boating.

Skiing is another sport that contributes to areas where outdoor recreation is an important business. Each skier spends an average of $23.30 each day in southern Vermont on lifts, lodging, food, and transportation. [1] The total effect of this one facet of forest recreation becomes apparent when the number of ski-visits is known. Throughout the country, U. S. Forest Service consessions had more than four million ski-visits in 1960. [10] Skiing enthusiasts increased in number by 75 percent from 1953 to 1956. This compares with a 100 percent increase in the number of campers and picnickers during the same period.

COMPATIBILITY WITH OTHER USES

Conservationists often align themselves with the recreation movement as called for in their version of multiple use of the forests. That concept of multiple use excludes timber values and calls for the forests to be used for hiking, sightseeing, camping, and other single purpose uses. The overall forested areas produce too many products to be limited entirely to one of them such as recreation. Most informed people recognize the continuing need for forest products; therefore, they seek some sort of harmony among all of the uses.

Of course, specific single purpose sites are needed for recreation, timber, water, and wildlife management. These are intensive use areas of small size and do not encompass an entire forest. However, wilderness areas and other large areas of unusual natural beauty have been established to preserve these areas in their natural state for the enjoyment of the public. The placement of large acreages into single purpose management for recreation and scientific purposes is the cause of much friction among special interest groups concerned with forested land.

The removal of large tracts of forest lands from timber production is brought about by the formation of wilderness areas and national parks. The timber industry views this removal of land from production as a threat to its well being. The timber industry argues that land presently producing tax-money will be removed from the tax-rolls when it becomes federal land. Timber land presently in federal ownership will no longer return a certain percent of stumpage returns to the local counties, as is the case when timber is being sold from federal lands. With the removal of timberland from the market, job opportunities will be adversely affected. In general, the timber industry believes that the depressing effect of a large wilderness area or national park in certain areas will not be offset by the economic benefits derived from recreation. The contention here is that wilderness areas or large parks are usually established in locales where a large part of the economy is based on timber and not near the large centers of population where the expected users live.

The advocates of large single purpose areas devoted entirely to recreation contend that such areas are needed in order to preserve some vestige of the nation's heritage. Since these areas benefit the entire nation, they should not be justified on the basis of local economics. Also, the advocates of large parks do not agree with the timber industry's contention that the large-scale withdrawal of land from the production of timber will have a depressing affect on the local economy. Their belief is that the income generated from park maintenance, park administration, and tourism will more than offset the depressing affect on the timber based economy caused by curtailing timber operations.

One of the best examples of achieving this harmony is taking place in the Passadumkeeg Mountain Region of Eastern Maine where a study has been made of the inter-relationships between timber production and recreation.[8] This study shows that a reduction in the timber harvest of only 1.7 percent would provide for the extensive recreation plans.

The advent of forest recreation does not mean that an area must give up its timber-based economy; but rather, that it can supplement that economy with the recreation industry.

REFERENCES

1. ANON. 1965. Brevity is the Word for Skiers. *New York Times,* January 17, 1965, p. XX31.
2. ANON. 1965. Steel Firm Disenchanted on Vacation. *Chambersburg Public Opinion,* March 10, 1965, p. 25. Chambersburg, Pennsylvania.
3. CLAWSON, MARION. 1964. *Leisure in America: Blessing or a Curse?* Monograph 4. American Academy of Political and Social Science, Philadelphia, Pennsylvania.
4. CRAFTS, EDWARD C. 1964. Launched: The Bureau of Outdoor Recreation. *Outdoor Recreation: Its Impact Today,* pp. 12–14. Soil Conservation Society of America, Ankeny, Iowa.
5. ERICKSON, RICHARD B. 1964. Urbanization and the Shooter. *The American Rifleman,* vol. 112, No. 12, p. 26. National Rifle Association.
6. GOULD, E.M. 1964. Forest Managers and Recreation Research. *Proceedings of the Society of American Foresters, Allegheny,* February 13–15, pp. 54–62.
7. KIMBALL, THOMAS L. 1964. For Public Recreation: Private Development of Hunting and Fishing, pp. 7–11. *Focus on Resource Conservation:* 1. Soil Conservation Society of America, Ankeny, Iowa.

Outdoor Recreation

8. MERRIAM, LUDING, AMMONS. 1965. *Glacier Park Chalet Visits: An Introduction to Wilderness.* Research Note No. 2, February 1965. School of Forestry, Montana State University, Missoula, Montana.

9. OUTDOOR RECREATION RESOURCES REVIEW COMMISSION. 1962. *Outdoor Recreation for America.* ORRRC Report to Congress. Government Printing Office, Washington, D.C. 246 pages.

10. OUTDOOR RECREATION RESOURCES REVIEW COMMISSION. 1962. *Paying for Recreation Facilities.* ORRRC Study Report No. 12. Government Printing Office, Washington, D.C. 88 pages.

11. OUTDOOR RECREATION RESOURCES REVIEW COMMISSION. 1962. *Federal Agencies and Outdoor Recreation.* ORRRC Study Report No. 13. Government Printing Office, Washington, D.C. 75 pages.

12. OUTDOOR RECREATION RESOURCES REVIEW COMMISSION. 1962. *Projection to the Years 1976 and 2000: Economic Growth, Population, Labor Force and Leisure, and Transportation.* ORRRC Study Report No. 23. Government Printing Office, Washington, D.C. 431 pages.

13. RECREATION ADVISORY COUNCIL. 1964. *A National Program of Scenic Roads and Parkways.* R.A.C. Circular No. 4. Washington, D.C.

14. RECREATION ADVISORY COUNCIL. 1964. *Policy Governing the Water Pollution and Public Health Aspects of Outdoor Recreation.* R.A.C. Circular No. 3. Washington, D.C.

15. SCHROEDER, GEORGE H. 1963. *Land Management Challenges for Industrial Foresters.* Special Publication No. 1, p. 43. Forestry and Conservation Station, Montana State University, Missoula, Montana.

16. SHANKLIN, JOHN F. 1964. Numbers and Types of Professionals Needed in Outdoor Recreation Leadership by Federal and State Agencies. *Proceedings of National Conference on Professional Education for Outdoor Recreation,* July 9–11, 1964. BOR, Washington, D.C.

17. TOLLEY, WILLIAM P. 1964. The American Heritage of Leisure. *Proceedings of National Conference on Professional Education for Outdoor Recreation,* July 9–11, 1964. BOR, Washington, D.C.

18. U.S. DEPARTMENT OF COMMERCE. 1964. *Statistical Abstract of the United States—1963.* Government Printing Office, Washington, D.C.

19. U.S. DEPARTMENT OF THE INTERIOR. 1962. Forest Conservation. *USDI Conservation Bulletin 42.* Government Printing Office, Washington, D.C. 82 pages.

Supply of Forest Recreation Areas

INTRODUCTION

In a sense, the entire 2.3 billion acres of the United States make up the potential supply of recreation land.[15] Sightseeing is one of the leading outdoor and forest recreation activities and it can take place anywhere. However, it is generally accepted that other forms of forest recreation such as camping and picnicking do require areas that meet certain conditions. Because of the requirements of setting, attraction, space, and climate, the area that can be considered as available for outdoor recreation is limited to places that meet the requirements. The total area of land that is suitable for some sort of forest recreation activity constitutes the theoretical supply for forest recreation. Today, there are approximately 775 million acres of forest land in the United States.[1] This seemingly large acreage of land must be many things to many people. Our population depends upon forest land for watershed protection, timber, wildlife habitat, recreation, and to a certain extent forage. All of these demands upon the forest are growing larger each year. The legal battles over water that are racking the Southwest highlight the desperate need for only one product of the forested lands. Many people rely upon forest products even while they are criticizing the forest management that made the products possible. Imposed upon this network of increasing pressures on the forests is the new surge for recreation. It is making heavier demands for a stronger voice in determining the use of forest resources.

Barring any catastrophic changes in our social system,

31

recreation will continue to grow. Therefore, it must be given a voice in formulating land management policy. However, forest land can not be turned over completely to recreation in spite of what some pressure groups may advocate.[23] Harmony must be reached among all forest land demands. Most of the demands are compatable with the others if there is a little compromising done by the land managers. Some forest demands seem to preclude other values; however, further inspection may often show that the first impression is not correct. The forestry practice of even-aged management, advocates clear cutting in small blocks. That means that all the trees within the cutting area are either cut or killed. The loss of den trees horrifies the squirrel hunter and the apparent destruction of the beautiful woods causes the sightseer to write to his Congressman. The hunter and the sightseer are partially in the right. A couple of compromises in the cutting techniques might have made everyone satisfied with the even-age management process. Den trees could have been left standing and strips of forest along the roads or in vista areas could have been left or cut under a less obtrusive system.

Aside from the fact that compromises could have helped the forest manager overcome some ruffled feelings, the process of timber cutting is not completely destructive to all aspects of the forest community. Into the clear-cut area come deer to browse for much needed food. The ruffed grouse is absolutely dependent upon such openings in the forest canopy.[25] The cutting has simply changed the wildlife cover and habitat from that suitable for squirrel and turkey to that required by deer and grouse. Although the esthetic values are sharply decreased at the time of cutting, they quickly return in the form of seedling and sprout reproduction. Sometimes the stand composition caused by planned cuttings is more pleasing to the sightseer than the previous, poorly formed second growth stand of timber that was removed.

The Allagash River in Maine is an example of the part that management plays in maintaining scenic areas. Organizations and governments have pushed for a national scenic and canoe area to protect the shoreline from destruction by its private owners. Actually, the entire shoreline has been under forest management for years and much of this so-called unspoiled area has been cut at least twice and has been open for public recreation for one hundred years.[6] Obviously, all cutting does not improve the scenery or the wildlife; but with an effort, the various demands on the forest can be harmonized and the growing demands for recreation, timber, and water can all be met.

The large forest areas are generally unused for recreation except for hunting. Even though each area cannot serve every purpose every moment, intelligent management will allow each activity to take place in a proper sequence. Camping and hiking can go on in areas that are not scheduled for cutting. Hunting can follow the managed cutting. Recreation is a powerful new force; but it should not become the only use of the forests. Putting too much emphasis upon estimated recreation dollar values would be attaching too much precision to too many variables.[23]

The actual supply of forest recreation land can include only those lands on which recreation is part of the present management plan or where it can be included with rational projections. Admittedly, any place might have recreational appeal to very narrow specialities such as snake hunters, rock collectors, or spelunkers. The more widely accepted endeavors such as camping, picnicking, hiking, hunting, fishing, and swimming generally require space, beauty, solitude, specific attractions, and water in the quantity needed for the area to be managed for recreation.

TABLE 3.1

THE GENERAL AND SPECIFIC REQUIREMENTS
FOR POTENTIAL RECREATION AREAS

General	Specific
Space	Attraction
Suitable climate	Setting
Accessibility	Water
	Public desire

Supply of Forest Recreation Areas

Although the presence of land and water acreage is the limiting factor for forest recreation activities, other factors influence the actual supply of forest recreation land. Accessibility, major attractions, and public desires play an important role in whether or not an area is really part of the recreational inventory. Even the attractions of a wilderness area must be reached by modern transportation if they are to be enjoyed. Some of the most wild and beautiful country within the United States lies inaccessible and therefore unused in Alaska.

DISTRIBUTION OF FOREST RECREATION AREAS

Physical Distribution

The supply of developed forest recreation areas is inadequate while the potential supply is much greater than could be required by any stretching of the imagination. More than 360,000 square miles of the United States surface is in public ownership and is open for outdoor recreation.[28] Many millions of acres of private and public forest land could be included to swell the already adequate figure. Unfortunately of for the easterner, most of the recreation land lies west of the Great Prairie. This means that most of the public land is in the West while most of the people are in the East. The population density is sixteen times greater in the Northeast than it is in the West and the recreation pressure can be expected to be at least proportionally greater.[28] A look at the ORRRC report figures given in Table 3.2 shows that while the Northeast had 25 percent of the population in 1960, it only contained 4 percent of the total public recreation land.[9]

Increased mobility and longer periods of leisure time provide for some individual release from the overcrowding by permitting families to travel to the sections where recreation areas are more extensive. Of course, these same two factors tend to increase the pressure on the inadequate areas near the megalopolis or city complex. The problem of getting people out of cities is now as acute as getting them into the cities was fifteen years ago. This paradox of oversupply and shortage is found within the individual states as well as throughout the United States.

TABLE 3.2

REGIONAL DISTRIBUTION OF POPULATION AND RECREATION AREA
(Excluding Hawaii and Alaska in 1960[a])

Population %		Recreation area %	
25	Northeast	4	Northeast
31	South	11	South
29	Central	12	Central
15	West	73	West

[a] ORRRC Report 1962.

By the very nature of its urban society, the United States has its population grouped into megalopolises where the people overwhelm any outdoor or forest type recreation that can be provided nearby. The detrimental effect of this heavy use lessens the effective area and makes the conditions worse. Many state parks that were designed in the 1930's have been placed in a high-density use situation that was not planned for. This heavy pressure has brought on deterioration of the facilities because the states, in an attempt to cope with the heavy use, have increased the numbers of campsites within their state parks beyond the limit that the areas can carry without adverse effects on the environmental conditions of the campground. From 1955 to 1960, the number of state operated campsites rose by almost 50 percent.[21] During the same period the number of campers has increased by approximately 100 percent and nullified any gains by the state park system.[16]

Distribution by Ownership

The fact that the physical distribution of recreation areas is in an imbalance with the need has previously been discussed. Besides physical distribution, the supply is affected by the

35

ownership and by the management of the land. Public forest recreation, as it is discussed in this book, takes place on land that is either in public or in private ownership. The matter of payment for use does not preclude private land from the public recreation area unless it is at a prohibitive cost or is accompanied by such standards as club membership or other precluding limitations. Usually, we should think of public-use recreation areas as those areas open to use by the general public regardless of ownership. This is opposed to land that is closed to public recreation use regardless of ownership. Approximately three-fifths of the country is in private ownership and is available for public recreation in widely varying degrees. All forms of government from the town to the federal level operate forest recreation areas.

TABLE 3.3

OWNERSHIP OF LAND IN THE UNITED STATES BY AREA AND PERCENT[a]

Owner	Area (million acres)	Percent
Private	1345	59
Public	873	41
Federal	771	34
State	84	4
County and Municipal	18	1
Indian	56	2
Total	2274	100

[a] ORRRC Study Report 1.

The four categories of ownership of recreation land are private, federal government, state government, and local government. Of these four categories of ownership of land, the federal land has been the most actively developed for forest recreation. The federal government has usually taken the lead in recreation. The states have shown interest in recreation; but until recently, they generally have been too late to act. Local governments enter into the forest recreation field only on a very limited

FIG. 3.1. Fishermen can pursue their sport on more than 40,000 miles of streams that flow through privately owned forests such as this one along California's Mad River. (American Forest Products Industries photo.)

FIG. 3.2. A public campsite near Effie, Minnesota is one of thousands that are provided by privately owned companies. One out of every five commercial forest-owning industries maintains public campsites. (American Forest Products Industries photo.)

scale. The local governments are more concerned with the pressing problems of urban recreation on a daytime basis. Playgrounds, ballfields, day camps, and supervised activities are needed to meet the needs of the community's youth. Some swimming and picnicking areas and urban organizations do provide local families with the opportunities for family-oriented recreation; however recreation at the community level is a subject of its own and is not covered in this text.

PRIVATE OWNERSHIP. Seventy percent of the non-urban land in the United States is in private ownership.[30] Of the 58 million acres of commercially owned forest land, all but 4 million acres are open to some form of public forest recreation. This means that the public has access to 92 percent of the commercial forest land in the United States. Also, fishermen can pursue their sport on over 40,000 miles of streams on these same commercial forest lands.[1, 2] The large forest landholding corporations keep their land open for public hiking, fishing, hunting, and camping and some go so far as to have campground areas established. Many of the larger landholders permit or encourage recreational use of their land more for good public relations than for profit. A blockade to the opening of some private land is the threat of liability for injuries to users. Often, landowners are afraid to encourage or even to permit the public to use their land for recreational purposes. There is the possibility of a lawsuit against the landowner by persons injured while on his land. Being judged liable for injuries sustained by others can be disastrous to many landowners. Even being judged innocent of liability can be an expensive proposition. The defendant must pay legal fees and miss much gainful employment as well as having the anxiety of a lawsuit. Large companies feel that they are often the target of unjust or exaggerated liability claims. Such claims are considered to be nuisance claims where people hope to gain some compensation even though the matter of liability on the part of the defendant is doubtful.

Landowners are not alone in this fight against liability claims. Medical doctors and well-meaning volunteers are susceptible to charges of injuries caused during unsolicited care at accident sites. In order to protect interested critizens and physicians from damaging lawsuits, some states have passed laws to protect persons performing acts of mercy. These statutes are commonly referred to as "Good Samaritan Laws". States such as Maine, New York, and New Hampshire where the public demands on private lands are heavy, have attempted to lift this liability. These states still recognize the owner's responsibility in wilful negligence but they are attempting to protect the landowner from the growing fear of "nuisance lawsuits".

The increasing need for forest recreation is reflected in the over-use of campgrounds. As the number of publicly owned campsites is increased, the demand increases and eliminates any actual gain on the need.[16] With an imbalance between the supply and the demand, the private investment system of capitalism comes into the picture. The use of private capital will permit areas to be developed on a risk and profit basis and thereby bring the supply in balance with the demand. Throughout the United States, private investors are developing forest recreation areas. The Florida Keys had no camping facilities in 1960; however, in 1965 they contained more than 1000 campsites.[20] Pennsylvania had 6 privately owned campgrounds operating in 1962. By 1965, the number had risen to 105 successful campgrounds.[24] Pennsylvania's state park system has helped to encourage this growth in private campgrounds by friendly cooperation with the owners and by not allowing pets into state park camping areas.

Private land is open to public recreation use for three reasons. The first reason is a passive approach by the landowner. People are welcome on his land as long as they do little damage to it. Another facet of the passive approach is that of enforcement. Even if the public was not welcome there, its exclusion would be too difficult for the landowner to enforce and might even have other distasteful side effects.

Public relations is the second reason that much private land is open to the public. Large companies must produce a good image in the public eye and they must meet certain obligations to the social system that is responsible for their existence. Attempts to avoid this responsibility cultivate ill will by the public towards the company. Good public relations are important to large companies for two major reasons. The first one is the obvious and the more direct reason of profit motivation. Rapid communication can spread a poor public image quickly and extensively to many potential consumers. A publicized company policy or action that causes widespread public disapproval can erase the benefits of a million dollar advertising campaign. A more subtle reason for large landholders to cultivate good public relations is the threat of legislation that might influence the use of the forest land. Legislative attempts to alter or control land use are common at all levels of government. Owners of large forest holdings must gain the confidence of the voter and prove to him that the landowners' methods are best for the general good of the community.

The third and the fastest growing reason for opening private land to public recreation is the expectation of profit. The profit motive implies active participation by the landowner. He must develop facilities and manage the area wisely in order to turn a profit on his investment. The private ventures range from a small backyard campground to the elaborate developments featuring lodges, ski lifts, artificial lakes, and camping all rolled up into one large speculation. Hunting and fishing enterprises are developing in areas where people are willing to pay a fee for game or fish taken.

Government officials realize that public agencies can not meet all the demands for forest recreation. They believe that the privately owned lands and the private capital will become more important in meeting the future recreation requirements. There will be a continual proliferation of privately owned campgrounds of varying size and quality. Organizations of campground owners are being formed to help the investor and the user. Unfortunately, private campgrounds got off to a bad start because of poor planning, poor management, and hopes of high returns. Now that responsible managers have succeeded in business and have organized, they are filling much of the need for campsites. More people are realizing that 5 dollars for each pheasant shot on a hunting preserve is a lower cost per bird than they would end up paying on open hunting areas if all the costs were tallied. Utility companies, paper companies, and other large landholders will increase the development of recreation facilities on their land to foster good will and to head off government control over the use of the land. Along with meeting their obligations to society in general, the large companies are expanding their lease arrangements with the Federal Bureau of Sport Fisheries and Wildlife. These agreements allow government biologists to maintain and manipulate game habitat while the land is under private ownership.

FEDERAL OWNERSHIP. The biggest forest recreation operator is the federal government which owns one-third of the country. Approximately 771 million acres belong to federal agencies, departments, or commissions.[19] More than thirty agencies of the federal government operate approximately one million recreation areas throughout the United States.[7,19] The federal government's prominent position in recreation is justified by three assumptions. The first and most basic assumption is that the public has the right to use its own land. Since the people are the government, they are in a sense the real owners of all federal land. The second assumption states that the public has the right to obtain any values created by the use of public land. In a capitalistic society, the investor is entitled to the profits; therefore, the public should receive any profit that results from the use of its land. The federal government's third assumption is that if the public is going to use its own land, it should use adequate and safe facilities. These adequate and safe facilities must be supplied by or under the auspices of federal agencies.[22]

Until the formation of the Bureau of Outdoor Recreation in 1962, no federal agency had ever been given the job of providing recreation for the American public; however, every one of the federal land managing agencies had been providing for the needs of recreationists for many years. The national forests and the national parks meet the general and specific requirements for potential recreation areas that are listed in Table 3.1 in that most of them are spacious, accessible, and have an attractive forest setting. The National Park Service

TABLE 3.4

FEDERAL AGENCIES MOST INVOLVED IN OUTDOOR RECREATION

Bureau of Outdoor Recreation	(BOR)
Forest Service	(USFS)
National Park Service	(NPS)
Bureau of Sport Fisheries and Wildlife	—
Bureau of Land Management	(BLM)
Corps of Engineers	(CE)
Bureau of Reclamation [a]	—
Agricultural Stabilization and Conservation Service	(ASCS)
Soil Conservation Service	(SCS)

[a] The Bureau of Reclamation cannot consider recreation values except when specifically authorized.

and United States Forest Service are the hosts to more than 164 million recreationists a year. The Forest Service maintains 50,846 campsites in 41 states while the Park Service operates approximately 28,000 campsites. [13]

The huge water impoundments that have been constructed by the Tennessee Valley Authority and the Corps of Engineers have placed those two agencies squarely into the recreation business. In 1960, the Corps of Engineers acted as host to more recreationists than any other agency. Table 3.5 shows that recreation visits to Corps of Engineers' impoundments rose from 16 million in 1950 to 106 million by 1960 and then to 156 million by 1964. [22]

The other major builder of large water impoundments is the Bureau of Reclamation which was not authorized to include recreation as a value on most of its projects until recently. In 1965, the Federal Water Project Recreation Act gave the Bureau of Reclamation limited authority to develop recreation opportunities on their projects. It is still the policy, as it was prior to the 1965 Act, to transfer major recreation areas to other federal agencies or to state and local governments for administration whenever possible. [5]

TABLE 3.5
RECREATION VISITS TO SELECTED FEDERAL LANDS

Administrating agency	Number of visits		
	1950[a]	1960[a]	1964
National Park Service	32,780,000	72,288,000	102,711,000
Forest Service	27,368,000	92,595,000	133,800,000
Tennessee Valley Authority	16,645,000	42,349,000	47,638,000
Corps of Engineers	16,000,000	106,000,000	156,000,000
Bureau of Reclamation	6,594,000	24,300,000	34,300,000

[a] ORRRC Study Report 13.

The Tennessee Valley Authority has adopted the policy of local development. That means that the TVA has encouraged recreation development in its areas by the state and local governments and by the other federal agencies that are interested in recreation. As of 1961, the recreational developments along the margins of the TVA lakes included 66 municipal and county parks, 13 state parks, and 365 water access areas. Several thousand cabins and hundreds of private recreation businesses have been built along the lake shores. Some lake frontage was sold to civic, service, or religious organizations; however, a reversionary clause was included in the sale contract to guarantee that the land was used for the purpose for which it was sold.

TABLE 3.6
PUBLIC LAND ADMINISTERED BY THE THREE
MAJOR RECREATION HOSTS IN 1960

Agency	Number of areas	Acres
Forest Service	155	181,500,000
Park Service	191	26,103,000
Corps of Engineers	250	3,223,000

As a direct result of the Outdoor Recreation Resources Review Commission Report to Congress in 1962, the Bureau of Outdoor Recreation was established. The BOR is responsible for the overall recreation planning throughout the United States. Because it does not administer any land, the BOR does not compete with other federal agencies for power and authority in the recreation field. However, it has established regional offices in various parts of the country and is considering doing its own research. Some people in the outdoor recreation field contend that these steps do put the BOR into competition with other federal agencies. Its presence in the government bureaucracy has begun to ease some of the inter-agency battles among the Corps of Engineers, the Forest Service, and the Park Service over the control of certain recreation developments. The BOR administers the money allocated to states under federal recreation legislation such as the Land and Water Conservation Fund Act of 1965. This money provides assistance and stimulation to the state recreation programs. A third charge given to the BOR is the encouragement of recreation research and the exchange of ideas and knowledge on that subject. It cooperates with higher institutes of learning by aiding in programming research and seminars and in publishing proceedings in the recreation field.

The BOR recognizes that the states are the logical level of government to develop outdoor recreation; therefore, it operates through state contacts that have been appointed by each state governor. These contacts are state employees of the cabinet level that are in a position to appraise the state's recreational stance. In most cases, they are the state director, or his equivalent, of the forest or park system.[27] The BOR also recognizes that private investors will make the greatest new contribution to recreation; therefore, it will give a great amount of assistance to the private sector of recreational development.[8]

The Wilderness Act and the Land and Water Conservation Fund Act are two major pieces of legislation that have been enacted by the United States Congress on the recommendations of the BOR. The Wilderness Act calls for the setting aside

43

of federal land in its natural state. Vehicles, roads, and all developments are excluded from the areas. All primative areas of federal land are to be considered for inclusion into the Wilderness System so that approximately 45 million acres of federally owned land could be included in wilderness status by 1974. [4, 10, 21]

The Land and Water Conservation Fund Act of 1965 is one of the most significant pieces of legislation ever enacted to support recreation. The act provides funds to state and local governments and to federal agencies for the development of outdoor recreation on a planned, nationwide scale. The expressed purpose of the Land and Water Conservation Fund Act is to bring the supply of the nation's recreation facilities up to its needs. The enormity of this program becomes apparent when the amount of money involved is considered. It is estimated that approximately 180 million dollars a year of federal money will be used to give the act life. Sixty percent of the 180 million dollars is designated to go to the state governments on a fifty-fifty matching basis. That means that for every dollar the state contributes to its planned outdoor recreation program under this act the federal government will contribute one dollar until the state limit of federal assistance is reached. The technique of using matching funds will add approximately 100 million dollars per year to the total money available under the Land and Water Conservation Fund Act. The remaining 40 percent of the funds will remain with federal agencies for the acquisition of needed recreation land or to help pay for selected developments. [11] The United States Forest Service has stated that it will spend approximately 80 percent of its share on land acquisition in the eastern states. [12]

The revenue needed for this operation is raised by the following three methods. Entrance fees are charged to certain recreation areas; motorboat fuel tax money is used to support this act; and the revenue obtained from the sale of surplus real property is included in the money available. The enormous sum of federal money needed to operate this program is raised without increasing the taxes of the general public. The basic premise behind the entrance fee is the tenet that the user should bear most of the cost. Also, when entrance fees are charged, private recreation areas are not placed in the impossible position of competing with wholly tax-supported facilities.

The Land and Water Conservation Fund Act provides for fees to be charged only at certain areas and specifically prohibits charges at other areas. All of four conditions must be met before the admission fee may be charged. They are: (1) the area must be designated and posted as a fee area; (2) a federal agency must administer the area; (3) the facilities or services have been provided at federal expense; and (4) the area must be administered primarily for scientific, historical, cultural, or recreational purposes. Recreation fees can not be charged for the use of public water; travel through a designated area in a private vehicle on a public thoroughfare; access to inholdings; for any non-recreational commercial activity; or as a federal hunting or fishing license.

The Land and Water Conservation Fund Act and the Wilderness Act are the two largest steps into outdoor recreation that the federal government has ever taken intentionally. The first half of the 1960's marked the beginning of forest recreation on a planned and grand scale. Many more steps will follow in the form of regional development bills such as the Appalachian Aid Act that will use federal money to open up vast new recreation opportunities in regions of the country that need an economic stimulus. [3]

STATE OWNERSHIP. Approximately 4 percent of the United States is owned by the individual states for roads, parks, forests, and fish or game areas. More than 5300 full-time professionals are engaged in recreation work at the state level where they work for more than 500 state agencies. [26] The majority of the state forest recreation usage takes place in approximately 2800 areas that comprise the state park systems where the attendance exceeded 270 million visits in 1961. [28] The states have been given the pivotal role in outdoor recreation under the Land and Water Conservation Fund Act of 1965. How much public outdoor recreation is developed and

Supply of Forest Recreation Areas

Table 3.7

Types of Area Used for Forest Recreation
and Their Administrating Agencies

Type of area	Administrating agencies

Forests	Federal
	    U.S. Forest Service (USFS)
	    Bureau of Land Management
	    (BLM)
	State
	Municipal
	Private

Parks	National Park Service (NPS) State Municipal Private
Wilderness Areas	USFS and NPS
Primitive Areas	USFS
Gamelands	State and Private
Recreational Areas	
National Recreation Areas	NPS and USFS
Canoe Areas	Private, State, USFS, and NPS
Impoundment Shorelines	Private, State, Corps of Engineers, Tennessee Valley Authority, USFS and NPS

Ski Slopes, Lodges, Marinas,
   Picnic and Camping Areas,
   Cabin Sites, and Trails
	Federal, State, Municipal,
	and Private

Roadside Rests	State and Private
Scenic Areas	State and NPS and USFS
Grasslands	NPS and USFS

what forms it will take largely depends upon the attitudes of the state governments. How much planning will the states do? How much money will they raise? How much flexibility will the state political systems allow? State recreation systems vary widely in facilities and services although all the states claim to provide the same basic commodity of outdoor or forest recreation.[21]

States are beginning to realize that it is their responsibility to provide balanced forest recreation opportunities for their citizens. Between 1955 and 1962, the states have made a 60 percent increase in individual campsites.[21] Michigan opened 800 new campsites in 1963 and 900 more in 1964 to raise that state's total number of campsites to approximately 11,000.[16] Simple proliferation of facilities does not appear to be the answer to overuse or to the overwhelming demand for forest recreation. Apparently, an adequate supply of satisfactory facilities attracts more people into the ranks of the participants or it encourages shifts from other areas or other interests to the satisfactory facilities.

TABLE 3.8
SUMMARY OF STATE PARK SYSTEMS[a]

	1950	1961
Areas	1725	2792
Acreage	4,657,000	5,799,000
Attendance	114,291,000	273,484,000

[a] Statistical Abstract of the United States—1963.

The federal Land and Water Conservation Fund Act will pour more than one hundred million dollars each year into the state programs on a matching basis. The states must have a statewide recreation plan approved by the Bureau of Outdoor Recreation to be eligible for the federal share of the matching funds. Even before the lure of federal money came along, many states had embarked on ambitious recreation development plans. Table 3.9 shows a partial list of state programs that had been started by 1966. These plans are extensive and costly as they stand by themselves. When they provide only the state's share of matching funds, the sums to be spent on outdoor recreation appear to be astronomical. To those state park users who are familiar with the sight of hand scythes instead of expensive power mowers, the thought of this amount of money being put into recreation is staggering.

Supply of Forest Recreation Areas

TABLE 3.9

PARTIAL LIST OF STATE RECREATION PLANS STARTED BY 1966 SHOWING
THE COST OF THE PLAN AND THE PROJECTED USE OF THE FUNDS

State	Amount (dollars)	Purpose of money
California	150 million	Grants to cities and counties for acquisition and development—50 million
		State park acquisitions—80 million
		Development of recreation areas—20 million
Florida	—	Land acquisition
Kentucky	176 million	4.5 million for state parks
Maine	10 million (continuing)	Guaranteed mortgage loans to private operators
Minnesota	55 million	—
New Jersey	60 million	"Green-acres plan"—40 million for land acquisition 20 million for matching local government funds
New York	100 million	35 million for land acquisition 65 million for matching local government funds
Ohio	55 million	Land acquisition and recreation area improvement and related purposes
Pennsylvania	70 million	Regional parks near urban areas—40 million
		Grants to local governments—20 million on matching basis
		Wildlife—10 million
Rhode Island	5 million	Acquisition and development of recreation lands
Washington	10 million	Acquisition of recreation lands

CARRYING CAPACITY OF THE LAND

The supply of forest recreation land cannot be measured in acres alone. The simple acreage figures do not provide the land manager with adequate information to plan for specific developments to meet a given demand.[9] Most of the land tied up by recreation is not physically occupied by the user. The user does not intentionally consume the land that he occupies; however, he is doing that very thing. Deterioration of the occupied portions is the greatest threat to established recreation areas. The very presence of large numbers of people in one place changes the ecology of that area in many ways. The soil is compacted and eroded by millions of footsteps. Vegetation is killed directly by trampling or indirectly as a result of soil compaction when the infiltration and perculation regimes of the soil are altered and the pore spaces are eliminated. Normal wear and vandalism alter the site in an adverse manner. This deterioration of the occupied area is a real problem in the wilderness areas as well as in the eastern state parks.[14,17,29]

The amount of use that an area can support without any change in the recreational quality of the site is termed its carrying capacity. Wagar describes recreation quality as the degree to which a recreation area normally contributes to the user's physical and psychic well being.[29] Carrying capacity determines how durable the site is for recreation in the terms of man-days use. Every visitor is counted each day to provide the figures for man-day use. It is the ability of the individual sites to hold up under user impact, or the carrying capacity, that determines how large a supply of recreation land really does exist in the United States.

Space requirements per man-day of use have been roughly established to guide land managers in maintaining a given level of recreation quality. However, variables such as the level of recreation quality desired, soil characteristics, weather, season of the year, and the use of the area make such figures general "rules of thumb". Each site must be evaluated individually to determine its optimum carrying capacity. Site influences affecting this evaluation are discussed in detail in Chapter 5.

The management decision concerning the desired level of recreation quality must be made before the carrying capacity can be determined. Wagar gives the following example to explain the carrying capacity of forest recreation lands.[29]

(a) Picnicking and its benefits would be at a certain level if the picnic area received 100 man-days of use each day.

(b) If the daily use were increased to 200 man-days, the character of the picnic area would change. It would adjust to the impact of the heavier use. Some wearing of the soil, a loss of grass, a higher noise level, and a loss of solitude would occur.

(c) If the daily use were held at 200 man-days, the area would reach a new level of recreation quality and stabilize there. The area would now maintain that quality with a carrying capacity of 200 man-days use per day.

The U.S. Forest Service standards for the carrying capacity of its wilderness areas is 3 acres per man-day of use each year. A 300,000 acre wilderness area would be able to have 100,000 man-days of use per year. Unfortunately, this carrying capacity is already being exceeded in some areas. The National Park Service suggested carrying capacities range widely with the type of attractions. They vary from 1000 man-days use per 15 acres for areas of local significance to 1000 man-days per 200 acres on areas of national significance. Insufficient research has been completed to give a sound basis for establishing carrying capacities. The ones listed here are only estimates based upon generalities and observations.

REFERENCES

1. AMERICAN FOREST PRODUCTS INDUSTRIES. 1962. *Forest Land Use— Everybody's Concern.* First Forest Land Use Conference, September 1961. AFPI, Washington, D.C.

2. AMERICAN FOREST PRODUCTS INDUSTRIES. 1960. *Recreation on Forest Industries Land.* AFPI, Washington, D.C.

3. Anon. 1965. Appalachia Aid Bill to Expand Highway System. *South Penn Motorist*, May, p. 6. Chambersburg, Pennsylvania.
4. Anon. 1964. New Wilderness Program. *Journal of Forestry*, November, vol. 62, No. 11, p. 8.
5. Bureau of Reclamation. 1964. *Reclamation's Recreational Opportunities*. Government Printing Office, Washington, D.C.
6. Clepper, Henry. 1962. The Allagash: Wilderness in Controversy. *Journal of Forestry*, vol. 62, No. 11, pp. 777–81.
7. Crafts, Edward C. 1964. Launched: The Bureau of Outdoor Recreation. *Focus on Resource Conservation*: 1. pp. 12–14. Soil Conservation Service, Ankeny, Iowa.
8. Crafts, Edward C. 1962. National Outlook Quotation. *Journal of Forestry*, vol. 60, No. 8, p. 572.
9. Davis, Kenneth P.1964. Accomplishments of the Ann Arbor Conference on Outdoor Recreation Research. *Proceedings of National Conference on Professional Education for Outdoor Recreation*. BOR, Washington, D. C.
9a. Dominy, F.E. 1965. Multiple Purpose Reclamation Projects Provide Public Recreation. *Proceedings of the Society of American Foresters*. Annual Meeting, Detroit, Michigan.
10. 88th Congress of the United States. 1964. Land and Water Conservation Act of 1965. P.L. 88-578 and H.R. 3846.
11. 88th Congress of the United States. 1964. Wilderness Act. P.L. 88-577.
12. Freeman, Orville. 1964. Land and Water Conservation Fund. National Outlook. *Journal of Forestry*, vol. 62, No. 10, p. 778.
13. Godbout, Oscar. 1965. The Camper Hits the Road. *New York Times*, May 16. Section 13, p. 1.
14. Hutchison, S. Blair. 1962. *Recreation Opportunities and Problems in the National Forests of the Intermountain Region*. Intermountain Forestry and Range Experimental Station, Ogden, Utah.
15. Johnson, H.A. and Tharp, M. 1963. Meeting the Demand for Outdoor Recreation. *USDA Yearbook*, p. 309. Washington, D.C.
16. Kent, Joseph. 1965. Are Private Campgrounds the Answer? *Better Camping Magazine*.
17. Lutz, H.J. 1945. Soil Condition on Picnic Grounds in Public Forest Parks. *Journal of Forestry*, vol. 43, pp. 121–7.
18. Outdoor Recreation Resources Review Commission. 1962. *Recreation for America*. Government Printing Office. 246 pages.
19. Outdoor Recreation Resources Review Commission. 1962. *Public Outdoor Recreation Areas—Acreage, Use, Potential*. ORRRC Study Report No. 1. Government Printing Office, Washington, D.C. 200 pages.
20. Outdoor Recreation Resources Review Commission. 1962. *Private Outdoor Recreation Facilities*. ORRRC Study Report No. 11. Government Printing Office, Washington, D.C. 88 pages.

Supply of Forest Recreation Areas

21. OUTDOOR RECREATION RESOURCES REVIEW COMMISSION. 1962. *Paying for Recreation Facilities*. ORRRC Study Report No. 12. Government Printing Office, Washington, D.C. 88 pages.

22. OUTDOOR RECREATION RESOURCES REVIEW COMMISSION. 1962. *Federal Agencies and Outdoor Recreation*. ORRRC Study Report No. 13. Government Printing Office, Washington, D.C. 75 pages.

23. ROCKEFELLER, LAURENCE S. 1962. The Future of Outdoor Recreation. *Journal of Forestry*, vol. 60, No. 8, pp. 521–4.

24. SANDY, C. R. 1965. Newsletter. *Campground Association of Pennsylvania*, vol. 11, No. 3. Mercer, Pennsylvania.

25. SHARP, WARD M. 1957. *Management of a Poletimber Forest for Wildlife Food and Cover*. Agricultural Experimental Station, University Park, Pennsylvania.

26. STOUT, NEIL. 1965. The Role of Forestry in the Recreation Boom. *Proceedings of Society of American Foresters, Allegheny*, pp. 18–25.

27. SULLIVAN, JOHN. 1965. *Sobering Statistics*. Northeast Outdoor Memo, p. 3–65. BOR, Philadelphia, Pennsylvania.

28. U.S. DEPARTMENT OF COMMERCE. 1964. *Statistical Abstract of the United States—1963*. Government Printing Office, Washington, D.C.

29. WAGAR, J. A. 1964. The Carrying Capacity of Wild Lands for Recreation. *Forest Science Monograph*, No. 7. Society of American Foresters, Washington, D.C.

30. WOOTEN, H. H. and ANDERSON, J. R. 1954. Major Uses of Land in the United States. *Agr. Information Bulletin*, vol. 168, p. 31.

CHAPTER 4

Forest Recreation Planning

INTRODUCTION

Forest recreation planning is the intelligent use of the recreation resources in providing satisfactory recreation facilities and areas to meet present and future needs of the population. It helps to determine types, quantity, location, and timing of recreation development. In order to make intelligent use of the recreation resources, the planner must understand the need for recreation in his area. He must know how much development is needed for each type of recreation and when it should be ready for public use. Also, he must know what sites can be developed for each type of recreation that is needed and what impact their development will have upon other forest uses.

Planning will prevent a hit-and-miss system of recreation that could put too much of the wrong thing in one place and not enough of anything in another. Haphazard developments based on available funds, sudden interests, or reaction to overcrowding will be partially avoided by a well-developed recreation plan. Anticipation of public needs is possible when investigations are properly performed and competently analyzed. By knowing what, where, when, and how much to develop, the private landowner and the public administrators will be in a better position to undertake successful recreation development ventures.

The recreation plan aids in the creation of related complexes of recreation opportunity instead of individual, unrelated, and competing facilities. These complexes should be grouped in such a way as to compliment one another. Hiking trails should be accessible to campers; however, the trail should not penetrate the campground. Fishing stream improvement could be coupled with small campsites and day-use areas developed near population centers, around boat launching areas, and adjacent to beaches. By grouping recreation complexes together in a rational manner, the planner can do much to fill the recreation need, increase dispersal of use, and reduce operation costs.

The forest is many things to many people; however, it is also only one thing to each of many others. To these, it is a place for growing and harvesting timber; a place to scrape away in order to get at valuable minerals; a place to keep sacred and undisturbed; or a place to collect and store water. Now that recreation is moving into the forest environment, it is colliding with the established uses of forest land and causing serious conflicts. Established and necessary uses of forest land are being attacked by recreationists who need more area. Also, some different types of recreation are incompatible when attempted in the same area. The conflict between skiers and wilderness enthusiasts in Southern California has obtained national prominence in recent years. Even at the local levels fisherman and water skiers are continuously battling. Recreation planning will help to make these collisions less inflannatory by pointing out potential conflicts in the use of the land before they happen and by suggesting ways of mitigating the impacts.

Timing of recreation development is very important for providing the optimal mix of facilities with the minimum investment.[7] Much of the total costs depend upon the advanced planning and the direct purchase of land. By looking ahead at the predicted need, the planner can make decisions on land purchases that could save substantial sums of money spent for land acquisition. Advanced planning is very important when long "lead-time" periods required for action could permit a high rise in the land value or allow commercial exploitation of the area before the recreation development could be started.

Timing is important even when the land is already administered by the government agency or private owner who is doing the planning because future recreation developments must be worked into the area's management plan. Management of forested areas requires long term plans that give the forest resource manager an outline of the operations to be undertaken on the forest. If recreation planning information were available to the forester far enough in the future, possible recreation sites could be saved, specially cut, or cut far in advance of the time they will be needed for recreation. This advance notice of land use for special purposes is commonly referred to as "ear-marking". Sufficient lead time will permit lower costs for acquisition and ear-marking of presently owned lands for future recreation uses.[7]

RESPONSIBILITY

Responsibility for recreation planning lies with the private landowners as well as with every level of government. The farmer who is considering converting part of his farm into a campground must make plans that are parallel to those made by the U.S. Forest Service. True, the farmer's plans are not as large in scope or magnitude as are those of the U.S. Forest Service; however, they are similar in intent. That is, they give a comprehensive report on the needs of the potential users and the resources available or required to meet those needs.

At the national level, the Secretary of the Interior is responsible, through the Bureau of Outdoor Recreation, for preparing a nationwide recreation plan. The federal role in recreation planning is primarily one of encouraging action by other levels of government and by private landowners. With the passage of the Land and Water Conservation Fund Act of 1965, P.L. 88–578, the federal government obtained a very useful tool for encouraging recreation action at all levels of government. This law authorized matching funds equal to fifty percent of costs to the states for acquisition and development of recreation land. In order for a state to receive federal

55

money under this program, it must have completed a state-wide recreation plan. As the states complete their recreation plans, the federal government adds them into its national recreation plan.

Being the largest landowner in the country, the federal government finds itself deeply involved in forest recreation. The Bureau of Outdoor Recreation is the federal government's agent for coordinating the recreation activities of over thirty other agencies. The purpose of this coordination effort within the federal level of government is to manage the federal lands for optimum recreation benefits so long as recreation remains consistent with other uses. There are some cases where the original purpose of the land management conflicts with recreation and therefore takes precedence over it. Military depots such as the sprawling Letterkenny Army Depot in Pennsylvania are often opened to public hunting; however, recent developments in Vietnam have caused munitions movements that occasionally interfere with public access and shooting on these depots. Fragile water-sheds that could not withstand the trampling of millions of feet are not developed for intensive-use recreation because of the danger of permanently damaging the original value of the area.

In addition to developing a nationwide recreation plan and coordinating the actions of its own agencies, the federal government coordinates and encourages the recreation programs of other parties. Concession systems are encouraged on federal recreation land to encourage the use of private capital in fields where the federal government does not operate. Technical assistance and planning aid is available to rural landowners who are interested in outdoor recreation enterprises. Unfortunately, technical assistance is the least important ingredient in a successful outdoor recreation enterprise. Management skills, foresight, and capital resources are the things most required for success; however, these very conditions usually are lacking in the submarginal agricultural communities where the federal government is so active in pushing its technical assistance.

The state role in outdoor recreation is considered to be "pivotal" by the Bureau of Outdoor Recreation. The BOR expresses the policy that the states should take on the responsibility of recognizing, developing, and managing public recreation resources that fall between national and local government control.[13] Many states have already completed comprehensive statewide, long-range plans for outdoor recreation. Besides compiling the statewide plan, the state should coordinate all outdoor recreation within the state and assist the local governments in their recreation programs. In state programs the concession method of encouraging private investment is used but to a more limited extent than at the federal level.

The local governments are the closest to the needs of the local population and should be able to transfer this need into action. Actually, this does not appear to be true for the planning and development of forest recreation facilities. All too often, small towns and counties consider nearby state parks as their own community recreation area and do little or nothing beyond the political wrangling required to get the state to take care of local needs. Some local governments at the city and county level are planning and developing such intensive recreation areas as picnic grounds and campgrounds. In most cases, these have been a direct benefit to local users. However, since outdoor recreationists are often travelers, the local governments are often catering to tourists' money rather than to recreation needs of local citizens when they establish overnight facilities.

INVENTORY

How much of what types of recreation are needed and when will the areas be required? In order to answer this question, a recreation planner must analyze the need for recreation within the area to be served by the plan. Also, he must compile the facts on available recreation opportunities and compare the sum of available facilities with the sum of the

57

demand. By subtracting the available opportunities from the need, the planner can ascertain the net amount of facilities required.

Recreation demand is the amount of outdoor recreation opportunities that the public wants. The BOR refers to recreation demand as, "an expression of total participation in general outdoor recreation activities that could be expected if adequate facilities were available."[2] Therefore, demand really is composed of the actual use of existing facilities plus a latent demand that is not being reflected because of the lack of sufficient facilities. The general variables affecting participation in outdoor recreation are discussed in Chapter 2. For use in planning, the demand analysis is divided into four parts.[2] The four steps or parts of demand analysis are:

1. Determination of effective population.
2. Adjustment of participation rates.
3. Determining existing demand.
4. Estimating future demand.

Effective Population

The size and distribution of the study area's population determines the "effective population". While the actual number of people has a direct bearing on the effective population, the distribution of those people within the zone of influence will govern the pattern of need. The majority of people live in metropolitan areas; but they seek outdoor recreation opportunities in rural and forested areas. Research shows that 90 percent of all outdoor recreation takes place within 125 miles of the participant's home.[3] Therefore, any metropolitan area that is within 125 miles of the study area should be considered as being within the zone of influence.

Sixty percent of outdoor recreation participation takes place within the day-use zone that has a radius of 40 miles. The weekend-use area has a radius of 40 to 125 miles and accounts for 30 percent of the recreation visits. The remaining 10 percent of the visits are made up of extended trips. Perhaps these

zone radii will change with increased interstate travel; however, they are presently proving to be satisfactory figures with
which to make estimates of demand.

In order that the effective population within the study area
can be determined, each metropolitan area is centered in a
circle with a 40-mile radius representing the day-use zone of
its population. Also, a 125-mile radius circle is used to depict
the weekend-use area for that metropolitan area. The area of
the portion of the day-use circle falling within the study area
is measured with a planimeter and expressed as a percent of the
entire circle area. Since 60 percent of the recreation use occurs
within the day-use circle, 60 percent of the metropolitan
area's population should be multiplied by the percentage of
the circle within the study area to obtain the effective population within the day-use zone.[2] By using the same reasoning, the effective population for weekend-use can be determined by using 30 percent of the metropolitan area population
as discussed above. The same procedure is followed for each
metropolitan area and the total added to the non-urban population inhabiting the study area to obtain an estimate of
the total effective population within the zone of influence.

This methodology assumes that the non-metropolitan population living within the study area will have its recreational
demands satisfied there. The amount of loss of non-metropolitan population outflow would be offset by inflow from
contiguous areas.

Demand is more than a reflection of population. It is a
product of population and rate of participation in outdoor recreation. The determination of effective population for the
zone of influence can be determined by the method given above.
This means that the next step in ascertaining demand is the
analysis of the participation rate for the effective population.

Adjusted Participation Rates

In order to estimate demand, the effective population's
rate of participation must be determined. Chapter 2 dis-

cusses the variables that affect user participation. Research does show that participation rates remain relatively constant for each social-economic segment of the population.[2] The Outdoor Recreation Resources Review Committee Study Report Number 19 gives regional rates of participation for selected activities. The figures in that study report are based on interviews conducted by the United States Bureau of Census.[11] The regional participation rates as given in the ORRRC study report are shown in Table 4.1.

TABLE 4.1
ANNUAL PARTICIPATION RATES FOR SELECTED ACTIVITIES BY REGION[a]

Activity	Days per person in effective population				
	United States average	North-east	North-central	South	West
Swimming	6.47	7.97	5.34	5.54	7.63
Sightseeing	5.91	5.11	6.64	5.09	7.46
Picnicking	3.53	3.77	3.64	2.77	4.30
Boating (all forms)	2.59	2.39	2.68	2.54	2.65
Nature walks	2.70	2.79	2.42	2.67	2.88
Camping	0.86	0.55	0.65	0.79	2.00
Hiking	0.42	0.41	0.35	0.35	0.72

[a] ORRRC Study Report 19.

An adjustment of the regional participation figures can be made to make the data more suitable for state or area use. This adjustment to reflect more localized conditions can be based upon an index that considers all of the factors influencing participation in outdoor recreation; however, such an index might be confounded by the interactions among variables or be too difficult and expensive to determine. A simpler adjustment of participation rates can be made by using *per capita* income comparisons, since *per capita* demand is closely related to disposable income. Most of the variables such as age, education, and occupation are relatively the same in most metropolitan populations or else they are reflective of *per capita* income. In determining an adjustment factor, the *per capita* income within the study area for 1960 should be used because the ORRRC report data is based upon that year. This factor should be used to adjust the participation rates to local conditions.

Determining Existing Demand

The current recreation demand by activity is the product of the existing effective population and the adjusted participation rates. An example of current recreation demand tabulation is given in Table 4.2.

TABLE 4.2

PRESENT DEMAND FOR FOREST-ORIENTED OUTDOOR RECREATION IS ESTIMATED BY MULTIPLYING THE EFFECTIVE POPULATION BY THE ADJUSTED PARTICIPATION RATE

Activity	Effective population (thousands)	Adjusted annual participation rate	Annual activity occasions (thousands)
Sightseeing	2555	7.07	18,064
Swimming	2555	5.96	15,228
Picnicking	2555	3.88	9913
Boating[a]	2555	2.85	7281
Camping	2555	0.69	1763
Nature walks	2555	2.58	6592
Hiking	2555	0.37	945
		Total	59,786

[a] Including water skiing, canoeing, and sailing.

The standard unit for determining primary outdoor recreation benefits is the recreation day and not the recreation occasion that has been determined in Table 4.2. Since research has shown that a participant engages in an average of two and a half activity occasions for each visit to an area, the activity occasion figure should be divided by 2.5 to get the proper estimate of recreation day-use.[2]

61

Those people who travel over 125 miles for extended trips are not considered directly in demand estimation because there is no valid way to determine their contribution to the recreation demand within the study area. It is believed by most planners that this 10 percent of recreationists, the extended vacationist, do contribute a significant portion of the demand. For this reason, recreation-use figures that are compiled for recreation plans are conservative in spite of what some critics might suggest.

Estimating Future Demand

The simplest method of obtaining an approximation of future recreation demands is by multiplying the predicted population by the predicted participation rate. By using the years 1976 and 2000 as target years, the planner can utilize the projection given in the Outdoor Recreation Resources Review Commission Study Reports 19 and 26.[11,12] The estimated future demand is based upon assumed availability of sufficient resources to completely satisfy the demand.

An acceptable prediction of the percentage increase in

TABLE 4.3

PERCENTAGE INCREASED IN PARTICIPATION RATES OVER 1960
BASE FOR SELECTED ACTIVITIES BY 1976 AND 2000[a]

Activity	Percent increase 1960–1976[b]	Percent increase 1960–2000
Swimming	90	300
Sightseeing	108	374
Picnicking	67	209
Boating	96	317
Nature walk	c	c
Camping	149	545
Hiking	148	511

[a] ORRRC Study Report No.19.
[b] With full opportunity.
[c] Lack of sufficient data.

participation rates based upon the ORRRC Study Report No. 26 is given in Table 4.3. The planner can apply the predicted percentage increases shown in Table 4.3 to the base figures given in Table 4.1 to arrive at the participation rates for the years 1976 and 2000. The estimated future demand is the product of the increased participation rates and the predicted populations for each target year.

An increase in both quality and quantity of recreation facilities on a *per capita* basis is assumed for the data in Table 4.2. Because of this, the predicted demand is not restricted as a result of insufficient satisfactory facilities. At first appearances, this assumption leads to liberal predictions; however, in the light of the overcrowding and the drawing powers of newly developed recreation areas, the "full opportunity" predictions may prove to be conservative ones.

SUPPLY

The planner must compare the available and planned supply of recreation facilities to the present and future demands in order to estimate the area's needs. This requires an inventory that accounts for all the recreation areas that are open for public use, regardless of ownership. Also, it should analyze the land-use patterns of the study area to determine what acreage of land will be available for future recreation development. Generally, the three-stage time sequence used in tabulating the data is: (a) the areas that exist at the time of the inventor must be tabulated, (b) all areas that are programed for completion by 1970 should be included, (c) the inventory should include all those areas that have been identified as potential recreation sites by the administering agency or landowner.

Existing Recreation Areas

Areas that are small can be inventoried personally by the planner; however, large areas present too great a problem for first hand inventorying. Also, the work has already been done

63

by some public agency that will cooperate in supplying the needed information. The Bureau of Outdoor Recreation has inventoried the publicly owned areas as part of its work on a nationwide recreation plan. This inventory includes all federal, state, and county areas larger than ten acres. All areas in cities with populations greater than 50,000 and a sampling of smaller cities are included in these inventories.[4] The Public Sector Inventory lists each area by name and gives its government administration level, size, use, location, and major classification of development as appears in Table 4.4.

TABLE 4.4
RECREATION AREA CLASSIFICATION SYSTEM[a]

(A) Class	(B) Description	(C) Man-days use/acre/year[b]
I	Intensively developed and managed for mass use	2000
II	Extensively developed for general out-door recreation	75
III	Natural environment; little or no development available	2
IV	Outstanding natural area	—
V	Primitive	—
VI	Historic and cultural area	—

[a] BOR Public Sector Inventory.
[b] Based upon Clawson, *Land for the Future.*

For planning purposes, the six BOR inventory classes are often grouped into three groups. Because of similar use and facilities, the six classes are combined as follows:[2]

1. Intensively developed – Classes I and VI
2. Extensively developed – Classes II and IV
3. Undeveloped – Classes III and V

State recreation plans, the Soil Conservation Service, the National Association of Soil Conservation Districts, and various state campground associations can supply the planner with information concerning private and public recreation facilities within the study area.

The land areas available to recreation are affected in a large measure by the land-use patterns within the study area. Therefore, a review of the land-use within the study area is necessary to determine what percentage of the land is available for outdoor recreation activities. Urbanized areas, cropland, and pastureland usually are not available or desirable for outdoor recreation. The BOR lists forest lands, water, and miscellaneous land as having the highest recreation resource potential.[2]

The use-capacity of the existing land can be estimated by using the use-figure given in column C of Table 4.4 for each of the three development intensity groups. This is probably the simplest method of determining the resource capacity. It is necessary to convert supply from area to recreation days-use for comparison to recreation demand by multiplying the man-days-use recommended in column C by the number of acres available.

The distribution of the recreation supply must be analyzed to see if it adequately serves the study area. Although sufficient land area might exist within the study area, it might be distributed in such a way as to be inaccessible to most of the population. It is at this point where the planner must make or ask for a policy decision governing the user group. Should the recreation developments be user-oriented, resource-oriented, or mixed?

The Bureau of Outdoor Recreation is striving to get developed areas placed where they are most readily available to the largest number of people at the risk of using less grand settings than exist elsewhere.[2,5] This philosophy of recreation planning is occasionally attacked on the grounds that it mistakes the spending of time and of money for actual enjoyment. In defense of this philosophy, it must be said that tax money, at any level, must be spent to the greatest advantage of the taxpayers. Private operators can look toward other philosophies, but not public agencies. A certain percentage of the sites should be developed in inaccessible areas where the land is inexpensive; however, these areas should be considered a small segment of the planned recreation "mix".

DETERMINATION OF AREA NEEDS BY USE-TYPE

By comparing recreation-day demands with recreation-day supply, the total surplus or total deficit of supply can be determined. The planner must then decide how to turn a total deficit of recreation days into meaningful terms that would be applicable to the development of a forest recreation area.

Some regional offices of the Bureau of Outdoor Recreation have derived the methodology to obtain the total average required for each type of use planned for the study area. [3] The methods given here can be used to determine area requirements by use-types for the development plan that is discussed in the next chapter.

The first step to take is to determine the developed area or the area that is actually occupied by the facilities. The second consists of converting developed area into total area. Since the predictions of use are based upon maximum use of the facilities, the use-days are determined by totaling the number of weekdays, weekend days, and holidays and equating them to weekend days.

A summer season usually reaches from Memorial Day through Labor Day and includes 14 weeks. The 14 weeks have 98 days of which 30 are weekend days or holidays. By assuming that 3 weekdays of use equals the use on one weekend day or holiday, the planner can equate the weekday use to holiday use by dividing the 68 weekdays in the period by 3. This resultant is added to the 30 weekend days occurring in the summer period. This means that the facilities are based upon 53 capacity days per year. Swimming is an exception to this assumption. Because of its susceptibility to being curtailed by inclement weather, swimming is computed at 80 percent of its capacity. Therefore, 42 days of swimming are assumed for each summer season.

All of the land required for one person to engage in the selected activity is included in the figures given in Table 4.5. This includes all the development that is necessary for that person.[3]

The information in Table 4.5 can be inserted in the formula given here to determine the area required to meet the predicted demand.

TABLE 4.5

ASSUMPTIONS AND STANDARDS USED IN DEVELOPING CONVERSION FACTORS FOR TRANSLATION OF DEMAND INTO ACREAGE NEEDS[a]

Activity	Number of people per car	Area required per person including parking (sq. ft.)	Turnover factor (TF)
Swimming	4	302[b]	1.5
Boating	3	544[c]	2.0
Picnicking	4	2725 to 726[d]	1.5
Camping	4	3640 to 907[e]	1.0

[a] Based upon the Report on Water Oriented Outdoor Recreation. Lake Erie Basin.

[b] Includes beach area.

[c] Includes ramp, car, and trailer.

[d] 4 to 15 tables per acre.

[e] 3 to 12 camping units per acre.

$$\text{Acreage required} = \frac{\text{Demand for activity} \times \text{area/person in sq.ft.}}{\text{Capacity days} \times \text{Turnover factor} \times 43{,}560}$$

$$= \frac{D \times a}{CD \times TF \times 43{,}560}$$

Sightseeing and walking require relatively little additional developed land and do not figure in the process of estimating required acreage. Therefore, the summation of the four listed activities will present an approximation of the developed area required to meet the recreational needs of the study area.

Extensively developed land has approximately 15 percent of its area developed. This means that for every acre of developed land, an extensive recreation area would have

67

$6\frac{7}{10}$ acres of undeveloped land. Class I or intensively developed land has approximately 70 percent of its area developed. Therefore, for every acre of developed land that it has, an intensively developed recreation area has $1\frac{4}{10}$ acres of land.

The extensive use factor of 6.7 and the intensive use factor of 1.4 can be averaged together to get a working index factor of 4 to apply to the demand acreages. By multiplying the index factor of 4 by the number of required developed acres, the planner can estimate the total acreage needs of recreation in the study area.

THE RECREATION PLAN

The recreation plan is a report that presents decisions concerning the recreational development of the study area. It is an outline of what is to be done in order to establish the recreation areas needed to meet the present and future demand deficits that have been estimated by the demand and supply inventories. A three-part recreation plan is used to present the proposed program for recreation development.

Part I of the recreation plan deals with the policy decisions concerning the type, quantity, placement, timing, and cost of the recreation facilities within the study area. This part should include statements to aid in the interpretation of the graphic section that follows.

Part 2 deals with the conflicts with other uses. It should recognize any conflicts that will result from the implimentation of Part 1 of the recreation plan. Specific steps should be laid out in this part of the plan to coordinate with all interested parties to alleviate any conflicts that will be caused by the development of recreation facilities within the study area.

Statements explaining policy on water pollution prevention, fire protection, hunting and fishing, and timber production should be included in this part of the report. Another topic that fits in here is the discussion on economic considerations resulting from the planned recreation facilities. This explains the

FIG. 4.1. Charnita, an all private outdoor recreation development, is located in south-central Pennsylvania where it lies on
the edge of the eastern megalopolis.

effect on the local tax base; the new service type facilities such as gasoline stations, motels, and restaurants that will follow the development phases; and the expected effect on regional employment that will be the result of increased recreational use of the study area.

Part 3 of the recreation plan is the graphic or visual aids section. It includes the maps, overlays, and photographs that are combined with the acreage and facility requirements to give an overall picture of the study area. The graphic section should be arranged very carefully so as to facilitate its use because it is the section of the plan that will be of interest to most people. Maps and graphs should be included to show the distribution of the effective population, of the recreation supply, and of the planned development areas.

The recreation plan should contain all the information and make all of the policy decisions that are needed to begin the development plans for each planned area. The recreation plan is neither a discussion of on-the-ground resource development nor is it a management plan for the study area.

TYPES OF USERS

Whatever facilities are built should depend upon their users. The types of facilities and the amount of site modification should depend upon what the user wants. User-wants are difficult to sample because use or even satisfaction does not mean preference. Enjoyment, enthusiasm, and satisfaction are relative with the individual and the situation. Campers may be satisfied to stay in a worn out, underserviced, and ill-equiped campground because they have never been to better facilities or because it is the only campground nearby their destination.

A resource-oriented study made by the National Advisory Council on Regional Recreation Planning recognizes the four user-oriented categories of sportsmen, family campers, resort users, and sightseers. [9] This text employs the facilities-oriented categories outlined by the Outdoor Recreation Resources

Review Commission since a major portion of planning is concerned with facility location.

FINANCING RECREATION DEVELOPMENT

The planner must realize what forms of financing recreation facilities are available to private investors and to government agencies. It is one thing to sit at the drawing board and plan recreation developments; but it is another problem to find the money for financing them. With the emphasis on user-oriented recreation areas where large effective populations exist, more costly facilities are needed to satisfy the ballooning demands. As more people become outdoor recreation-oriented, they want more variety in the selection of activities available. Beaches and marinas of the summer are being supplemented by ski-tows and toboggan runs during the winter months. Lodges, rental cabins, and elaborate camping areas probably will continue to be in demand. These are all very expensive facilities that may be out of reach of many landowners and government agencies. There is the possibility that a shortage of capital for these facilities could prevent their being available to help meet the growing recreation demands by the public.

A comprehensive discussion of recreation financing from a public agency viewpoint is presented in the ORRRC Study Report No. 12.[10] This report explains some of the financing methods available to recreation planners as well as outlining problems involved in financing this form of investment.

Many problems beset the planner who must be concerned with where the money comes from. He must count on construction work to progress on a seasonal basis and in locations where costs probably will be high because of inaccessibility. As mentioned earlier in this chapter, the facility may be under construction at the very time the public is losing interest in that form of activity. To help lessen the danger of obsolesence, the planner should include as much flexibility as possible. While flexibility helps to protect the capital investment, flexibility also raises the costs.[7]

TABLE 4.6
CATEGORIES OF FACILITY-ORIENTED USERS[a]

Categories	Brief description
1. Wilderness enthusiasts	Want no commercial development; perhaps no site modification that would interfere with their sense of isolation; relatively small group.
2. Sportsmen	Desire minimum of facilities; adhere to parts of wilderness approach, but conflict sharply on others; accept the need for capital investments for improvements better than any other group.
3. Day-use participants	Picnickers and swimmers generally accept and even require much site modification; willingness to pay; produce the most number of private successful ventures in some regions.
4. Campers	Generally families; fastest growing segment of forest recreation; widely varying opinions on site modifications; willingness to pay for elaborate facilities.
5. Winter sports enthusiasts	Rapidly growing in number; require the largest capital outlays; obtain biggest returns.
6. Boating enthusiasts	Great impact in recent years; cruising, waterskiing, and fishing have developed with reservoir construction in areas where recreation opportunities were previously scarce. Adequate facilities of marinas, lodging, and service are very expensive.
7. Resort users	Go to resorts, not to an activity; use urban facilities in outdoor or forest setting; various activities enhance stay at resort.
8. Sightseers	Extensive recreation users; use vistas, roadside rests, curio shops, marked trails, restaurants, and similar service facilities.

[a] ORRRC Study Report No.12.

Four of the five broad classes of financing outdoor recreation facilities that are listed in Table 4.7 are based upon those described by the Outdoor Recreation Resources Review Commission. One additional category has been added in this text to give credit to private enterprise for being in forest recreation without government prodding.[10] Each category is described briefly in the following paragraphs.

TABLE 4.7
BROAD CLASSES OF FOREST RECREATION FINANCING

No.	Class	Capital	Land-ownership	Management	Comments
1.	All private	Private	Private	Private	Own attractions
2.	Satellite	Private	Private	Private	Dependent upon nearby heavy-use public facilities
3.	Concession	Private	Public	Private	Large, government administered attraction
4.	Combination	Public and private	Public	Private or public	—
5.	All public	Public	Public	Public	—

All Private

Over 70 percent of the rural land in the United States is in private ownership.[15] Therefore, the use patterns of private lands will have a great influence on the development of forest recreation in one form or another. Although the Bureau of Outdoor Recreation is trying to remedy the problem, the unfortunate fact remains that most of the publicly administered forest, parks, and water frontage lie far from the population centers.[14] The United States Department of Agriculture claims that, "It is inevitable that a very high proportion of future outdoor recreation in this country will take place on or in association with privately owned facilities." [14]

Private enterprise can stand on its own two feet in forest recreation at any size level. Smaller private endeavors included in this class must have some attraction to bring visitors, be situated to gather in the en route transients, or fill a local need for that particular type of recreation. Large resort developments can create their own attractions such as lakes, golf courses, ski-tows, lodges, and cabins. The need for these forest resort cities is acute in the eastern Megalopolis as has been demonstrated by the instant success of the large ventures that have opened there during the last couple of years.

Private enterprise has the advantage over public development because private investment does not have to justify itself directly to the masses of taxpayers that must be served by publicly financed recreation. Therefore, private capital can be placed into specialized projects that meet a more limited desire than can public capital. [8]

In recognizing that private land and private capital must play a widespread role in supplying the needed recreation facilities, the federal government took steps to encourage private enterprise to enter this field by supplying technical assistance and even financial help in the form of loans. The main emphasis of this effort has been aimed at the rural landowner who could diversify his activities and get into outdoor recreation for a profit.

Unfortunately, many people at all levels of government view recreation as an "out" or the "missing industry" of poverty areas. As a result of this thinking, much of the federal assistance has been slanted toward marginal farmers. The assistance has been limited mostly to design details, planning assistance, and low cost credit while ignoring the more important problems of business management.

Managerial skill probably is the most important factor in making the business venture a success. [1] Also, foresight and available capital are two other leading reasons given for success or failure of a recreation enterprise. Managerial skills, foresight, and available capital are not generally processed by the marginal farmer that the government is now inviting into the recreation business. [7]

Satellite System

The second method of obtaining capital for recreation facilities is the reliance upon the satellite class of development. The satellite class, or gateway system, is made up of private capital on privately owned and operated areas near and dependent upon a large public recreation area. This system is officially recognized by the proponents of large public recreation areas as a way to preserve areas in a more natural state. Because of the mobility of today's visitors, public parks can be serviced by facilities located off the public land; thereby encouraging private investments that are dependent upon the park to draw the users.

The typical example of the satellite system in operation can be observed around Gettysburg, Pennsylvania. Here, the Gettysburg National Monument attracts tourists and Civil War buffs by the hundreds of thousands without providing them with any facilities or services other than information and minimal toilet facilities. Visitors to the national monument must rely entirely upon private capital ventures for all services and facilities.

A secondary satellite system has developed around a well known state park that receives much camper-use from Gettysburg tourists. Since dogs are excluded from Pennsylvania state parks, would-be campers are turned away to seek facilities elsewhere. Three private campgrounds have been established around this state park to cater to the needs of the dog-owners and overflow crowds. So the camper that has been attracted to the Gettysburg National Monument is excluded from the state park and ends up staying in a private campground.

The satellite system has received much criticism from those who believe that it creates a "honky-tonk" or "tourist-trap" atmosphere. True, the public agency's lack of control over the private development could prove to be a serious disadvantage. Poor quality accommodations and low caliber services can spring up under these situations.

Proponents of private enterprise can answer the criticisms on the lack of controls by reviewing the theory of supply and demand. If these tourist-trap conditions exist, as they often do, it is a result of the user-public's need. As this need for goods and services becomes large enough, competition becomes keen and the overall quality of the private developments increases. The pleasant environment and high standards of development surrounding the Gettysburg National Monument are credits to both an interested local population and private enterprise.

Whatever the arguments, the satellite system is working and it will continue to expand. Hopefully, the tourist-trap atmosphere will not gain the upperhand and spoil the entrances to all the heavily used park areas.

Concession System

The use of private capital and private management on public land makes the concession system of financing recreation.[10] This permits private capital to come into large public areas where there is heavy use and to operate a business without competition. The price paid for this privilege is regulation. The public agencies set standards for structures, services, and profit. A compromise between restrictions and profit is necessary in order to make this system work.

This compromise must be based upon some common sense assumptions in order to establish an equitable solution. The concession system is needed to obtain facilities and services to meet the growing recreation demand. Its success depends upon the fairness of this compromise between the public agency which is obligated to protect the public interests and the private investor who wants to make a profit. Table 4.8 lists some of the problems that a concessionaire must consider when

75

entering into a concession agreement with a governmental agency.

TABLE 4.8

SUMMARY OF ADVANTAGES AND DISADVANTAGES
OF THE CONCESSION SYSTEM FOR THE INVESTOR [a]

Advantages	Disadvantages
1. Attractive location maintained by government 2. Lack of competition 3. Captive clientile 4. Free publicity 5. Successful concession is in public interest	1. Shifting government policy 2. Harsh and uncertain wording of the contracts appear to favor the government 3. Political interference

[a] ORRRC Study Report No. 12.

Federal agencies have been the biggest exponent of the concession system, although the states have participated to a limited extent. The Departments of Agriculture, Interior, and Defense are the major agencies involved in supervising concessions within their jurisdiction. Of the individual bureaus, the Forest Service is the most deeply committed with over fifteen hundred concessions involved. [10]

Combination Class

The combination of private management of publicly owned facilities on public lands is the fourth basic method of financing recreation facilities. This method has been widely used by the states and to a limited extent by the federal governments.

This method of financing recreation facilities has worked with varying degrees of success; however, it has produced facilities when they would have been lacking otherwise. By charging rent for the facilities, a government agency relieves the operator from the long term investment of funds. This is often the situation at state owned day-use areas where the public wants to buy prepared food, curios, and miscellaneous necessities.

The other advantages of this system to the operator are captive clientile, lack of competition, and attractive surroundings which are similar to those advantages of the concession system. The disadvantages to the operator of political interference, fluctuating policy, and unequal appearing contracts are also similar. In this system, however, the operator may be less of a businessman than those involved in the large concession ventures. He may view the operation as a part time undertaking to provide his family with a summer's vacation. True, efficient businessmen do perform well in this system; however, the poorer managers have a good chance of becoming involved in these activities even though they do not have to have large sums for investment to qualify for the concession system class. True, the agency having the responsibility for the public interest in the area does have the final control over quality of operation in that it can refuse to renew the lease agreement.

All Public Class

Public ownership and management of facilities on public land is the fifth basic method of financing recreation developments. This method is very popular with state organizations who often view it as a way of avoiding concession-caused problems, maintaining absolute control, and producing a profit for the state. Private businessmen might question the efficiency of the state employee who does not have a true profit incentive.

One obvious problem here is that this situation favors political interference. All too often these facilities simply become another source of patronage jobs to be handed around by the politicians in power.[10] When this happens, the quality of employee drops.

77

REFERENCES

1. AGNEW, R. 1965. *Profitable Private Campground Construction and Operation.* Rajo Publications Inc., New York, N.Y. 50 pages.
2. BUREAU OF OUTDOOR RECREATION. 1966. Outdoor Recreation Requirements for the Upper Mississippi River Basin. Unpublished. Lake Central Region, BOR, Ann Arbor, Michigan.
3. BUREAU OF OUTDOOR RECREATION. 1966. Water Oriented Outdoor of Recreation, Lake Erie Basin. Unpublished. Lake Central Region, BOR, Ann Arbor, Michigan.
4. BUREAU OF OUTDOOR RECREATION. *Public Sector Inventory—Numerical List.* Northeast Region, BOR, Philadelphia, Pennsylvania.
5. CLAWSON, M. 1963. *Land and Water for Recreation.* Policy Background Series. Rand, McNally and Company. 145 pages.
6. CLAWSON, M. *et al.* 1960. *Land for the Future.* Resources for the Future, Inc. Johns Hopkins Press, Baltimore, Maryland. 500 pages.
7. GOULD, E.M. 1964. Forest Managers and Recreation Research. *Proceedings of Society of American Foresters, Allegheny.* Baltimore, Maryland.
8. LANE, R.D. 1964. Private Recreation Enterprises—Pie in the Sky? *Proceedings of the 19th Annual Meeting Soil Conservation Society of America.* Jackson, Mississippi.
9. NATIONAL ADVISORY COUNCIL ON REGIONAL RECREATION PLANNING. 1959. *A User—Resource Recreation Planning Method.*
10. OUTDOOR RECREATION RESOURCES REVIEW COMMISSION. 1962. *Paying for Recreation Facilities.* Study Report No. 12. Government Printing Office, Washington, D.C. 93 pages.
11. OUTDOOR RECREATION RESOURCES REVIEW COMMISSION. 1962. *National Recreation Survey.* Study Report No. 19. 394 pages.
12. OUTDOOR RECREATION RESOURCES REVIEW COMMISSION. 1962. *Prospective Demand for Outdoor Recreation.* Study Report No. 26. 61 pages.
13. RECREATION ADVISORY COUNCIL. 1964. *General Policy Guidelines for Outdoor Recreation.* Circular No. 2. Washington, D.C.
14. U.S. DEPARTMENT OF AGRICULTURE. 1962. *Rural Recreation—A New Farm Business.* Washington, D.C.
15. WOOTEN, H. and ANDERSON, J. 1954. Major Uses of Land in the United States. U.S. Department of Agriculture. *Agr. Information Bull.* No. 168. 31 pages.

CHAPTER 5

Site Selection

INTRODUCTION

In selecting the place, or site, of any recreation development, the planner is limited or guided by a set of principles and a number of basic site influencing factors. These principles and factors as discussed in this chapter are applicable to any form of forest-oriented recreation. Generally, the higher investment and more identifiable intensive-use areas receive most of the planner's attention. Camping, picnicking, skiing, and boating are typical examples of activities that require a relatively high degree of development. Other activities such as hunting and sightseeing have as many or more participants; however, hunting and sightseeing are less identifiable as activities requiring development of sites except in the large picture of highways, restaurants, and gas stations.

The configuration and variability of forest land presents a host of problems to the planner who is attempting to locate the most desirable site for an intensive-use recreation development. Everything will not be perfect. It is most likely that every site investigated will have some characteristic that will adversely influence the quality of the site's recreation potential. In each situation, the planner must weigh the advantages of the site against the price of overcoming its disadvantages. It must be looked at in this manner rather than advantages versus weaknesses because many site selection criteria become limiting factors if they are unfavorable. A swampy area would not serve well for a golf course; however, under unusual circumstances site modification could be done to permit such an establishment. The relative demand for such a development must be coupled with the available sites within the general location of the recreation development.

Site Selection

Three general principles of site selection should be observed in choosing sites that are to serve as recreation areas. First, the primary purpose of a recreation development must be to satisfy the user. The user must be satisfied with the development or eventually it will fail. This principle applies as readily to private enterprise undertakings where one might readily consider the making of money as the primary purpose. Profit is certainly the motive for going into business; however, the profit realized will usually depend upon the extent that the users' requirements are satisfied. If a public agency establishes recreation areas without serious regard to user needs, that agency is self-seeking or negligent in its duty to the tax-paying public.

Second, user convenience must be the prime reason for the selection of a site. Forest recreation is becoming people-oriented rather than resource-oriented. Therefore, development areas must be selected with regard to their convenience for the public rather than to the convenience for the resource manager. This principle has been part of the private investor's thinking right along. Public agencies and large landowners not seeking a profit from recreation have long considered recreation as a byproduct to be fitted in at the convenience of resource management. If the site can not be chosen for user convenience, that convenience must be built in. If sufficient lake frontage is unavailable to supply a lodge with a marina, then lagoons must be dug or lake frontage created to bring the users and the attraction together for the users' convenience.

Easy access to the area is a must. Back-pack hikers must first get to the wilderness area before they begin their hike into the back-country. In this case, convenience to the user refers to high quality access roads. Other forms of convenience might include such things as running water, charcoal burners, or even fully furnished cabins such as are available at West Virginia's Blackwater Falls State Park.

The third principle is concerned with the relationship between resource and user satisfaction. The resource must be adequate to provide sufficient enjoyment for the users. Tennessee Valley Authority lakes, Yellowstone National Park, and Vermont's Battenkill river are proven attractions that provide the users with almost unlimited opportunity for enjoyment. The recreation developments mentioned have adequate resources to fulfill the users' need. There are attractions to bring the visitors to the area. Also, each has a sufficient amount of land around the area or as part of it to provide for sufficient developed sites, proper setting, and additional side attractions. Some private recreation areas have invested thousands of dollars to bring the resource level up to that required to attract users. Additional attractions can stretch the resources of an area. A golf course at a ski area is an accepted way of keeping the public satisfied all year around. Also, the lake that serves as a hazard on the fifth or sixth hole can supply the water for the snow-making machines in the winter.

SITE INFLUENCING FACTORS

Certain physical factors influence the quality of recreation that can be developed on an area. These factors limit the type of development possible on a given site. The higher quality site will have a favorable summation of these influencing factors. Although individual factors can be ignored if the planner has unlimited capital, they are important enough to be limiting without the expenditure of funds to change them. Each site influencing factor constitutes a scientific field of its own and can not be covered completely here. This chapter briefly relates the role of each factor to its influence on an intensive recreation area. Table 5.1 lists the five major site factors that influence the quality of an intensive forest recreation area.

TABLE 5.1
SITE FACTORS INFLUENCING QUALITY OF FOREST
RECREATION AREAS

Climate
Topography
Soils
Water
General environment

Site Selection

Climate

Climate is defined by Webster as, "the average condition of the weather at a place over a period of years". The climatic data that is compiled over many years is composed of the many elements of weather such as temperature, humidity, precipitation, and prevailing wind direction. Climate is generally considered to mean a summary of weather variations on a regional basis.[1] Therefore, the argument can be raised that this chapter is dealing with microclimate; that is, the local weather conditions that exist at one small area and are influenced by the conditions at that area. The major weather elements that form the climate of an area are temperature, major air movements, and precipitation. Microclimate on any given site is influenced by the factors of temperature, aspect, air drainage, exposure, wind, rainfall, and position on the slope.

Microclimate

TEMPERATURE. Data concerning temperature give the planner a great deal of insight into the expected quality of site. Daily or monthly mean temperatures can be compared with the regional means to determine if the site is adversely or favorable affected by microclimatic influences. Mean summer temperatures will influence the vegetation that can be grown on an area and therefore has a direct relationship with forest recreation.[1] Temperature ranges are important in site selection. A large spread between the mean daily high temperature and the mean daily low temperature is undesirable for recreation areas. Sites with more uniform temperatures should be sought. The mean daily high (or low) temperature can be determined by recording the highest (or lowest) temperature reached each day of a month and averaging those figures.

Although pressure systems and frontal changes influence the weather regionally, they have slightly varying impacts on each different site. These varying impacts are brought about by the factors affecting the microclimate of a site. Aspect, exposure, elevation, and air-drainage influence the temperatures at a

82

given site and cause some sites to be more favorable than others for recreation.

ASPECT. The compass direction in which a slope faces dictates its aspect. Foresters have long recognized that certain aspects are better than others for timber growth. Timber growth is only of parallel interest to recreation; however, the things that cause better or poorer timber growth could have some affect on forest recreation quality. The east slope receives morning sunshine and afternoon shade and may be the best aspect for campgrounds. The morning sun can warm the rising campers and dry out the damp site. Since most camping is done in the summer, afternoon heat is a problem. By placing the campground on the east slope, the planner can take advantage of the afternoon shade to cool the campground. In far northern states, any aspect might be satisfactory for winter sports. Perhaps the southerly slopes will help to warm skiers or skaters. However, in most locales, the north slopes are most favorable because of the protection they offer to the snow. West or southerly aspects are best for swimming beaches. People tend to swim during the afternoon and generally prefer the sun to shade. Vistas and scenic overlooks must be placed where they are most effective; however, a northerly aspect is best whenever a choice exists. The northerly aspect places the sun at the observers back and not in his eyes. Also, the sunlight gives better accent and lighting on the scene when viewed from this aspect.

AIR DRAINAGE. Air drainage plays an important role in microclimate in that it affects temperature, humidity, and fog. Colder air sinks to the lower levels. Cold air and humidity collect in low areas where they remain during periods of quiet air. During clear, calm evenings heat is lost by radiation, causing a further reduction in temperature. If the air temperature is lowered below saturation point, radiation fog is formed.[1] Although smog is usually associated with cities it is common in campgrounds and picnic areas where poor air drainage exists. A blue-grey blanket of smoke and cooking gases hangs over many crowded campgrounds. This problem is not serious if there is a wind strong enough to form turbulance and thereby improve the air drainage. Smog is a local phenomenon that occurs when air temperatures rise with increasing altitude instead of falling with altitude thereby prohibiting the fouled air from escaping by normal convection currents.

Poor air drainage areas can be avoided by keeping the recreation area out of the low places and off stream bottoms. Air drainage can be improved within picnic and campground areas by creating "chimney effects" in the overhead cover to permit better ventilation.

EXPOSURE. The exposure of an area to sunlight plays an important role in determining microclimate. Exposure differs from aspect in that exposure refers to the ability of sunlight to fall on an area. The southern aspect would be expected to have the greatest exposure; however, the lower portion of the slope may lie within the shadows of another mountain and thereby have a low exposure time. Sites with high exposure times tend to become hot and not desirable except as swimming areas or for use in late fall, winter, or early spring when the heating effects of long exposure time are welcomed.

WIND. The prevailing wind should be considered when positioning cabins, tents, and camping unit interiors. The door of a cabin or tent should not face directly into the prevailing winds nor should the tent pad be located just downwind from the fireplace. Wind blowing over a long water surface can cause relatively large waves on lakes; therefore, boat landings should not be placed at the end of the long axis of a lake when other sites are available.

Winter sports are severely affected by wind. Ski slopes and sledding hills can be scoured clean of snow by winds. On the other hand, constant drifting at an inconvenient location will require snow removal funds to be expended. Ice skaters prefer to skate where there is little or no wind; therefore, an artificial barrier might be required if the site does not lie in the lee of a natural windbreak. Climatic data obtainable from the local weather station will provide the overall picture concerning the winter weather over the area; however, on site, investigation

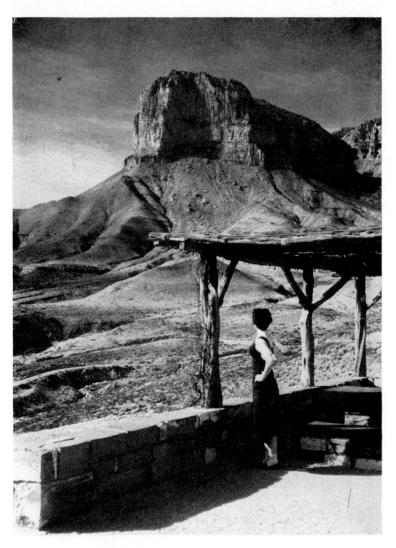

Fig. 5.1. Shelter to protect picnickers from New Mexico sun.

should be made to determine the prevailing wind directions during the snow season. On the ground observations will give an indication of what to expect. Also, the valuable knowledge of local citizens probably will provide the investigator with the most specific information.

RAINFALL. The amount of rain that falls is generally uniform over a large region so that alone it does not influence the individual site selection to a great extent. However, when combined with other site influencing factors, rainfall becomes very important in influencing the quality of a recreation site. Satisfactory outdoor recreation areas have been developed on the wet Olympic Peninsula of Washington as well as on the Big Bend National Park in Texas. However, the amount of rain that falls does affect greatly the impact that other factors have on the quality of the site.

Dampness, dreary weather, mud, and damage to the ground are problems that occur more readily in areas that are wet during the heavy-use period. More day-lighting or removal of overstory vegetation is required to dry out areas. Also, more shelters are needed to provide people with wet weather activity space. In the hot, dry Southwest, shelters are constructed to provide shade for the users.

Dust, limited vegetation growth, and recreation area damage are problems to be faced on dry site recreation areas. Irrigation may be necessary to provide enough water for the vegetation to recover from trampling and to grow. Plantings of all kinds may be necessary to provide an adequate ground cover and shade in areas of dry-season use.

POSITION ON SLOPES. The placement of the recreation area on the terrain is important to the user because this decision has a great bearing on user comfort throughout the life of the development. The hillside should be divided into the lower, the middle, and the upper third of the slope and each third considered as to its affects on recreation. The position on slope has some effect upon the exposure of the site to sunshine, air drainage patterns, and temperature extremes. Although exposure is related to aspect, it is not identical. Lower slopes are exposed to sunshine for a much shorter period than the upper slopes of the same aspects; therefore, the lower slopes tend to be cooler and damper with poorer air drainage. As a result of poor air drainage the smoke filled and moisture laden air lingers on the lower slopes. Convection currents move the cool air downslope at night so that the cold air collects in the bottom of valleys.[1]

The upper slopes have the greatest extremes in temperature. They get very hot during the day when they are exposed to the sun. In the eastern mountains, the overstory vegetation is of poor quality on the upper slopes as a result of exposure and dryness of site. The poorer quality overstory that is found on the upper slope permits more sunlight to strike the forest floor. In the evening, the sparser vegetation permits relatively more heat loss by radiation than do the closed canopies on the lower slopes. The upper slopes are more exposed to wind than the other slope positions and are considerably drier as a result. Fire, which is the third major problem in recreation, is a relatively more serious threat on the dry, wind swept upper slopes than it is on the lower slopes.

The middle slopes offer the best microclimatic conditions for recreation area development. Morning updrafts and evening downdrafts produce good ventilation and provide a moderating effect on the temperature. Middle slopes may lack sufficient benches or other gently sloping terrain to extablish recreation areas without a great amount of earth moving. However, middle slope sites are superior to upper and lower slope sites and should be considered for development whenever possible.

Topography

The relative configuration of the land or topography plays a major role in determining the recreational quality of a site. The influence of land relief exhibits itself as the steepness of slope, the position on slope, the aspect of the slope, and the relative position of attractions to possible hazards or detractants.

86

A site's steepness, or its percent of slope, play a basic role in determining its use for recreational development. Obviously, moderately steep slopes make better ski runs than softball fields. Since campgrounds should be developed on slopes that are less than 10 percent, the location of such gentle sloping areas strongly guides the placement of campgrounds and picnic areas.[2] While the rugged mountains provide a picturesque setting, the more level spots provide the sites for recreation site development. If level places do not exist for parking, tenting, and playing, they must be made. Steeper slopes mean greater costs for building level sites.

Steeper slopes require longer trails, more steps, or steeper grades. Road and trail layout is restricted by steep slopes which also limit accessibility. Also, the dangers of erosion and slides are greater than they are on more gently rolling land. However, level land is not without hazards. Level areas might be poorly drained and therefore unsuitable for dispersal fields, heavy traffic, or structures.

In some parts of the West and Southwest where forest and bush fires are hazards to human life, certain features of topography become important. Box canyons with only one easy exit should be avoided in site selection. The dangers of flooding or wash-outs should influence the choice of sites along rivers and streams.

The relative positions of the selected sites to the attraction, ease of movement between them, and access to the sites are reflections of the general configuration of land. Cliffs, rock outcrops, and swamps can be attractions or hazards to recreation development depending upon their nature and location.

Soils

The problems associated with soils are many and difficult to overcome. Generally, an understanding of the physical properties of the soils in an area is needed in order to avoid problem soils and to choose ones favorable to the selected use. Erosion, compaction, trafficability, drainage, and slope are five of the physical properties of soil that must be considered in site selection. These five properties are considered as hazards to any kind of management that takes place on the ground. Unfortunately, use restrictions due to soil conditions are even less practical in forest recreation management than they are in any other kind of forest resources management.

Recreation areas should be located on gently sloping areas that have deep, well drained soils that are of medium textures. The heavier soils of silt and clay are more susceptible to puddling,† surface runoff, and erosion. Very coarse soils such as sands are not as desirable as the loams of the medium textured soils because the coarse textured soils tend to be droughty. As a result, they will not support the grasses and understory that is so desirable in recreation areas. One advantage to the very course soil material is the lack of dust and mud.

Adverse soil conditions do not always preclude the use of an area; however, they do demand special attention if the area is to prove satisfactory. Experienced, trained soil scientists should be consulted to gain information about the soils in specific spots.

Water

Water is an essential ingredient of most recreation areas. It is required for the existence needs of cooking, washing, and drinking and for the recreational needs of swimming, boating, or fishing. Chapter 15 deals extensively with the supply of water needed to meet existence needs. The problems of water quality, quantity, source, treatment, and distribution must be considered by the planner to develop a safe and adequate water system.

Recreation water is required for the successful operation of most forest recreation areas. It is an attraction; therefore, sites should be located with a view of the water whenever possible.

† Puddling refers to loss of soil structure because of use when too wet or too dry.

Care must be taken to avoid locating the development along the edge of the water where the development could spoil the attraction. Although recreational water quality need not be so high as existence water, minimum standards do exist. Some states

TABLE 5.2
SOURCES OF WATER FOR EXISTENCE AND RECREATION NEEDS

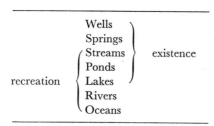

permit public bathing in water with a coliform organism count of 2400 per 100 ml of water. Most areas consider the safe limit for bathing water to be 1000 coliform organisms per 100 ml of water.[3] Hazards such as dangerous undertow, swift current, or rocky bottoms should be considered in choosing a site with water as an attraction.

General Environment

A junkyard and the county dump would not make good neighbors for a forest recreation area. In general, the quality of an area is affected by the esthetic level of its surroundings. The problem of the character of the surroundings falls into the category of general environment. Is the area large or small? Is it accessible? What is the cover type of the area? What building materials are natural to the area? These are some of the questions concerning the general environment. In general, a planner should search for accessible areas within a setting that would not be adversely influenced by adjacent developments. Occasionally, the area to be developed is the local eye-sore such as was the case with Kickapoo State Park in Illinois that is an abandoned strip-mine turned into a state park complete

89

with camping, picnicking, and fishing. As the size of a recreation area increases, the impact of the surrounding developments decrease. When the recreation areas cover thousands of square miles, the internal facilities can remain somewhat immune to the conditions outside.

The nature of the vegetation cover is of some concern to the planner because it tells him how much modification will be required to raise the site-quality to the prescribed level. The percentage of wooded or cleared land can help him determine the costs of cutting or of planting. The presence of noxious weeds such as poison ivy or poison oak will mean an eradication program.

The presence of local building material may prove to be a cost reduction factor as well as a good way to provide a more natural flavor to the construction projects.

No matter how many site influencing factors are considered in site selection the most important thing to strive for is the primary purpose of a recreation area. The primary purpose of a recreation area is to produce user satisfaction.

References

1. Neuberger, H. and Stevens, F. 1948. *Weather and Man*. Prentice Hall Incorporated, New York. 272 pages.
2. U. S. Forest Service. 1963. *Recreation Management*. Title 2300 of *Handbook and Manual*. U.S. Department of Agriculture, Washington, D.C.
3. U. S. Public Health Service. 1965. Environmental Health Practice in Recreation Areas. U.S. Department of Health, Education, and Welfare. *Public Health Service Bull.*, No. 1195. Washington, D.C.

CHAPTER 6

Recreation Area Development

INTRODUCTION

The next step after recreation planning is the development of specific recreation areas. How many campsites? How many picnic tables? Where will they be located? Can day-use and overnight areas be developed on the available spaces? Where will the roads be located? How will the drinking water be supplied? These questions and others are answered in the development plan. The purpose of the development plan is to get the on-the-ground layout plans completed.

As considered here, a developed area is a relatively small area of contiguous land that will be administered and managed by one supervisor and whatever staff is required to assist him. Development plans are confined to specific locations that are joined together by the same attraction. As such, development plans are resource-oriented in that they are based upon the recreation resources of the designated area that can be used to satisfy the recreation demand. The recreation plan as discussed in Chapter 4 is generally population-oriented and provides the general information needed to arrive at the number of various types of facilities required. This chapter on recreation area development is concerned with the on-the-ground problems associated with the creation of intensive-use recreation sites. The actual selection of individual sites, the design and layout of recreation areas, and construction specifications for the facilities are part of recreation development.

Certain assumptions are made at the beginning of the development program.[7] These assumptions are based upon data compiled in the recreation plan. For small areas or private land where no overall recreation plan exists, these assumptions are based upon the landowner's desire and upon information gathered during the early stages of development planning. Examples of the basic assumptions needed for the creation of a specific development plan are:

1. The recreation development is wanted, authorized, or needed.
2. The predicted use is given or is obtainable.

Generally, the development plan is based upon the predicted use and the land available. These factors are brought together in the investigation phase which is the first half of the development plan. By working with the resources and demands, the developer can create the working report which is the second half of the development plan.

For its purposes in area planning, the United States Forest Service usually limits development areas to approximately one hundred acres.[15] However, this size constitutes the area of substantial modification and does not include the general environment or setting requirements. For the purpose of this book, the development area will be dictated by the resources available and the quantity of land that can be managed and administered under one superintendent and his staff.

INVESTIGATION OF THE PROBLEM

The purpose of the problem investigation is the location, selection, and the layout of the recreation facilities. This is accomplished by determining what facilities are required to meet the demand and then by placing them on the most desirable sites whenever possible.

Types of Activities

The type of recreational activity developed will be dictated by the decisions made in the planning stages. These decisions will be influenced by the expected demands of the perspective users and by the resources available. A scarcity of land will

limit both the type and the quantity of recreation development. On the other hand, large tracts of available land with a
varied landscape offer many opportunities for diversity in
development. A small area near a large population center will
be able to serve the greatest number of people if it is developed
for day-use activities such as picnicking where there can be a
high turnover rate among users and where a high density of
use can be achieved. If the day-use demand is not overwhelming, a small tract of land in a scenic setting and near an attraction could be developed into a campground. Since the larger
tracts of land permit versatility of design and more variety of
types of activities, they are more desirable to work with. The
presence or absence of recreational water certainly will alter
decisions concerning the type of recreation. Water for swimming is practically a must for successful private recreation areas
and very desirable for all day-use areas.[9]

Available funds might limit the actual development in spite
of what the plan might call for. Private developers might
operate on a fractional level to test public response or to gain
income. Also, costs of campgrounds might force their post-
ponement in favor of the more profitable picnic areas when
funds are limited. Even though these approaches to the problem might prove to be detrimental to the success of private
recreation areas, they are resorted to as a result of insufficient
capital.[8]

Predicted Use

The predicted use of the different types of facilities can be
obtained from the recreation plan, from estimates based on
location and attractions, or by checking on use at nearby
developments that offer similar facilities.

Required Facilities

Turning the predicted use figures into required facilities is
a trick that often appears to be sleight-of-hand. The most
reliable technique for this operation is that of using constants

to convert predicted use into required acres of land for each type of use. A complete discussion of this technique is included in Chapter 4 of this text. The use of the constants technique is included in Example B of the Development Plan given later in this chapter.

Many central camps approach a density of twelve camping units per acre and some states are attempting to achieve a picnic table density of fifteen per acre. Observation has shown that density on privately operated areas probably varies with nearness to major attractions. [1, 10] In areas where land values are high and the demand is heavy, the units are crowded more closely together for the purpose of gaining more use per acre of land. By using the same logic, one can reason that the private operator must offer something more attractive when his land is not overrun by people desperately clamoring to camp or picnic at a very popular resort.

As mentioned earlier in this chapter, the size of the development might be limited by the available resources and by the desire of the landowner. After the basic assumption that the recreation area is needed has been made, the resources available might dictate the types and quantity of recreation facilities even more than the predicted use. If recreational water is available, it should be developed for swimming and boating. [8] The site selection factors that are discussed in Chapter 5 should be reviewed so that the developer is familiar with the physical factors that influence the recreational quality of the site. The amount of land that has high potential for recreation will help determine size, location, and amount of the recreation facilities.

Another resource to consider here is that of operating personnel. Some types of developments need more watching or administration than do others. If operating personal will be a problem, the size or type of developments will be limited. Family operated picnic grounds may be based upon the amount of work each member of the family can contribute. The hiring of reliable outside help might be too expensive or even impossible.

Inventory

The heart of the investigation is the inventory of the area. What possibilities exist? Where are the most desirable locations? What limitations must be placed on their use? Are they accessible? These are just some of the many questions that the inventory will answer for the developer. Before he can act wisely, the developer should have a thorough working knowledge of the area. He must know:

1. The legal boundaries of the area and have them clearly marked.
2. The configuration of the landscape as it includes drainages, ridges, slopes, springs, cliffs, and other topographical features.
3. The geology of the underlying rock.
4. The soils that comprise the area.
5. The vegetation types and associations that cover the soil mantle.
6. All cultural improvements that lie on or that directly influence the area to be developed.
7. Past management history.
8. Any zoning or planning ordinances that might restrict his decisions.

GRAPHIC RECONNAISSANCE. There are many tools available to the developer who is willing to gather them together. The most basic step in the graphic reconnaissance is that of obtaining a copy of the legal plat or map of the property. The plat and legal discription of the property are on record at the county Recorder of Deeds' office and are usually obtainable through the County Surveyor's office. If there is any doubt concerning the property boundaries, the County Surveyor should be contacted. In the event that the property boundaries require relocation, the landowner's capital investment will not have been placed in jeopardy by the developers lack of investigation and poor professional competence.

The title should be checked for encumbrances that could cause legal problems in the future. In many cases, a relatively

95

small investment in legal assistance at this point in the investigation will save much heartache and cost later on. The legal fees and even the resurveying costs are small prices to pay for the security and benefits they offer.

Some other tools available in making the graphic reconnaissance are topographic maps, aerial photographs, geology maps, and soil maps. Skilful interpretation of the information displayed on these publications will enable the developer to compile much pertinent data concerning the site. These maps were compiled by experts in each of the fields and thereby present more information than any developer could collect by himself. The topographic map, soils map, geology map, and aerial photograph useage in graphic reconnaissance is discussed in the following paragraphs.

Topographic map. The most familiar tool in the graphic investigation is the United States Geologic Survey quadrangle sheet. The quadrangle sheet or "contour map" is produced by the Army Map Service and published for civilian use by the United States Geologic Survey. It graphically displays such topographic features as land configuration and streams; cultural features such as roads and buildings; and, optionally, such vegetative cover as forests and orchards. The original USGS sheets included 15 minutes of longitude and 15 minutes of latitude and usually were printed at the scale best suited for general use in that portion of the country. In areas where problems of national significance occur, the scales of 1:31,680 or 1:24,000 were used. Areas of average national importance were surveyed for publication at a scale of 1:62,500.

After World War II the 15 minute guadrangle was generally abandoned in favor of the $7\frac{1}{2}$ minute quadrangle sheet which shows greater detail. Most of the nation is now scheduled for resurvey into $7\frac{1}{2}$ minute quadrangles. The new quadrangle sheets give a very good presentation of the natural and cultural features of the land. Unfortunately, four $7\frac{1}{2}$ minute quadrangle sheets now replace one 15 minute sheet. This means more shuffling of papers in the office or field to get the proper coverage. The use of scissors and rubber cement will pay great dividends before the project is complete. It is strongly recommended that one map showing the entire tract and its immediate surroundings be constructed from what ever number of $7\frac{1}{2}$ minute sheets are required.

TABLE 6.1
SCALES COMMONLY USED ON USGS STANDARD TOPOGRAPHIC MAPS

Reference fraction	Engineer's scale	Contour interval
1:24,000	1 inch = 2000 feet	1 to 100 feet
1:31,680	1 inch = $\frac{1}{2}$ mile	1 to 100 feet
1:62,500	1 inch = 1 mile (approx.)	10 to 100 feet
1:63,360	1 inch = 1 mile	(Alaska only)
1:125,000	1 inch = 2 miles (approx.)	20 to 250 feet
1:250,000	1 inch = 4 miles (approx.)	20 to 250 feet

Status maps showing the completed survey work for each state are available from the Geological Survey Distribution Section, Washington, D.C., for areas east of the Mississippi River and from the Geological Survey Distribution Section, Denver, Colorado for states west of the Mississippi River. Also, a free folder explaining the topographic maps and symbols can be obtained from the same places.

The quadrangle sheets can be obtained at local distribution points within each state as explained on the back of the state's status map. However, highly satisfactory service is rendered to those who choose to deal directly with the regional distribution sections in Washington and in Denver. Order forms and the price list accompany the status maps and should be used in ordering maps whenever possible. The current price is 30 cents per sheet with a discount of 20 percent on orders exceeding 10 dollars.[17]

Geology maps. Geology maps are available for each county from the state office of the U.S. Geological Survey. These are generally high quality maps that are accompanied by an excellent description of each geologic strata and its effect upon the landscape. Knowledge of the underlying rocks is helpful in interpreting the topography, evaluating possible sites, locating roads, and searching for water supplies.

Soil maps. The United States Soil Conservation Service has the responsibility for soil correlation and mapping in the United States. Copies of soil association maps are usually available from the County Work Unit Conservationist or from the state office of the Soil Conservation Service. This department is readily available and quite willing to help on all soil and related problems. The soil association map should be accompanied by brief descriptions of the soils found in each association stating their capabilities and limitations. A knowledge of the soils in the area is of the utmost importance if future problems are to be minimized. In limited areas, the U.S. Forest Service soil scientists have produced outstanding maps of soils occurring in and around national forests. Information can be obtained from these maps by contacting the appropriate forest supervisor.

Aerial photographs. The use of aerial photographs for graphic reconnaissance is rapidly becoming very popular. A wealth of information concerning topography, vegetation, geology, and existing roads and structures can be obtained from aerial photographs. Much information can be gained from simple imagery interpretation if the observer has some knowledge of aerial photographs. More specific facts can be obtained by basic photogrametric techniques of height and distance measurements.

Aerial photographs are intended to be taken with the camera perpendicular to the earth's surface or at a planned angle from the perpendicular. The former, or vertical photography, is the most commonly used and the easiest to obtain. The latter, or oblique photography, shows a good perspective scene but is not suited for accurate interpretation by anyone except highly trained and well equipped specialists. The oblique photograph does have a display value for the recreation developer. The relative landscape is more discernable to the public when viewed on the familiar high oblique that shows the horizon than it is on the vertical photographs. These high oblique photographs are more difficult to obtain; however, they do help in advertising or in public relations when they can be obtained.

The vertical photograph can be easily obtained at various scales from the regional office of the Agricultural Stabilization and Conservation Service (ASCS). The ASCS distributes the photographs taken for other agencies as well as those flown for ASCS purposes. If the owning agency is unknown, the order should be handled by the Coordinator of Aerial Photograph Work at the Washington office of the ASCS. The regional laboratory offices of ASCS are:[2]

Eastern Laboratory	Western Laboratory
Aerial Photography Division	Aerial Photography Division
ASCS—USDA	ASCS—USDA
45 South French Broad Avenue	2505 Parley's Way
Asheville, North Carolina 28801	Salt Lake City, Utah 84109

The first step in purchasing the required photographs for the job is to obtain a photo index sheet of the county concerned. The photo index sheet is a picture taken of all the aerial photographs that have been matched together on a flat surface so as to give the appearance of a county map. More than one photo index sheet may be required to give entire county coverage. These index sheets can be viewed at the local ASCS office, the Soil Conservation Service office, or by contacting the county agent of the State University Extension Service if such a program exists. The index sheets can be requested from the regional ASCS office for a cost of $2.00 per sheet.

In most cases, existing photographs are adequate for the purpose of recreation development. They are taken on black and white panchromatic film with high precision equipment and are printed on single or double weight semi-matte paper. If the ASCS supplied photographs are not adequate for the developer's needs, he can contract with any of several competent private businesses to fly the required photographs. One note of caution should be sounded here. Reliable firms with long records of success should be contacted. If color film is to

99

be used, the cost of the delivered prints may run twice as much as for panchromatic film; therefore, avoid contractors that have not had a great amount of experience in color photography. [6]

TABLE 6.2

PARTIAL DATA CONCERNING AERIAL PHOTOGRAPHS AVAILABLE FROM THE AGRICULTURAL STABILIZATION AND CONSERVATION SERVICE

Scale (approx.)	Engineers scale (approx.)	Print dimensions (in.)	Cost per print[a] in quantity		
			1 — 5	6 — 100	100 +
1:20,000	1 in. = 1667 ft	10 × 10	$1.00	$0.90	$0.70
1:15,840	1 in. = 1320 ft	14 × 14	$2.30	$2.00	$1.70
1:12,000	1 in. = 1000 ft	18 × 18	$2.50	$2.20	$1.90
1:7920	1 in. = 660 ft	26 × 26	$3.00	$2.60	$2.30
1:4800	1 in. = 400 ft	40 × 40	$7.00	$6.00	$5.00

[a] Costs are given for double weight semi-matte paper.

Although the single vertical aerial photograph is not a map in the photogrametric sense, it does serve as a very good guide to the landscape. An experienced interpreter can evaluate several factors that aid in identifying images shown on aerial photographs. Avery lists shape, size, tone, pattern, shadow, topographic location, and texture as the seven most important factors. [2]

Single photographs, usually at a scale of 1:15,840, make excellent field sheets and are often carried by soil scientists and foresters who make notes directly on the photograph surface with soft pencil. This mapping or sketching technique permits spots to be pinpointed on the photograph by the man looking at that location. The location of specific landmarks both on the photograph and on the ground eliminates any need for mistake producing measurements.

By the use of conjugal pairs, or overlapping photographs, a third-dimension model of the overlapped area can be viewed. This third dimension, or stereoscopic model is the same view that an airplane passenger would have when looking vertically downward upon the photographed area.

Fig. 6.1. The final working map gives the diagramatic outline
of the proposed recreation sites.

Fig. 6.2. The telescopic alidade and statia method will produce a very satisfactory plane table map showing a five-foot contour interval.

The use of conjugal pairs and a few simple photogrametric techniques will enable the trained interpreter to select possible sites for the developed facilities, to layout roads, to analyze the vegetative cover, and to make other tentative development decisions.

By judicious use of USGS quadrangle sheets and aerial photographs, the developer will be able to pre-select several possible sites for the developed areas without making the expensive field trips that would otherwise be necessary. When the possible sites have been marked on the topographic map or on one aerial photograph, the developer can make his way directly to each one for an on-the-ground reconnaissance. This will greatly reduce the time required in investigating the area and help to prevent the developer from wondering around in the woods hoping to stumble onto a suitable site.

Working map. A final working map will be needed to develop the second portion of the Development Plan. It is a good idea to begin the first draft of the working map while involved in the graphic reconnaissance. As data concerning possible sites are compiled, they can be recorded directly upon the working map. Also, as the graphic reconnaissance progresses, the picture of possible sites will become clear on the working map whereas it would be a jumble of facts and figures in a notebook.

Scales of 1 inch = 400 feet or 1 inch = 500 feet have proved to be satisfactory for development planning. The former scale is probably more favorable on areas of less than 1000 acres. An advantage of making the working map at a scale of 1 inch = 400 feet is the similarity to the scale of the 40 inch × 40 inch aerial photograph enlargements available from the ASCS. Although the scale is neither uniform nor exact at all points on the photograph, it is approximate enough to use in locating cultural improvements and vegetative covers that are not shown on the quadrangle sheet.

Most quadrangle sheets are sufficiently accurate to serve as the working map. The purpose of the working map is to diagrammatically show the proposed recreation sites and the road network required to serve them. All the developer has to do is reproduce the desired portions of the quadrangle sheet at the proper scale for his working map. Changing scales is a real-itively simple problem that can be easily overcome. The steps for redrawing the topographic map at the larger scale when a projection table is not available are given below:[12]

Step 1. Block off the development area on the quadrangle sheet so that it forms a rectangle with the left side-line running north–south.

Step 2. Grid the rectangle. Construct parallel north–south lines with one-quarter inch spacing. Then construct parallel lines that are perpendicular to the north–south line with quarter inch spacing. This divides the area into blocks that are one-quarter of an inch square.

Step 3. Letter each north–south line and number each east–west line for identification. This gives each line inter-section an identity.

Step 4. Divide the desired scale by the quadrangle scale to get the conversion factor.

EXAMPLE:

$$\frac{\text{desired scale}}{\text{quadrangle scale}} = \text{C. F.}$$

$$\frac{\dfrac{1}{400}}{\dfrac{1}{2000}} = 5$$

Step 5. Grid the sheet of drawing paper with the lines placed so that they are spaced according to the product of the original spacing and the conversion factor. In the case of the example, the inter-line spacing should be 5/4 inches.

Step 6. Letter and number the grid lines as in step 3.

Step 7. Transfer data from the topographic quadrangle to the working map by using the points where the contours, natural features, and cultural improvements intersect the gridlines.

GROUND RECONNAISSANCE. Nothing will substitute for an on-the-ground inspection of perspective sites and water sources. The developer and whatever technical assistants that he requires must get out to take a look at the land. Aerial photographs and maps are only tools to assist the developer and to make his job easier. They do not replace the need for him to see the area with his own eyes; to walk over the ground; and to check out his graphic interpretations of slope, vegetative cover, soil, drainage, rock cover, and water sources. When he is on the ground at each site, the developer can use a check list of the recreation site influencing factors listed in Chapter 5.

Ground reconnaissance can be expensive if one simply strolls through the woods observing things as he goes. A developer's time is better spent in doing what he is being paid to do, which is to develop a recreation area. Therefore, he must rely upon his graphic interpretation for guidance unless the area is very small and easily traversed. Anyway, the stereoscopic view of the aerial photographs generally gives the observer a better perspective of the landscape than he can get by standing on the site. This is especially true in heavily forested areas.

While making the ground reconnaissance, the developer must make up his mind which sites will be best suited for each planned activity. He must locate the needed acres for picnicking, for camping, for bathing, and for whatever other activities are required by the master plan.

Site maps. After the sites are chosen, each site should be mapped to a scale of 1 inch = 60 feet to make the working drawing of that area's layout. Each campground, picnicground, beach, and other type area is shown on the master working map as a diagrametric outline along with its road network. The individual sites become the focus of attention while their internal layouts are planned. The detailed map of each area should be made in the field using either plane table

103

or transit methods. The telescopic alidade and stadia rod will produce a very satisfactory plane table map showing 5-foot contours. If a smaller contour interval is required, the transit and grid technique should be used. However, this technique is not too satisfactory on wooded land or where expenses are limited. Some U.S. Forest Service developers demand that a one-foot contour map be made. This is an expensive and even doubtful venture on wooded land; however, it may be necessary where the land is nearly flat, extensive paving is to be done, or doubt exists about the placement of septic tank drain fields and water lines.

Using the layout techniques discussed in Chapters 8 through 13, the different facilities should be drawn on the 1 inch = 60 feet working map so as to take advantage of the topography. The layout should show all roads, trails, structures, units, water lines, absorption fields, and power lines where applicable.

The Development Report

The Development Report describes the planned recreation sites, the proposed facilities, the proposed timetable of development, and the estimated costs involved. The facts gathered and the decisions made during the investigative phase of the development plan are presented and explained within this Report. A suggested outline for this Report is presented below. This outline is presented as a guideline and is open for modification to fit the circumstances. [1, 7, 16]

Suggested Outline for Development Report

    I. Introduction
        A. Objective of development plan
        B. Description of the area
           1. Size and ownership
           2. Location and setting
           3. General topography
           4. Accessibility

C. Statement of recreation needs in area

    1. Present and predicted use of nearby facilities

    2. Estimated use through year 2020 (Table 1)

II. Required Areas and Facilities

  A. Conversion of predicted use into facilities and costs (Tables 2 and 3)

  B. Proposed sites and their development timetable (Table 4)

III. Detailed Descriptions of Each Proposed Site

  A. Data sheet

    1. Name

    2. Type of recreation activity

    3. Location

    4. Size

    5. Area description

      (a) Vegetative cover

      (b) Topographic features

      (c) Advantages

      (d) Disadvantages

    6. Proposed facilities and costs

IV. Appendix A

  A. Working map

    1. Scale at 1 inch equals 400 feet

    2. Showing

      (a) Diagrametric outlines of each proposed site

      (b) Contours

      (c) Roads and trails

        (1) Proposed

        (2) Existing

      (d) Other topographic features

        (1) Natural

        (2) Cultural

      B. Detailed map of each proposed site

         1. Scale 1 inch equals 60 feet

         2. Showing

            (a) Contour lines (5 foot to 1 foot interval)

            (b) Detailed layout within area

      C. Detailed drawing of standard unit designs for applicable activities

         1. Picnic units

         2. Camping units

         3. Amphitheater

   V. Appendix B

      A. Engineering specifications and drawings

         1. Roads and trails

            (a) Size

            (b) Surface

            (c) Grade

         2. Water treatment and distribution

            (a) Equipment needed

            (b) Specifications

         3. Sanitation

            (a) Sewage

            (b) Refuse

         4. Structures and site modification

The suggested outline for the Development Report has four parts. In addition to the appendices, the Report covers (a) the general introductory material in Part I, (b) the required areas and facilities in Part II, and (c) a detailed description of each proposed site in Part III. This Report is constructed from specific data gathered in the investigative portion of the development plan. Much of the latter two parts of the Report are dependent upon that information as it is reflected in the working map of the area. It is the working map that graphically exhibits the selected sites for each facility.

Part I. Introduction

Part I of the Report is concerned with a general description of the area and of the anticipated demand on that area for recreation facilities. In the recreation planning stage, this demand should have been projected through the next 35 or 40 years so as to permit the construction of adequate facilities from the beginning. Although these are considered to be planning figures, the estimated-use figures should be shown in Table 1 of the introductory part of the Report so as to give a basis for making succeeding assumptions or estimates. An example of Table 1 is presented below to show predicted-use figures for a proposed Corps of Engineers impoundment on the Cheat River of West Virginia. Since the following examples are based upon standards for federal development, the appropriate cost figures are used.

EXAMPLE A

TABLE 1

PREDICTED RECREATION—DAYS USE WITH AND WITHOUT PROJECT

Use of area by purpose of visit class	Estimated 1960 man-days use	Predicted man-days use without project			Predicted man-days use with project		
		1970	1990	2020	1970	1990	2020
	(1000)	(1000)	(1000)	(1000)	(1000)	(1000)	(1000)
Campgrounds	2.0	5	10	15	20	35	60
Picnic sites	12.0	15	20	40	30	50	75
Swimming	3.0	6	12	18	15	35	55
Boating	0.5	1	3	5	20	50	90

Part II. Required Areas and Facilities

Part II of the Development Report is concerned with determining the types and numbers of facilities needed and their costs. If conversion factors are used such as they are by the U.S. Forest Service, they should be shown in Table 2 of the Report. Example B gives the format of Tables 2 and 3 as they should appear in Part II of the Development Report.

Recreation Area Development

EXAMPLE B

TABLE 2

USEABLE RECREATION ACRES NEEDED IN YEAR 2020

Area class	Estimated visitor day use	Converting[a] factors	Acres needed[c]	Number of units
Campgrounds	60,000	0.0016[b]	96	298
Picnic sites	75,000	0.0008[b]	60	240
Swimming	53,000	0.0001	6	5[d]
Boating	90,000	0.0002	18	5[d]

[a] Based upon formula for determining acreage requirements in Chapter 4.

[b] Three camping units per acre; four picnic units per acre.

[c] Rounded upward to nearest acre.

[d] Swimming and boating units are based upon usable locations required to satisfy the demand.

The method of using the converting factors is employed to save arithmetic on projects where visitor-day use is the only variable. When the space requirements of the user, length of season, and turnover factor remain constant for an activity, they can be worked up as a converting factor to be multiplied by the number of visitor-day use to estimate the required acres of development. The formula for estimating the area required is discussed in Chapter 4. An example of computing the converting factor is given below:

(a) Compute converting factor for campgrounds that will have three units per developed acre (formula in Chapter 4).

$$\text{Area required} = \frac{D \times a}{cd \times TF \times 43,560}$$

(b) Make a converting factor (y) by:

$$\text{Let } (y) = \frac{a}{cd \times TF \times 43,560}$$

(c) Therefore:

$$\text{Area required} = D(y)$$

108

The completion of Table 2 in Part II of the Development Report provides the developer with the number of units required by activity type. The next step to take is the cost determination for the project by completing Table 3. Table 3 is a cost summary of the recreation development. It uses the data from Table 2 to determine the number of each type of facility that is required and the estimated cost for it. Example C shows Table 3 as it should appear in the Development Report. Although the tables shown in the examples are for very large developments, they are still set up and used in the same manner for small developments.

EXAMPLE C

TABLE 3

Area class	Number of units	Unit cost	Total cost per class
Campsites	298	$1200	$357,600
Picnic sites	240	$1200	$288,000
Swimming	5	$12,200	$61,000
Boating	5	$17,800	$89,000
Total costs			795,600[a]

[a] U.S. Forest Service 1963 cost estimates. Not including 25 percent contingency, planning, and overhead fee.

Table 4 that is suggested in the outline for the development plan is a summary of planned areas and a timetable for their construction. It serves as the heart of the Development Report when used in conjunction with the working map. It gives a complete summary of the planned recreation development by the areas that are identified on the working map. The area names and numbers that appear in Table 4 must be the same as those shown on the working map that is part of the Report's appendix. Example D shows Table 4 as it should appear in Part II of the Development Report.

The sample outline and the examples listed above will help guide the developer in producing the Development Report. The

109

Example D

TABLE 4
SUMMARY OF PLANNED AREAS AND THEIR CONSTRUCTION TIMETABLE

No.	Location	Net useable area (acres)	Units				Completion schedule[a]			
			Camping	Picnicking	Boating	Swimming	% completed by			
							1970	1980	1990	2000
1.	Spring Run	30	24	40	1	1	100	100	100	100
2.	Bear Trail	45	24	25	1	1	—	—	100	100
3.	Big Bend	240	60	85	1	1	25	50	100	100
4.	Deer Flat	500	169	50	1	1	—	50	100	100
5.	Indian Creek	180	21	40	1	1	50	50	100	100
			298	240	5	5				

[a] Completion schedule dependent upon predicted use figures and available capital.

Development Report and the investigation phase should be presented in such a way as to make them as usable as possible. Emphasis should be placed on complete and clearly understood tables and summaries that can be correlated easily with the maps contained in the appendix.

If the developer is working for someone other than himself, he must of course render the best possible service to his client and perform in a professional manner. Beyond this, however, he should strive to make his report as interesting and as understandable as possible. Neat, colored maps or photographs with overlays are more than just "merchandizing"; they are important in aiding the client to quickly understand the development plan. If the developer has done a professional job of preparing the plan, he should not feel guilty in using a little "eyewash" to sell his product to someone who might not have the time, interest, nor technical understanding to read beyond the first couple of pages.

Part III. Detailed Descriptions of Each Proposed Site

The third part of the Development Report gives a detailed description of each proposed site. Each proposed site should be named by this point in the report so that easy correlations can be made between the detailed descriptions and the areas drawn on the working map. The detailed description of each site should contain information on the site's location, size, vegetative cover, and topographic features. Succinct statements concerning the site's apparent advantages and disadvantages should be included as part of the detailed description. Also, a list of the proposed facilities and their costs should be included.

The description for each site should be presented in tabular form so as to make the information readily available to interested readers. The tabulation format should be kept uniform whenever possible in order to lessen the time needed to locate details about the site.

The maps made of each site should be drawn at a scale of

111

1 inch equals 60 feet and included in Appendix A of the Development Report.

Parts IV and V. Appendices

APPENDIX A. Appendix A is the proper location for all pertinent maps that will be included in the Development Report. The working map of the development area should be drawn at a scale of 1 inch equals 400 feet (1 inch = 500 feet if the area is greater than 1000 acres) and should be included in Appendix A. Each of the site maps should be placed in the same order as the sites are numbered in Table 4 of Part II.

APPENDIX B. The engineering specifications and working drawings should be included in Appendix B so that they will not clutter up the body of the Development Report. Care must be taken to present the Appendix material in an orderly and uncomplicated fashion so as not to frustrate the user who is looking for the details that have been filed in the Appendix.

The average developer would like to believe that his work is completed without his worrying about engineering specifications and drawings. Unfortunately, things do not work out that way. The purpose of the development plan was stated at the beginning of the chapter. Its purpose is to get the on-the-ground layout plans completed. The person who is responsible for getting the job done must have the specifications and designs in order to determine costs, prepare for purchases, and obtain the necessary approvals by regulating agencies.

Much information concerning water supply, sanitation, and layout can be obtained from various chapters in this book. Working drawings of standard structures and facilities are easily obtainable. The U.S. Forest Service has assembled a set of working drawings into one publication entitled, *Working Drawings of Basic Facilities for Campground Development* that can be purchased from the Superintendent of Documents for 20 cents. [13] The use of the word campground in the title is somewhat misleading in that the working drawings included in that publication are for structures usable in almost any popular forest recreation activity.

112

Estimated average capital costs per site range from $130 to more than $1600.[11, 5] The lower cost of $130 per campsite as mentioned for Indiana landowners is an unrealistic figure while the BOR price of $1654 per unit, including all facilities and interior roads, is prohibitively high for most private landowners and should be used only when planning the most elaborate facilities. The best estimate of costs for the average campground development requires the capital investment of approximately $600 to $700 per unit.[14] This figure is estimated for smaller areas that contain ten units. Additional units cost slightly less to build since the roads and water lines are mostly in place.

Picnic units do not require as large a capital investment as do camping units; however, each complete picnic unit will cost approximately $235. The BOR cost estimate for a picnic shelter is an overwhelming $12,000; however, the U.S. Forest Service has published specifications for a shelter that costs approximately $1000 to build.[14] The estimated costs given in this chapter include both material and labor; therefore, much of the total outlay of money could be saved if the landowner supplied his own labor.

The general recreation cost figures used by the Bureau of Outdoor Recreation in some of its comprehensive studies are given in Table 6.3.[4] These are the costs as listed in the 1965 reports and are probably realistic in the light of the desired permanence of the planned developments. In addition to estimated capital costs of the facilities, the Bureau of Outdoor Recreation includes an additional fee of 25 percent of facility costs to cover planning, overhead, and contingencies. This planning, overhead, and contingencies cost is not included in Table 6.3 because it is the policy of federal agencies to total all the capital costs and then add a 25 percent increase of that total at the end.

Costs on individual items vary greatly according to circumstances; therefore, local bids should be solicited for materials and labor. The cost lists that appear in many publications are very good for general planning, but are not good enough for

113

specific projects. Some cost lists appear to be slanted to encourage landowners to get into the campground business. As a result of conflicting published cost estimates, the developer would do a more professional job by obtaining bids and determining the actual costs for the given project as part of his own work rather than relying upon published estimates for more than guidelines.

TABLE 6.3

CAPITAL COSTS OF GENERAL RECREATION FACILITIES AS ESTIMATED BY THE BUREAU OF OUTDOOR RECREATION [a]

Item	Unit cost (dollars)	Remarks
Picnic units	235	Unit-table, grill, trash container, and one parking space
Picnic shelters	12,000	—
Beach acres	12,197	$0.28 per square foot
Boat and water ski units	17,800	Single-lane concrete ramp, 12 ft × 500 ft at $10,000 and a 40 car and trailer gravelled parking lot at $7800
Parking	—	Activities other than boating and camping
Asphalt	132	per 300 square foot parking space
Gravel	99	per 300 square foot parking space
Sanitary units	—	Costs included in camping unit cost
Flush	14,500	
Pit	9000	
Campsites	—	Includes share-water supply, sanitary facility, roads and signs
Asphalt	1967	
Gravel	1654	
Roads	—	
Asphalt	52,500	per mile
Gravel	22,500	per mile
Walks	5280	per mile
Trails	450	per mile

[a] Bureau of Outdoor Recreation, USDI, Lake Central Region Comprehensive Studies.

REFERENCES

1. AGNEW, R. 1965. *Profitable Private Campground Construction and Operation.* Rojo Publication, Inc., New York. 50 pages.
2. AGRICULTURE STABILIZATION AND CONSERVATION SERVICE. 1966. Order for Aerial Photography. Form ASCS–441, Jan. 66.
3. AVERY, T. E. 1964. *Interpretations of Aerial Photographs.* Burgess Publishing Company, Minneapolis, Minn. 193 pages.
4. BUREAU OF OUTDOOR RECREATION. 1965. *Wabash River Basin Comprehensive Study—Big Walnut Reservoir, Downeyville Reservoir, Big Blue Reservoir.* Lake Central Region, BOR, Department of the Interior, Ann Arbor, Michigan. 21 pages.
5. BUREAU OF OUTDOOR RECREATION. 1966. *Wabash River Basin Comprehensive Study—Louiseville Reservoir, Helm Reservoir.* Lake Central Region, BOR, Department of the Interior, Ann Arbor, Michigan. 23 pages.
6. COOPER, C. and SMITH, F. 1966. Color Aerial Photography: Toy or Tool? *Journal of Forestry,* vol. 66, pp. 373–8.
7. DOELL, C. E. 1963. *Elements of Park and Recreation Administration.* Burges Publishing Co., Minneapolis, Minn. 340 pages.
8. HOLCOMB, CONKLIN, and WINCH. 1964. *Opportunities for Private Campgrounds as an Alternative Use of Land.* Agriculture Extension Service Circular No. 792. Virginia Polytechnic Institute, Blackburg, Virginia.
9. LANE, R. D. 1964. Private Recreation Enterprises—Pie in the Sky? *Proceedings of 19th Annual Meeting of Soil Conservation Society of America.* Jackson, Mississippi.
10. MACKIE, D. J. 1965. Site Planning to Reduce Deterioration. *Proceedings of Society of American Foresters Meeting,* 1965. Detroit, Michigan.
11. STEWART, B. E. 1964. *A Plan for the Development of the University of Maine Forest.* Maine Agricultural Experiment Station. Miscelaneous Publication No. 659.
12. TRACY, J. C. 1934. *Plane Surveying. A Textbook and a Pocket Manual.* John Wiley and Sons, Inc. New York. 162 pages.
13. U.S. FOREST SERVICE. 1962. Working Drawings of Basic Facilities for Campground Development. *Agriculture Information Bull.* No. 264. U.S. Department of Agriculture.
14. U.S. FOREST SERVICE. 1962. Forest Recreation for Profit. *Agricultural Information Bull.* No. 265. U.S. Department of Agriculture.
15. U.S. FOREST SERVICE. 1963. *Recreation Management.* Title 2300 *Handbook and Manual.* U.S. Department of Agriculture, Washington.
16. U.S. FOREST SERVICE. 1963. Supplemental Report of the Impact of the Proposed Rowlesburg Reservoir on the Monongabela National Forest. Unpublished. Regional Office, Upper Darby, Pennsylvania.
17. U.S. GEOLOGIC SURVEY. 1962. *Topographic Map Symbol Sheet.* U.S.G.S., Department of the Interior, Washington, D.C.

References

Part II

Introduction

THERE is a point at which planning must be turned into action. Someone must turn recreation plans and development reports into facilities that the public can use. Bridging the gap between paperwork planning and on-the-ground development is a difficult step. It requires an understanding of the planning reports and a knowledge of the specific improvements to be undertaken. Also, initiative is required on the part of the land manager if he is to maintain actual control over the development of the recreation areas.

Many facilities come about by management decisions or expansion improvements and not as a result of a large scale recreation plan. When the time arrives for the manager to concern himself with the specifics of getting the facility onto the ground, the manager must have an adequate source of detailed information concerning recreation developments and their operation and management. The planning stages of recreation areas are horizons apart from the successful construction, maintenance, and operation of a forest recreation facility.

Part II of his book provides a technical approach for getting the job done. It is the "how to" approach to recreation facilities, management, and operation. In Part II, the land manager can find the specifications and recommendations for sanitation, water supply, and various forms of developments. Also, he can obtain the suggestions, methods, and techniques for operating and managing recreation areas under varying circumstances.

119

Introduction

Although Part II gives many details concerning the design, management, and operation of forest recreation areas, it can not give the three qualities that are most important to a recreation area manager. A good recreation area manager must have initiative, interest, and imagination. He must find the opportunities to improve his areas wherever possible. A certain aggressiveness will be needed to obtain a positive approach to management.

CHAPTER 8

Campgrounds

CLASSIFICATION OF CAMPGROUNDS

Camping is one of the major forms of forest recreation. Although it does not compile the large days' use statistics as do sightseeing and picnicking, camping does provide the true image of forest recreation for most Americans. The mention of forest recreation conjures up visions of tents standing among the high reaching trees in some secluded forest glen. The number of campers more than doubled in the decade from 1955 to 1964 so that there were approximately 13 million of them by 1964.[6] Campground visitations rose from 18 million in 1955 to more than 40 million in 1964.[11]

Campers expected many different things of the campgrounds where they stayed. Thier tastes ran from expensive mobile campers to backpacks. However, they all demanded the three major features of sanitation, safety, and attractive sites. The U.S. Forest Service Handbook describes campgrounds as sites primarily developed for overnight use by campers.[18] Campgrounds are improved areas that provide visitors with attractive sites, sanitary facilities, and safe fire areas along with such general safety as can be accomplished through proper administration. However, the primary purpose for providing the campsite, or any other facility, is to produce user satisfaction.[2] Often, this purpose is lost because of indifferent bureaucracy within public parks, overzealous administrators, or over-restricting regulations. Most campers, hunters, and fishermen realize the need for certain limitations; however, they show justified resentment toward being treated as delinquent book-borrowers by bossy park superintendents or worrisome campground owners.

121

Campgrounds

Generally, campers are a loyal group and prefer to return to favorable sites year after year. Many campers even become possessive and refer to a particular campsite as their camping spot. These people are important to the camping movement in forest recreation. In many cases, they have been camping in an area longer than the park administrator has been on the job. These "regulars" can contribute much to the planning and managing of a campground; however, they are very sensitive to changes that are not compatable with their feelings.

Camping is the essential element of forest recreation for some people while it is just a means to an end for others. Many people spend their vacation camping because they enjoy the act of camping in a favorable spot. Other people camp in order to go places because of simple economics. A family of four would spend approximately 400 dollars on a ten-day vacation if it ate in restaurants and slept in motels.[6] Ten days of camping would cost the same family less than 100 dollars. The savings caused by camping will quickly amortize the investment in camping supplies.

There is a wide variation among campers as to their needs. Some want to be isolated back in a wilderness area while others enjoy the social emnities of city-like tenting. The campers seeking isolation want solace and relief from the frictions brought on by social contacts. On the other hand, enjoyable times occur for many other camping families as they get together with the campers crowded around them. There are other conflicting interests among campers. Some want conveniences to varying degrees while others prefer pure wilderness. There are those who demand easy accessibility and those who look forward to packing-in by foot or horse. Others want as much wilderness as they can drive to. Careful planning can make land available to meet most of the varying demands for camping areas.

This chapter treats the development of campgrounds that are to be used by the campers who are traveling or vacationing as families, as small groups, or as individuals. Camps used by organizations such as the Boy Scouts, YMCA, or church

122

groups have different problems of design and administration. The organization camps are discussed in a later chapter.

A system of campground classification is necessary in order to allow the land manager to choose the type of campground that is suitable for the needs in his area. This book has adopted the Wagar system of classification because of its flexibility and its overlapping types that permit freedom of use without over-classification. [2] Any new field needs definitions; however, it must fight off hair-splitting and overclassification. Wagar's system of campground classification should serve as a guide and not as a set of rules for campground development.

TABLE 8.1

CLASSIFICATION OF CAMPGROUNDS AND THEIR PURPOSE[a]

Classification	Purpose
Central camps	Provide maximum conveniences and headquarters for large numbers of campers.
Forest camps	Mix naturalness with conveniences.
Back-country camps	Unrestricted camping and no conveniences.
Peakload camps	Handle large numbers of campers for short periods of time.
Long-term camps	For campers staying one month or more.
Traveler's camps	Provide for needs of en route campers.

[a] J. A. Wagar.

Central Camps

Whenever the conditions occur that consistently will attract large numbers of people to a relatively small spot, the best class of campground to provide is the central camp. Central camps are just a few steps away from city living in that the camping units are crowded together in designated locations and each unit is oriented next to its neighbors in a geometric pattern. This placement of units allows maximum use of the land area and permits easy maintenance and administration.

The formal layout and closeness of the campsites permits intensive use of the area. The intensive use in turn justifies the

123

investment of capital to provide services for the camper. Because of this intensity of use, flush toilets are necessary to maintain satisfactory sanitary conditions. Hot showers, electrical hookups, a general store, and laundry facilities are part of life in a complete central camp. Many camping purists or some non-campers find the central campground, as it is described here, distasteful. Certainly, the person who camps for the purpose of obtaining seclusion and an expression of self-reliance would not be content to stay in a central camp. However, central camps do have many advantages over the more primitive forms of campgrounds. Central camps provide security, comfort, social life, and convenience.

Security is a need that must be recognized in camping as well as in hometown living. Few campers will admit in public that they consider their physical security when they select a campground; however, every serious family head is concerned with the safety of his family. Many camping families have driven into and then out of an isolated and deserted campground after dark. Everyday living brings people into constant contact with many other people in familiar surroundings where legal governments provide communities with police protection. Therefore, the individual is not equipped to provide for his own security. As most experienced campers know, any physical danger is very small; however, camping puts people into unfamiliar situations in places where no formal law enforcement is evident. The large number of people in a central camp provide a feeling of security, as well as justifying the salaries of the attendants and managers who are responsible for the camper's safety.

Comfort in camping is a relative term dependent upon the campers and upon their desires. Central camps provide the maximum comfort obtainable in normal camping situations. The comfort level of a central camp is one rung lower than it is for cabin living. Research has shown that the comfort level of a campground is one of the four major conditions affecting user satisfaction. [2] The many conveniences available in central camps raise the comfort level while overcrowding lowers it.

124

Major site modification is required to overcome the effects of high density use. Nature must be assisted by planting, fertilization, irrigation, and construction. Native vegetation is often replaced with more durable ornamental plants. Paving protects the roads, parking areas, and heavily used portions of the campsite from the deterioration effects of heavy traffic. The pretense of rustic construction is abandoned in favor of more suitable and less expensive materials to provide administration buildings, storage sheds, wash houses, and other required structures. Barriers of wood, masonry, or plants control the flow of traffic. [2]

The social instinct of people remains active while they are camping. Even those who venture into the back country remember the chance meetings with other hikers as highlights of the camping trip. Central camps bring people together from widely separated sections of the country. Although the campers are from different parts of the country and have diverse backgrounds, they all have camping as a common interest. Some experienced campers prefer to spend part of their camping vacation in large central camps in order to exchange fireside chatter with other campers. Many people who prefer central camps because of the available facilities and services are also those people that want to follow a daily living pattern that is not greatly different from their normal pattern. Their evenings are taken up by entertainment or a social engagement. The activities and the setting are different but the evening's format remains unchanged. Group singing or slide talks by park personnel replace television, and the fireside chat with neighboring campers takes the place of an evening of bridge or pinochle.

The convenience of the central camp is an important factor to the traveling vacationer or to the camper with limited equipment or limited experience. It is near the attraction that the camper will come to see and it will serve as a base of operations for him. From this base of operations, the camper can make day trips to nearby points of interest. Often, neighboring scenic attractions can be protected from destruction by trampling or by the encroachment of campsites if the campers can be congregated into a central camp.

A central camp must meet three minimum requirements to be successful. First, it must be very near a major attraction that will bring the crowds of campers that are needed to justify the high density development and the many facilities and services that are available at a central camp. This should be a durable attraction that will hold its value over an indefinite length of time and under heavy use. An extensive area of unusual beauty would satisfy this requirement but a small fishing stream would not. The heavy fishing pressure brought on by the users of the central camp would destroy the attraction by overuse. Second, it must be accessible from a major highway although the camp itself should be several miles off the highway. Central camp users are numerous, often touring, and they are not ready for a long, hard drive to an out-of-the-way place. However, the campground should be far enough off the major highway to discourage the curious motorist from taking a casual side trip through the camping area. Third, it must be flexible if it is to continue to provide returns on the initial investment. Methods of camping are changing and the campground should be flexible enough to accommodate the new methods as they become popular. At one time, most campers used tents. Now, over half of the campers are using camping trailers, tent-trailers, pickup truck campers, or specially designed vehicles for sleeping and living space. Tent designs are changing and are requiring different pad arrangements.

Central camps such as the ones at Yellowstone, Yosemite, and Crater Lake National Parks are large enough to include several hundred units and accommodate large numbers of campers. The smallest central camp should exceed thirty units in order for it to accomplish its purpose of supplying the maximum conveniences to the campers. It is the large numbers of campers grouped together that enable the central camp to support the cost of construction and maintenance of flush toilets, showers, laundry facilities, a general store, and the other conveniences associated with a central camp. Smaller central

126

camps can act as a base for surrounding campgrounds that maintain a more rustic atmosphere. In this case, the central camp can supply facilities and services that are not found or desired in the other classes of campgrounds that are nearby.

Forest Camps

The forest camp utilizes individual camping units that are designed to handle a family or a small camping group. The units are scattered to provide a degree of privacy; however, they are grouped enough to permit construction of limited facilities. The forest camp is the typical campground that is associated with forest recreation. The camping units are located along a looping road that winds through a wooded area where the natural environment has been maintained as much as possible. The forest camp is a blending of the formal campground layout with the naturalness of the forest.

Forest camps have the four strong points of family living, convenience, solitude to a degree, and site protection. Families have the campsites to themselves without much disturbance from passersby or neighbors. This situation allows the family or camping group to perform as a unit within its own campsite. Since families form the largest group of campers, forest camps are the most popular type of campground. The feeling of solitude that encourages family living is a feature of forest camps that comes from spacing the units at intervals of at least 100 feet. Many campgrounds are developed without regard to this minimum distance between camping units. The attempts to conserve space or money by crowding the units together is an unfortunate choice of conservation. Many state parks contain new campgrounds with a 50-foot spacing between the centers of the units. These subminimum spaced units do not produce a forest camp; but rather, they make a modified central camp. They do not fill the needs of a central camp nor do they meet the minimum requirements for satisfactory forest camps.

Convenience is a strong point favoring forest camps. The

127

user is able to drive right into the campsite that is laid out for his needs. The family can be set up for overnight living in a minimum of time. Water, sanitary facilities, and refuse collection stations are within a couple of hundred feet. The user has easy access to and from the campsite and to nearby attractions. Ease of access and limited facilities favor the visitor who does not plan a long stay. Many forest camps have a two week limit on occupancy to permit as many people as possible to use the camps. The same features are desirable for the campers who use the campsite as a base of operations while visiting surrounding attractions. The users should find the forest camp convenient to them while they are participating in certain forest recreation activities such as fishing, sightseeing, and hiking. It does not qualify as an outdoor motel in that it is not right on the major highway. The forest camps should serve a particular area or attraction and should be far enough away from the major throughway to discourage their use for picnicking or en route camping.

Solitude, as it is found in the forest camp, is not based upon isolation from other humans; but rather, it is developed by clever design of a relatively high density use area. As mentioned above, the spacing of the units helps to produce the feeling of solitude; however, the distance between units can be stretched so far before they become single, scattered campsites.

Site modification is the amount of change in a area during its improvement to campground status.[2] The site modification for forest camps is done in such a way as to maintain as much of the area's rustic flavor as possible. Improvements are made with natural material whenever possible. Buildings are constructed of logs or wood slabs and barriers are made from rocks, logs, or other native material. The layout of the campground is such that campers are not required to cut through other campsites when following the shortest route to the facilities such as toilets, water supply, or wash house.

The dispersal of the campsites acts to protect the site from destruction by overuse. Judicious location of forest camps can help to justify a central camp nearby. Forest camps are often located as satellites to a central camp that supplies their users with the more elaborate services and facilities that do not fit in with the spirit of the forest camp. Camping units within a forest are usually located in loops located along a road so that there are approximately fifteen units to each loop.

Back-country Camps

The back-country camp is designed to provide limited facilities for camping in wilderness areas that are far removed from civilization. They are in the wilderness or back country where they can be reached by walking, horseback riding, or boating. Back-country camps vary widely in the kinds of services and facilities that they supply; however, they maintain the wilderness flavor of the area as much as possible. A fireplace and a clearing is usually provided for each campsite. Other improvements might include such things as corrals, safe drinking water, and toilets according to the specific needs of each area. Site modification is limited to the facilities and clearing and is not applied to the general area. However, the increasing use of favorable camping spots is causing site deterioration. Site modification and rehabilitation is one technique of restoring a campsite to a condition approximating the original; however, wilderness campers do not want any site modification that would spoil the original purpose of the wilderness area.

Many people go camping in wilderness areas to escape from crowds and regulations. These wilderness campers like being free to wander and to camp where they want to without interference. In general, they do not want any cultural improvements to mar the solitude of the wilderness. Unfortunately, the campers' presence is enough to change the environment.[10] Even slightly used areas show considerable wear and tear. Also, wilderness campers have a tendency to follow familiar trails and to camp near the old camps of others. Site deterioration has been accelerated in wilderness areas by a sharp increase in their use. Pack animals and riding horses eat more vegetation in a week than they can carry. With an average of 2.5 horses per person in the wilderness, the forage is quickly consumed.[10]

Wilderness, back country, or primitive areas have slightly different connotations when used by different federal or state agencies; however, they are basically large tracts of land that have no public roads or other cultural developments. Campers gain their enjoyment in these areas by communing with nature without interference from crowds or regulations. The back-country campers make up a relatively small, but outspoken, segment of the camping public.[18, 7] In local areas, formal back-country camps tend to concentrate use during overnight camping and thereby protect the surrounding site. When used in conjunction with an established trail system, the back-country camps can be used to spread use over the entire wilderness preserve. Therefore, back-country camps serve to protect the wilderness character by concentrating camping use in widely scattered campsites. These camps will increase in number and in public acceptance as the user pressures on the wilderness areas continues to rise along with all other forest recreation pressures.

Peakload Camps

The peakload camp is designed to handle large numbers of campers for short periods of time with the minimum of services and facilities. This form of campground serves those people who arrive too late to occupy a regular campsite. A designed and well-marked peakload campground keeps the overflow crowds in a designated location where sanitation and regulations can be enforced. Without the overflow area, many campers would not stay in the area or they would set up their own campsites throughout the surrounding woods. Both of these alternatives are unsatisfactory.

Records show that campground use comes in spurts during short periods of seasonal attractions such as the opening day of the fishing season, hunting season, or the Fourth of July weekend.[3] Over 80 percent of income at private campgrounds is generated on weekends while the average occupancy is less than 10 percent of capacity for the entire season.[9] It would be economic folly to attempt to construct camping facilities to meet the peak demands that occur a few times a year. This would produce large, rambling, and empty campgrounds for the normal season. The costs of this pursuit would be ruinous; therefore, another solution to the peakload problem has been adopted. The peakload, or overflow, campground is provided to handle the crowds that cannot find a campsite in the forest or central campgrounds.

These overflow areas usually have portable facilities and a minimum of sanitary developments. Water is generally supplied by a tank trailer, if at all, and the fireplaces are usually portable iron grilles. Pit toilets are provided; however, they are centrally located to minimize the number required. Occasionally, picnic areas are planned so that they can be turned into peakload campgrounds when the need arises. This planning allows for better facilities and a more permanent development. Of course, this approach assumes that the peak demand for camping does not coincide with the demand for picnicking; therefore, the doubling up of the picnic and the peakload sites can be done successfully only in limited locations.

The degree of site modification for peakload camps varies widely and does not parallel the use. Generally, peakload camps are set up in an old field or clearing that is near the regular campgrounds. Sometimes, much site modification is done on a small area to provide for intense use. Native vegetation is planned to provide shade and barriers. Occasionally, open areas are mowed during periods of light use in order to maintain the grass cover and to keep out volunteer trees. In specific locations where very heavy use occurs sporadically, log barriers are constructed to limit motor vehicles to designated areas.

The advantages of peakload camps are site protection and user satisfaction during periods of extraordinary use. If the landowner allowed the indiscriminate locating of campsites,

131

he would be violating the definition of a campground. Facilities for fire and sanitation must be provided in a campground. These things would be unavailable or inconvenient in unrestricted camping. The area would be subject to serious deterioration and the visitors would be dissatisfied with the available facilities and the location of their camping neighbors. New trails would be formed indiscriminately and damage to the vegetation would occur over a widespread area. Although the peakload camps often do not provide a pleasant view, they still satisfy the user under the circumstances for which they were designed. Campers, fishermen, and hunters generally understand why they have been directed to a peakload camp and make the best of it.

Occasionally, some campers prefer to use the peakload camp instead of the forest or central camp because of their unusual equipment such as buses and trucks and their dislike for the more formal campsites. The peakload camp should be held for overflow crowds if it is to serve its purpose. The other campgrounds should be flexible enough to handle special camping equipment and to provide for various camping tastes.

Peakload camps are usually located near the campgrounds they serve; however, they should not be placed closer to the attraction than are the regular camps.

Long-term Camps

Long-term camps are designed to provide accommodation for campers who wish to stay in an area for more than two weeks. People who stay in one location can be centered in one area that is specially equipped to meet their requirements. By grouping the long-term campers in one place, the administrator keeps them from tying up the short-term camping facilities.

Cabins, tent-cabins, truck-campers, and camping trailers often are used for long-term camping.[10] The standard canvas tent is being replaced by these other facilities. The demand for

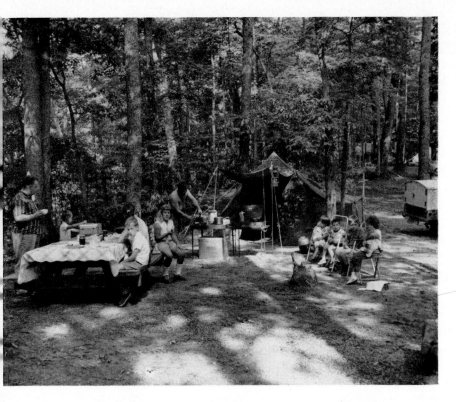

Fig. 8.1. A forest camp is a blending of a formal campground layout with the naturalness of the forest. Forest camps provide family living, convenience, a degree of solitude, and site protection. (U.S. Forest Service.)

Fig. 8.2. Peakload camp in use during deer season on the Monongahela National Forest, West Virginia. Peakload camps serve to satisfy the user who cannot find space in a regular campground. (U.S. Forest Service.)

FIG. 8.4. Cast iron fireplace common to most camping units.

FIG. 8.5. Concrete ring for disposal of lighted charcoal and for
containing wood fires.

more conveniences increases as the camper's stay lengthens. Hot showers and laundry facilities are needed for maintenance of personal health standards and ready access to stores is needed to keep the group supplied during the prolonged stay.

Public agencies usually attempt to serve the greatest number of people that they can; therefore, they tend to avoid establishing long-term camps. Campers who intend to stay in a camping area for a long period of time give a predictable income to a private campground. Because of this, private capital is interested in providing long-term camps to users on a profit motive basis.[14, 21] Some eastern states have removed rental cabins from their parks and placed a time limit on the camping areas in an attempt to cut down on long-term camping on tax-supported land. States can no longer justify expenditures for long-term campers while many more short-term campers cannot find adequate facilities. Federal recreation managers are encouraging private capital to meet the need of the long-term camper by the use of the lease and concession agreements.

Site modification is usually heavy around long-term camps because of the need for paving roads, trails, and living areas. Traffic control and artificial materials are obvious to the user.[2] Occasionally, long-term camps are established under more natural conditions; however, the general rule calls for many services and facilities. Flush toilets and running water are necessary for this class of campground. Garbage collection, washing facilities, hot water, and sometimes electricity are provided.

A major attraction is usually near a long-term camp. Many of the successful privately operated long-term camps are located within national or state parks where they accommodate the vacationing visitors. Although the users want to relax and live out of doors, they generally need something to maintain their interest in an area. Extensive scenic attractions, good fishing, or boating are some things that will help to make a long-term camp a success.

Campgrounds

Traveler's Camps

Campers en route between their destination and home often stop overnight at camps that have been designed to serve the traveler. A large percentage of campers stay at traveler's camps at sometime during their trip because these camps provide cheap and convenient accommodations.

Money saving and convenience are the major advantages afforded the users of these camps. Land managers recognize the values of having the traveling campers located together for safety, sanitation, and regulation. However, there is a question concerning federal and state development of traveler's camps. Should the public agencies get into an outdoor motel business? [2] Many western states and the federal government do provide this service to en route campers. Traveler's camps have proved to be a successful venture for private capital if they have good locations along a major highway and in an area where campers are traveling past.

Traveler's camps should provide the minimum facilities that the traveler needs to spend a night and to prepare his meals. Toilets, water, fireplaces, and tables are the usual facilities found at these camps. Maintenance of these areas is a larger problem than it is for other classes of campgrounds because of the rapid change of occupants. In most cases, the length of stay should be limited to one night if the areas are to serve their purpose. Site modification is usually very heavy because of the heavy use and smaller space requirements. No attempt should be made to maintain the natural setting. The units can be crowded together to 30-foot centers. Paving should cover much of the area that is to carry vehicular or foot traffic. Screening vegetation and barriers should be used to compensate for the lack of space in giving privacy and in protecting the site from excessive wear. [21] In general, the traveler's camp does not offer a scenic or recreation appeal. It provides overnight accommodation and should be located so that it does not become a peakload camp handling the overflow crowds from nearby campgrounds. [17]

Traveler's camps should be located adjacent to a major throughway in as pleasant surroundings as possible. Many small town Chambers of Commerce in New England and elsewhere have constructed traveler's camps to encourage en route campers to spend a day in their town. States are incorporating traveler's camps into their statewide recreation plans to encourage tourists to visit the state's attractions. [17]

APPLICATION OF CLASSIFICATION SYSTEM

As mentioned earlier in the chapter, this classification system of campgrounds should serve only as a guide in campground development. It has already had wide distribution through U.S. Forest Service publications and is generally accepted as a guide in many areas. Any attempt to force every campground entirely into one or another catagory would defeat the flexibility inherent in this system. A system of campground classification designed to accommodate every different interpretation of needs would be so cumbersome as to be completely useless except in classrooms.

Each situation requires its own solution in campground development. Quite often the manager inherits an existing campground that is completely inadequate to meet the demands of the campers. He must scrape together enough money to patch up facilities that will serve the number of users without much concern for their desires. When the time comes that the manager can begin to follow a development plan that refers to forest camps, central camps, and overflow camps, he is too saddled with the "Topsey-style" monster that just grew.

Many of the eastern states have attempted to combine the forest camp with the central camp. That is, they have attempted to preserve the natural beauty of the forest surrounding the family camping unit while placing the units on 50-foot centers. Presently this method is proving to be popular in the eastern states where extremely heavy use dictates crowded conditions. Many of these areas are relitively new and have not shown how well they will maintain the forest atmosphere under such heavy use. As dust, mud, and dying vegetation force the managers to turn to artificial measures such as paving and barrier plantings, these campgrounds probably will move into the central campground catagory. Necessity has fathered some very interesting innoventions in campground layout. The loops and turns of the interior campground roads provided many wasted sites because they did not provide vehicular access to each isolated spot. Also steep hills along an interior road had previously prevented the establishment of camping units there. Now these areas have become "walk-in" camping units. The cars are parked in a designated spot and campers walk approximately one hundred yards to their unit. This walk-in unit enables the manager to make use of those corners unaccessible by automobile. Also, it allows the camper to get a little way off from his neighbors so that he can have some isolation.

Many campers wish to hike a couple of miles into an isolated camp that has many of the facilities associated with an improved camping unit. They want to make an attempt at roughing it only in the fact that they must hike in to the area. Once there, they want the comforts afforded by the forest-type campground. Attempts to meet this demand are most notable on the West Coast. Certain campgrounds are operated in such a way that the campers leave their equipment and supplies at the managers office. The equipment and supplies are trucked over maintenance roads to the camping unit while the campers are hiking in.

Although each campground must be designed to meet the demands of its users, it must be based upon the sound principles of safety, comfort, convenience, economics, and conservation. It is the primary responsibility of the campground designer to provide camping units that are as safe as possible from hazards. Beyond that primary requirement, he can consider the other principles.

CAMPGROUND DEVELOPMENT

Camping Units

A camping unit is an area that has been developed to accommodate a party of campers. Usually a group of eight campers is the maximum design load for a camping unit. The three major purposes for a camping unit are:

1. To provide for the comfort, living, and activity requirements of the campers.
2. To provide the camper with a planned area for fires and sanitation.
3. To provide definite use and traffic patterns within the campgrounds.

Although there is some variation among formal camping units, there is an overall similarity in their composition and arrangement. The usual camping unit is 25 feet wide and 30 feet long with a buffer zone surrounding it. The buffer zones are strips of woodland that have been left to provide privacy and to help protect the soil and vegetation from destruction. The width of the buffer zones between camping units varies from 25 feet in central camps to over 100 feet in forest camps.

In order for a camping unit to provide adequate accommodation, it must contain a stove or fireplace, a table with benches, a tent or trailer space, and a parking space. [20] Water and sanitation are major facilities that affect the location of camping units within a campground. However, water and sanitation generally are not provided within each camping unit.

The interior of the camping unit should be planned to provide ease of movement from table to tent, car, or fireplace. The table is the center of camping activity and should be placed between the parking area and the tent space. For convenience, an exception is made if the unit is designed for trailer camping because of the practicality of keeping the trailer on or near the parking area.

Campgrounds

Tables and fireplaces have changed very little since their design evolved in the pre-World War II period.[22] The tables should be made of pressure-treated wood and bolted into place to prevent movement. Concrete piers should be used under each leg to assure that the bench remains level. Fireplaces generally should be of the small, low design that is shown in Fig. 8.4. They do not need to be the elaborate stone structures that were built by the Civilian Conservation Corps prior to 1940.

FIG. 8.3. Camping unit layout with perpendicular parking spur.

Private campground owners have built adequate fireplaces from scrap pipe and cement block for 2 to 6 dollars per unit. The U.S. Forest Service pays approximately 30 dollars for each installed metal fireplace.[16] The fireplace should be placed so that it is downwind from the tent and table during periods of the prevailing winds. Fireplaces have become secondary cooking places for the many campers who use gasoline pressure stoves or other cooking devices such as charcoal grills.

The need for the disposal of burning charcoal in camping and picnic areas has led to the use of concrete rings for

138

containing the discarded charcoal. These concrete rings are 2 to 3 feet in diameter and 12 to 18 inches high. They are placed in contact with mineral soil so as to provide a safe receptacle for burning material. Campers have accepted the use of the charcoal ring. In many cases, they prefer to build their fires in the safe confines of the ring instead of in the fireplaces. Some park administrators state that they are replacing fireplaces with the concrete "fire-rings" in new sites to save on development costs.

A camping unit should be oriented so as to take advantage of any scenic view and of the land conformation. Besides increasing the attractiveness of the unit, judicious orientation minimizes the need for major site modification by heavy, earth-moving equipment. Site modification is usually necessary to provide the required comfort levels. The forest canopy must be opened to allow for the admission of sunlight and to provide for air movement. The deep shady forest generally does not provide man with a good living atmosphere for camping. Tents, clothes, and other material are wet in the morning and will require sunlight to dry out. Smoke, gasoline fumes, cooking odors, and other smells will linger under a closed canopy that does not allow for the proper air drainage. Sunlight will dry the campsites and cause convection currents in the air that will carry off the collected fumes and replace them with fresh air. Enough trees should be left to provide adequate shade and to maintain the natural setting of the camping unit. The remaining or "leave" trees should be chosen for their apparent health, size, location, and species, in that order of importance.

The area within the camping unit should undergo a periodic cleanup to remove dangerous snags or diseased trees that threaten the safety of the camper. In some cases, organic litter and vegetation should be removed to reduce the possibility of fire spread. However, the litter protects the soil from compaction and helps to prevent site deterioration.[12] In most cases of heavy use, the ground litter should be augmented instead of reduced. Sawdust or shredded bark is frequently

139

Campgrounds

AUTO PARKING SPUR

TYPE-A
BACK-IN
TRAILER PARKING

Fig. 8.6a. Details of parking spurs. (U.S. Forest Service.)

spread over the camping unit to protect the soil from wear and to help keep down the dust.

Although camping units should be on slopes of less than 10 percent, they are seldom level enough for proper tent pads or tables; therefore, some mechanical grading must be done.[18] In some of the more formal camping units, the tentsite is designated and the spot modified to provide tie downs and a level pad. The specified tent location centralizes wear in one spot that can receive special treatment. Many state

140

TYPE-B
BACK-IN
TRAILER PARKING

FIG. 8.6b

TYPE-C
BACK-IN
TRAILER PARKING

FIG. 8.6c

parks and private campgrounds do not have designated tent-sites within the camping units and permit the tent to be set up anywhere within a loosely defined area. This practice leads to damage of all the trees and vegetation within the unit.

Each camping unit should include a parking area for at least one car and in some cases for a trailer. Since camping

141

units generally are designed to accommodate one family, it is usually assumed that one parking space is adequate. However, approximately one fourth of single family camping units are occupied by two or more families even when empty units are available.[9] Occasional units should be designed as multifamily camping units; however, the majority of camping units should be operated as single family units with one parking space.

The car should be parked within the camping unit on a gravel or paved parking spur that is at least 12 feet wide and 30 feet long. The spur should be located so that it will provide the campers with easy movement between the car and the table. Log or stone barriers should be placed so as to restrict the car to the parking spurs.

Proper placement and construction of the parking spurs are very important considerations in the establishment of safe and efficient camping units. Generally, the parking spurs are located perpendicular to a two lane road and at a forty-five degree angle to a one lane road. The perpendicular spurs are designed as head-in parking areas while the forty-five degree spurs are either head-in or back-in parking places.

Evolution of safer and more efficient camping unit design is continuing to take place to meet the needs of the campers. Back-in parking spurs are becoming the most popular design in newly constructed camping units. The large increase of trailer campers has created a need for larger parking spurs. The minimum standard size for a trailer parking spur is a width of 14 feet and a length of 55 feet.[16, 19] They should be of the back-in or of the newer drive-through design. The drive-through parking area is a small loop just off the campground road. It allows a car and trailer to enter at one end, park parallel to the campground road, and exit at the other end of the loop. The exit end of the parking loop serves as a back-in parking spur for the car while the trailer remains set up for camping.

Trailers and truck back sleepers require certain considerations since they are used by approximately half of the campers. The users of truck back sleepers do not need a tentsite but

142

they do want to back their pickup trucks further from the road to obtain more privacy. Trailer doors open on the right-hand side of the trailer; therefore, camping units should be designed so that the door faces away from the road and into the camping unit. [18] Tree limbs should be trimmed to allow clearance for the trailers. [16]

Campground Layout

The campground should be designed, or laid out, to provide for the comfort and enjoyment of the user, for efficiency of maintenance, and for the preservation of natural beauty. The campground layout is concerned with the placement of camping units, roads and trails, sanitation facilities, and water supply.

There are many kinds of campers; therefore, the campground layout should be designed for the campers who will use it. [16] Fishermen and hunters are less concerned with privacy in the campground than are vacationing families. Site selection and predicted user groups should be considered carefully in the planning stages that are discussed in Part I of this book.

The proper location of individual camping units in forming a campground is necessary in central, forest, and long-term camps. Most of the requirements are the same for the central and the forest camps except that of spacing. Long-term camps, a very small segment of the total campgrounds, are basically either central or forest camps depending on their location and design. [2] At least 100 feet should separate the camping units except in central camps where they are set together with 50 feet between center points. [18] The American Camping Association recommends that the number of camping units be limited to three per acre. [1] However, the placement of four to seven camping units per acre is more common throughout the country.

The centers of the units should be placed at least 50 feet from the edge of campground roads and at least 100 feet from

143

streams or lake shores. People following their desire to camp as close to water as possible are causing serious damage to many shoreline areas; therefore, camping units should be placed away from the water as much as possible within the designated campground. The units should be oriented in such a way that the campers in one unit do not travel through other units to reach the major attractions. In most cases, the actual location of the individual units should take place after the internal campground roads have been located.

Campground roads are classified as either entrance or internal roads. Entrance roads are designed to allow movement between the major highways and the campground. The entrance roads are an important part of the campground setting because they present the first and last impressions of the campground they serve. These roads must be designed so as to allow reasonably rapid travel at the same time that they provide the proper setting expected for a campground. They should be well identified by signs, two lanes in width, and surfaced with crushed stone or paved. The sharpest curve permitted in an entrance road should have a fifty foot radius of curve. The turn off from the main road onto the entrance road should have a radius of curve that is greater than 100 feet.

Entrance roads should be marked with a sign that is clearly visible from 300 feet on a main highway or from 150 feet on a forest road. Deceleration lanes should be constructed along the main highway for 150 feet in both directions from the intersection.[1]

The internal roads of a campground should be one way loops whenever possible. Traffic flow and topography will require some two directional roads; however, these two lane roads should be kept to a minimum for safety to the camper and for lower costs to the builder. The roads should be laid out in gentle loops that have 200 feet minimum diameters to allow for the placement of units and facilities within the loop. One way loops permit better utilization of existing grades, encourage slower driving, and allow flexibility in placing units and central facilities. Occasionally, an internal road will end in a turn around area. In this case, the road should be at least one and a half lanes wide with intervisible turn outs to allow for passing. Internal roads should be hard surfaced or covered with crushed stone to make them usable in wet weather and to prevent blowing dust in dry weather.

Internal campground roads should be kept at least 200 feet from the water's edge. Access to the water should be provided by a boat landing road if necessary and also by well marked trails. Formal trails are an important part of the campground layout because they channel the people's movement within the area. A well marked trail system will assist the camper to find his way around; it will help to keep the campers on given routes and out of other people's camping units; and it will aid in preventing the widespread destruction of the campground setting by keeping the trampling feet in the designated routes of travel. Admittedly, some campers will take short cuts or wander all over the other camping units; however, the majority of campers will be eager to use a well designed trail system within the campground. In areas of unusually heavy use such as around wash houses or toilets, the trails will require surfacing to prevent soil wear and to eliminate muddy spots. Trails should be 5 feet wide and cleared to a height of 7 feet.[8]

The location of the water supply and the sanitary facilities is a critical decision in campground layout. The high costs of installation and maintenance must be balanced against user satisfaction and safety. Sanitary facilities are more often criticized than any other part of a campground.[4] The U.S. Forest Service considers one outlet to be the minimum water supply for every four camping units.[18] A non-threaded, self-closing faucet should be placed within 150 feet of each camping unit if water under pressure is provided. Also, some threaded faucets should be available at intervals for fire protection. Small or remote campgrounds can be served adequately by hand pumps or springs. Some peakload camps have water supplied at pickup stations by tank trucks. However, this is unsatisfactory except as an emergency step in the overflow camping areas where people should stay for only one night.

145

Water under pressure encourages excessive use.[20] Standing water in puddles around faucets will quickly turn the area into an unsightly and unhealthy mess. Water should be drained away from faucets by underground drains or surface paving. Sanitary water disposal becomes a problem wherever water is available to a large number of campers. Too often, no facilities are supplied for the disposal of wash water or dishwater so the water is thrown into the brush around the camping unit. The soil in the camping area becomes saturated with chemicals and grease contained in discarded dishwater. Aeriation and normal infiltration of water in the soil are blocked causing damage to the protective vegetation. Under severe conditions, waste water causes sanitation problems as well as aesthetic devaluation. To cope with the problem of waste water disposal, slop sinks should be conveniently placed throughout campgrounds that receive heavy use.

Liquid waste drains or slop sinks should discharge into the general sewer system if one exists. Where sewer lines are not available, the slop sink should drain directly into a seepage pit that has been constructed exclusively for liquid waste from washing and cooking. This type of disposal needs the approval of the local health authority.[20]

Another major consideration in campground layout is that of refuse disposal. The U.S. Forest Service expects garbage collection to become big business in its camping areas by the year 2000 when the cost of garbage disposal is predicted at over five million dollars per year. Some ranger districts are already operating municipal type garbage trucks.[10] Each camper produces approximately $1\frac{1}{2}$ pounds of refuse per day.[20] This refuse must be collected and disposed of as part of a daily maintenance operation.

The four reasons for refuse removal that are listed in the U.S. Forest Service manual on recreation management are:[18]

1. To eliminate conditions favorable to disease-spreading insects and rodents.

2. To minimize obnoxious odors.

3. To prevent the pollution of the water supply.
4. To prevent the defilement of natural beauty.

The campground layout should include a refuse can for each camping unit. The use of one can may be stretched to serve two camping units, but this practice is not recommended for areas of heavy use. The refuse container should be located at the front edge of the camping unit or adjacent to the road so that it will be accessible for pick up as well as convenient to the users. The conventional 20 or 30 gallon, galvanized cans with tight-fitting lids are usually satisfactory refuse containers. These cans are watertight, non-absorbent, and easily washed. Disposable plastic liners are available at an approximate cost of 3 cents each.[15] The plastic liners aid in maintaining cleanliness and reducing the need for frequent washing of the containers.[20] In campgrounds where bears or dogs are a nuisance, some modifications must be made to prevent the animals from scattering the refuse. The containers should be made of a heavier gauge metal and they should be securely anchored to the ground. Specially constructed swinging lids help to block the entrance of the animals into the cans.

A campground should be laid out so that there is a toilet within a 300 foot radius of every camp and one toilet for each sex for every ten units. Although some state health codes require the distance between a camping unit and a toilet to be less than 200 feet, private investors prefer to stretch the minimum distance to 500 feet in order to provide more elaborate and therefore more expensive facilities.[13, 7] Six types of sewage disposal systems that are used in campgrounds are:[18]

1. Simple sanitary pits.
2. Watertight, pump-out pits.
3. Chemical tanks.
4. Incinerator vaults.
5. Septic tanks.
6. Sewage treatment plants.

The sanitary pit, pump-out, and incinerator are satisfactory where use is light or running water is not available.[18] The

147

privies are acceptable if they are kept orderly, clean, and relatively odorless. Although the privies are cheaper than flush toilets to construct, they are more expensive to maintain. Chemical tank toilets should be used in places where pit toilets can not be used because of possible high water conditions.

Flush type toilets require an adequate water supply, soil conditions that are favorable for a dispersal field, and heavy enough use to justify their costs. Specific details on sanitation facilities are given in the next chapter.

Placing of the toilets too close to camping units is as bad as placing them too far away. People prefer to be more than 50 feet from the toilet buildings to avoid obnoxious odors and heavy pedestrian traffic. Toilets should be well marked and easily located. Barrier plantings are desirable to screen the toilet structures; however, the screening should not hide the buildings from view.[5]

REFERENCES

1. ANON. 1962. *Tent and Trailer Sites*. American Camping Association, Bradford Woods, Indiana.
2. BURCH, WILLIAM R. Jr. 1964. Two Concepts for Guiding Recreation Management Decisions. *Journal of Forestry*, vol. 62, No. 10, pp. 707–11.
3. BURKE, H.D. and RUSHMORE, F.H. 1963. *A Planning Guide for Outdoor Recreation in Washington County, Maine*. Department of Public Information and Central Services, University of Maine, Orono, Maine.
4. FINE, I.V. and WERNER, E.E. 1960. *Camping in State Parks and Forests in Wisconsin*, vol. 1, No. 3. University of Wisconsin, Madison, Wisconsin. 18 pages.
5. FORBES, R.D. and MEYER, A.B. 1961. *Forestry Handbook*. Roland Press Company, New York. 1200 pages.
6. GODBOUT, OSCAR. 1965. The Camper Hits the Road. *New York Times*, May 16. section 13, page 1.
7. HALCOMB, CONKLIN and WINCH. 1963. *Opportunities for Private Campgrounds as an Alternate Use of Land*. Agricultural Extension Service V.P.I. Circular No. 792. Blacksburg, Virginia. 16 pages.
8. HEATH, EDWARD I. 1954. *A Plan for the Development of Nature Trails in the University of Maine Forest*. Miscellaneon Publication No. 663. Maine Agricultural Experimental Station, University of Maine, Orono, Maine. 16 pages.

148

9. Hopkins, Walter S. 1965. Outdoor Recreation on Small Woodlots. *Proceedings of the 62nd Annual Meeting of Association of Southern Agricultural Workers.* Dallas, Texas, February 1.

10. Hutchison, S. Blair. 1962. *Recreation Opportunities and Problems in the National Forests of the Intermountain Region.* Intermountain Forest and Range Experiment Station. Paper 66. Ogden, Utah. 33 pages.

11. Kent, Joseph. 1965. Are Private Campgrounds the Answer? *Better Camping,* February 1965.

12. Lutz, H.J. 1945. Soil Conditions on Picnic Grounds on Public Forest Parks. *Journal of Forestry,* vol. 43, pp. 121–7.

13. Ohio Department of Health. 1964. *Camp Sanitation-Laws, Regulation, and Recommendations.* 22 pages.

14. Outdoor Recreation Resources Review Commission. 1962. *Paying for Recreation Facilities.* ORRRC Study Report No. 12. Government Printing Office, Washington, D.C. 88 pages.

15. Sandy, C.R. 1965. Advice to the Forlorn. *Campground Association of Pennsylvania. Newsletter,* vol. 11, No. 3, p. 6. Mercer, Pennsylvania.

16. U.S. Forest Service. 1962. Forest Recreation for Profit. *USDA Agriculture Information Bulletin.* No. 265. Government Printing Office, Washington, D.C. 26 pages.

17. U.S. Forest Service. 1960. *National Forest Recreation Survey.* California Region. U.S. Forest Service. 184 pages.

18. U.S. Forest Service. 1963. *Recreation Management.* Title 2300. *Forest Service Handbook.* Government Printing Office, Washington, D.C. 315 pages.

19. U.S. Forest Service. 1962. Working Drawings of Basic Facilities for Campground Development. *Agriculture Information Bulletin,* No. 264. U.S. Department of Agriculture. 23 pages.

20. U.S. Public Health Service. 1965. *Environmental Health Practice in Recreational Areas.* P.H.S. Publication No. 1195. Government Printing Office, Washington, D.C. 134 pages.

21. Wagar, J. Alan. 1963. *Campgrounds for Many Tastes.* Intermountain Forest and Range Experiment Station Research Paper Int. 6. Ogden, Utah. 10 pages.

22. Wagar, J.V.K. 1946. Services and Facilities for Forest Recreation. *Journal of Forestry,* vol. 44, pp. 883–7.

CHAPTER 9

Picnic Areas

INTRODUCTION

The word picnic is so much a part of the everyday language that it rarely needs definition. As just about every American knows, a picnic is an outdoor meal where the members of the party consume the food they brought along with them. Commonly, a picnic implies a trip away from home and not dinner on the patio. Television commercials still picture a picnic as a basket and blanket set on the ground near a sportscar by a young, cigarette smoking couple. Although picnickers may or may not smoke cigarettes, they are not epitomized by the young couple. Rather, picnickers tend to be family or organized groups that use tables and other facilities in a developed recreation area.

Although picnicking does take place endemically throughout the forests and along the roads, it is generally considered to be an activity requiring developed facilities. Developed facilities not only add to the convenience, safety, and enjoyment of the users but they also serve to keep the people grouped together in places designed to accommodate them. This centralizes wear, reduces soil and water pollution, consolidates the rubbish, and facilitates cleanup and maintenance.

If researchers did not count the sport of just relaxing, they could name picnicking as the most popular forest recreation activity. [9] The forest setting is ideal for picnicking in that it is shady, pleasant, and in some cases quiet. Most certainly, it is different from the dining room. Picnicking is classed as a day-use type of activity. That is, the users participate during a portion of the day or evening and do not require overnight accommodation. Actually, many publicly administered picnic areas have established closing times. In areas where recreation water for swimming or boating is not plentiful, picnicking is the dominant day-use activity. When water for recreation is available, picnicking becomes codominant with such activities as swimming, boating, fishing, and water-skiing.[9]

Most successful picnic areas are within 30 miles of a population center so that people can make the one way trip in less than 45 minutes.[4] Many states are keeping this travel distance in mind when planning new day-use recreation facilities by striving to build a park within 25 miles of every citizen. Investigations of privately owned picnic areas bear out the 30-mile premise in that most of the ones operating with a profit lie within this area.[7] McCurdy's study of Ohio's forest picnic business determined that these establishments received 85 percent of their income from users living within 30 miles of the facilities.[8]

THE PICNIC UNIT

The picnic unit is approximately 400 square feet in size and is oriented around the table. In addition to the table, a picnic unit usually contains a fireplace of some sort and a refuse container. Water supply, sanitation facilities, and a parking spot are located nearby to the picnic unit. When many units are placed together to form a large picnic ground, fireplaces are not included with every unit because most people prefer to bring prepared foods or to do their cooking on gas stoves or charcoal grilles.

The table should have the seats attached and be made from durable materials. Although pressure treated lumber costs more than untreated lumber, it lasts so much longer that it is worth the extra cost. One argument for using non-pressure treated wood is that the costs are low enough to permit disposal of rotted tables. This sounds reasonable but does not work out in practice. Regardless of economics, the tables are not thrown away until they have passed through several seasons in poor condition, while the rot was getting extensive enough to justify disposal. Some managers do store and refinish picnic tables each winter to preserve them; however, this is a costly and difficult way to protect wood.

Combination wood and metal tubing table-bench combinations are becoming popular in many larger picnic grounds. These are made of wood plank table tops and benches connected together with metal tubing. Apparently they are being accepted by the user-public in the Lake States recreation areas where they are commonly used in spite of the fact that metal tubing does not fit into the preconceived idea of naturalness that picnicker's might expect.

It is becoming more evident with heavy use of picnic areas that tables should be tied down so that they cannot be moved. That is because there is an area of concentrated wear that occurs around a picnic table. This wearing and compaction of the soil kills the overstory vegetation and opens up the area to direct sunlight. In order to gain the benefit of shade, the users move the table out of the sunny spot and into the shade; thereby moving the circle of wear. By tying down the tables, the manager can stop the circle of wear from creeping outward and destroying the shade-producing vegetation in widening areas.

The idea of fastening down picnic tables has been advocated for more than 25 years; however, it has been resisted by some park managers for various reasons.[5] "Why shouldn't the users have the privilege of placing the tables where they want them?" is one argument against permanent table locations. Another one claims that it would cost money to build tie-down points and therefore the park could not afford to do it.

The latter argument can be summarily dismissed by stating that the park management cannot afford not tying down tables if it wishes to protect the quality of the area. The former point of public privilege requires more tact. After all, the users are either paying customers or taxpayers. Either way, they have a right to demand that their needs be fulfilled. The site must be protected from destruction as a service to all taxpayers including the immediate users or as a capital investment by the private owner. If the public wants the tables moved about, it is obvious that their needs have not been met in the layout design. All too often, the movement of tables is permitted as a cover-up for poor layout design or managerial laziness.

Fireplaces are not as important in picnic unit designs as they once were; however, they cannot be eliminated. People still want the experience of the campfire, some even prefer to cook in fireplaces, and other people need a place to dump burning charcoal. The waist-high cast iron charcoal grille that is used by the State of Michigan is an ideal departure from the ground level oriented concept of picnic cooking. These grilles are set at approximately waist height by a heavy metal post. In areas where use is limited to daytime, these grilles are very satisfactory.

The concrete fire rings described in Chapter 8 that are made from sections of sewer pipe have proved to be an inexpensive and easily installed container for fire in that they cost less than 10 dollars each. Each ring is more than 30 inches in diameter and weights approximately 300 pounds. The walls are 3 inches thick and 10 inches high. The size and weight of the concrete rings deters most picnickers from moving them.

The refuse container should be located near each table but in a position that facilitates its being emptied by the maintenance crews. These containers should meet the standards outlined for refuse containers in the chapter on sanitation (Chapter 12).

PICNICGROUND LAYOUT

Picnicgrounds must serve a variety of users under differing circumstances. Although picnicking is classed as a day-use activity, all participation is not limited to daylight hours. Certain users prefer picnics as a summer's evening activity eventhough most picnicking is done in the daytime in conjunction with other day-use activities. Picnicking is usually thought of as

153

a destination type of use; however, with the increase in mobility, there has come an increase in en route picnicking that is reminiscent of the railroad tour stops of past decades.

The picnicground should be situated in such a position as to afford the best view possible; however, it should be kept back at least 150 feet from the water's edge. This 150-foot buffer strip is recommended for two reasons. First, the presence of the picnicground near the water will concentrate the use where it will do the greatest damage to the area's natural environment. Second, the picnicground is kept back from the water's edge to discourage swimming in unauthorized areas.

Well marked trails are necessary to tie a recreation area together. Trails and stairs should be constructed when necessary to guide the user to such nearby attractions as the beach or the boat landing. In order to satisfy the differing needs of picnickers, this text recommends four general classifications of designed picnicgrounds. They are (a) the general use picnicgrounds, (b) the reserved group area, (c) the forest cluster, and (d) the en route picnicground.

General Use Picnicgrounds

The general use picnicground probably is the most commonly designed picnicground. It incorporates flexibility by catering to most forms of picnicking tastes. The unit density varies from ten to fifty per acre; however, fifteen tables per acre is the most favorable density in the general use areas.[6] This is the maximum level that, under normal use, will permit growth of durable grasses.

The entrance road should divide into one way loops that provide access to the parking lots. This keeps traffic flowing into and out of the lots in one direction only; thereby lessening the traffic danger to pedestrians. Service roads needed to maintain the area should be 8 feet wide and closed to the public's vehicles. This way they can serve as trails within the picnicground.

General use picnicgrounds should contain at least one

154

Fig. 9.1. Picnic tables that were dragged into a semicircle around a bonfire.

Fig. 9.2. Group picnic area in foreground is separated and screened from the family campground in the center of the photograph. (U.S. forest service.)

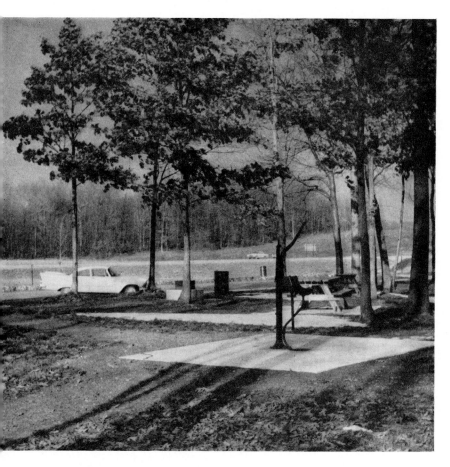

Fig. 9.4. Roadside rest on U.S. Interstate Highway 81.

hundred units to make them efficient to operate and to provide enough flexibility.[12] Approximately half of the tables should be placed in groupings of twos or threes to serve small user groups that require more than one table. When units are coalesced into a grouping of tables, one fireplace or barbecue pit can serve the multiunit grouping.

Those users who desire to participate in evening picnicking around a bonfire will need to be considered in the layout design. People like to sit next to the fire in the evening. Since the ground around picnic fireplaces usually is dusty or muddy, peoble sit on the tables and attached benches. If the tables are not properly oriented to the fire, they will need to be turned before they are satisfactory for use as seats. Figure 9.1 shows a group of tables moved into a circle around a fireplace by evening users. True, tables permanently implaced would be difficult to move. However, the real purpose of designing a picnic area is not to frustrate the users but to anticipate his needs. The purpose of design layout is to give the user satisfactory and safe facilities while protecting the quality of the natural environment at the highest level compatible with use. Therefore, allowances should be made to satisfy the evening picnicker by arranging small groups of tables around fireplaces at a couple of points within the area.

The trails leading to the evening picnic sites should be clearly marked and well maintained. Since these units will be used after dark, they should be readily accessible from the parking lot. This makes night travel between the units and the parking lot less hazardous and also permits easy checking at closing time.

Drinking water is less essential to picnicking than it is to camping because many picnickers come ready equipped for the meal and have a limited need for additional water.[11] They need little or no water for cooking or dish washing. Therefore, the water outlets need not be very close to each unit. They should be placed so that every picnic unit is within 50 to 70 yards of drinking water. This method of placing water outlets differs from the method used in campground layouts in that it is based upon approximate radii and not directly upon the number of units.

The U. S. Public Health Service recommends that water be available within 150 feet of each picnic unit.[12] This is a specification that should be adhered to in a high-density, heavy use area; however, the distance can be stretched to approximately 200 feet in less heavily used areas. All faucets should be self-closing and non-threaded to conserve water. Exceptions to this faucet design should be made where strategically placed outlets are designated for fire suppression purposes.

Since the turnover factor for picnic areas is estimated to be 1.5, more than one family or group will use each table on a given day.[1] Also, some administrators believe that the shorter staying picnickers are not as careful to maintain the cleanliness of toilets and washhouses as are campers. The toilets can be as much as 500 feet away from picnic units and still meet the U.S. Public Health Service suggested standards concerning distance.[12] Flush toilets should be used in all general use areas whenever possible because of the heavier use from each unit and the larger number of units within the effective radius of each toilet facility.

The parking of the automobiles poses an interesting problem in layout design because of the importance placed upon nearness of the automobile to the picnic unit. Research by Burke shows that people want to picnic within 250 feet of their automobiles and that they will not use a table that requires a walk of more than 400 feet to reach it.[3] Investigations made in New York State indicate that the public desires nearness to the parking area above all other considerations.[5]

Parking facilities can provide a good control over usage of a picnicground if parking can be restricted to the designated areas. The theory here being that one table in use means one car in the lot.[6] Unfortunately, there is the problem of parking on the grass, in the woods, and in other unauthorized places. Posts, high berms, ditches, curbs, and other barrier materials can be incorporated in the layout to help restrict vehicles to the roads and parking places. The barriers used to restrict vehicles should be as subtle and unobtrusive as possible.

Parking lots should be hard surfaced or graveled according to intensity of use. The costs for asphalt surfaced lots are approximately one-third higher than for gravel covered lots.[2] Asphalt surfaced lots are preferable to graveled lots because the maintenance costs are lower and the user satisfaction level is higher. Three hundred square feet of paving is recommended for each parking space within the lot. This permits room for parking, for backing up, and for manoeuvering.

Two or three central parking lots are recommended for general use picnic areas rather than several small ones. Narrow forested strips should be used to break up the central lot and prevent the larger lots from looking as though they belong to the suburban shopping center. If the wooded strips are oriented in an east to west direction, they will provide shade for much of the paved areas of the lot.

General use picnicgrounds must be planned to incorporate the collection of units into the natural beauty of the area. Cox points out that this incorporation requires a well thought out blending of man made angles and lines with nature's curves and colors.[5] The designer must not confuse informality with haphazardness. The placement of each unit must be considered on the basis of individual site problems as well on its part in the overall esthetics and operation of the picnicground.

Group Picnicgrounds

Approximately one-half of all the income at Ohio's private picnic areas comes from groups that contain more than fifty people.[8] These group picnic outings are popular with civic, social, professional, and labor organizations as well as with church and educational groups. Group picnicking is a common activity throughout the United States and should be recognized as a need during recreation planning. These groups should be catered to by providing a separate area.

157

Picnic Areas

The separate area for large groups has many advantages that should help the manager as well as the user group. First, the group has a place to have a picnic that was designed to accommodate a large group. Because of administrative policy, the area can be reserved during certain days for large organized groups or open to the general public during heavy-use days. Second, the group obtains privacy in separation from the general use area. By having their own area, the group does not overrun sections of the general use picnic area and place an overload on the facilities there. Bus loads of people invading a general use area conflict with the families and small groups of users that feel pre-empted from the facilities or annoyed by the overcrowding.

The group picnicground should be separated from the general use area by enough distance to prevent casual invasion by non-group members. This means that parking, water, and sanitation facilities must be supplied for exclusive use of the groups. Entrance roads should pass the other picnic areas prior to reaching the group picnicground so as to minimize the need for restricting signs and gates to keep out non-group users.

Plays areas and special cooking areas for barbecues or clambakes are favored by large groups because these users tend to engage in planned play activities and commonly prepared meals. By placing the tables into formal arrangements, the designer places the group together for meals and business meetings. The formal grouping of the tables provides more unoccupied space for play areas and general environment. Also, it concentrates wear and rubbish into one location. This reduces the destruction of the surrounding forest and makes cleanup easier.

Shelters are of particular importance to the success of group picnic areas. By providing protection from inclement weather, they permit planned group outings to continue when they would otherwise be cancelled because of rain.

Cluster Picnicgrounds

The cluster picnicground is a low density picnic facility that is designed for use by families and small groups that desire privacy. These areas have a density of four units per acre and incorporate the least site modification of all types of picnicgrounds. The units are grouped in clusters of three to five units for lower construction costs and easier maintenance. Approximately 100 feet spacings are left between each unit within the cluster.

FIG. 9.3. Sketch of cluster picnicground layout.

A longer walk from the road to the unit is more justified at the cluster units than in the general use areas. The longer walk may be necessary to achieve privacy while keeping the road construction cost down. Unpaved, one-lane service roads can serve as trails throughout the cluster areas and thereby reduce the development costs.

The cluster units cause a dispersal of users over a large area;

159

therefore, they should be limited to lighter use locations or in conjunction with large general use picnicgrounds. Pump-out pit toilets might be satisfactory in these areas because the lighter use will not justify the cost of flush toilets.

The units and layout of the cluster picnicground are somewhat similar to the units in the forest type of campground except that the parking spurs can be 400 feet from the unit and there are no tent pads. The variable distance from the parking spur accounts for the need to consider clusters of units instead of the uniform spacing that is found in the forest campgrounds that are described in Chapter 8.

Although maintenance of cluster areas is somewhat more difficult because of the traveling distance, the flexibility of layout is a great aid to the park manager. Cluster picnic units can be fitted into rough terrain or into small areas of particular scenic interest without destruction of the attraction. A certain spreading of the wear circle will occur even though the table is anchored in one place; however, wear circles should remain confined to the location of each unit and not coalesce into one big bare spot. The recreation area manager must remain prepared to limit use and rehabilitate the sites when wear becomes excessive.

En Route Picnicgrounds

One of the heaviest used recreation facilities is the roadside picnic table on a major highway. Roadside tables and rest areas have long catered to the traveler who wishes to prepare a meal rather than to visit a restaurant. With the increased numbers of people taking longer and more frequent trips, the demand for these facilities is rising rapidly. It is possible to travel along the major turnpikes of the eastern states all day without seeing an empty roadside picnic table. The proliferation of single tables simply complicates the problem because it makes cleanup costly and involves the motorist in a miserable game of "luncheon roulette" while trying for the next table down the highway.

Roadside rest areas that contain many tables appear to be the answer for en route travelers on the major highways. With the interstate road system devoid of restaurants, more motorists probably will begin to combine picnicking with long distance traveling. By having the tables grouped in evenly spaced rest areas, the planner facilitates operation and maintenance and enables the traveler to plan on the rest stop ahead of time.

Roadside rests should include picnic tables, sanitary facilities, and drinking water as well as a safe place to pull off the highway. Grilles and fireplaces should not be included in the layout because the rest area is designed for rapid turnover. Flush toilets should be installed whenever an adequate water supply is available and soil conditions are satisfactory for a disposal field (Chapter 12).

REFERENCES

1. BUREAU OF OUTDOOR RECREATION. 1966. *Water Oriented Outdoor Recreation*. B.O.R, Lake Central Region. U.S. Department of the Interior, Ann Arbor, Michigan.
2. BUREAU OF OUTDOOR RECREATION. 1966. *Wabash River Basin Comprehensive Study–Louisville Reservoir, Helm Reservoir*. B.O.R, Lake Central Region. U.S. Department of the Interior, Ann Arbor, Michigan.
3. BURKE, H.D. 1964. Picnic-Table Use Depends upon Distance from Parking Area. *Journal of Forestry*, vol. 62, No. 10, p. 753.
4. CRITES, R.S. 1966. *Handbook of Outdoor Recreation Enterprises in Rural Areas*. Farmers Home Administration, Government Printing Office, Washington, D.C. 122 pages.
5. COX, L.D. 1940. The Design and Development of Picnic Grounds. *Bull. New York State College of Forestry*, vol. XIII, No. 3–c. Syracuse, New York.
6. MACKIE, D.J. 1965. Site Planning to Reduce Deterioration. *Proceedings of the Society of American Foresters*. Annual Meeting, Detroit, Michigan.
7. McCURDY, D.R. 1964. Making Woodlot Recreation Pay. *Proceedings of the Society of American Foresters*. Annual Meeting, Denver, Colorado.
8. McCURDY, D.R. 1965. *A Survey of Ohio's Forest Picnic Business*. U.S. Forest Service Research Note CS-37. Central States Forest Experiment Station, Columbus, Ohio.

Picnic Areas

9. OUTDOOR RECREATION RESOURCES REVIEW COMMISSION. 1962. *The Quality of Outdoor Recreation as Evidenced by User Satisfaction*. ORRRC Study Report No. 5. Superintendent of Documents. Government Printing Office, Washington, D.C. 95 pages.

10. RICE, W.W. 1965. *A Rigid-frame Picnic Shelter from Hardwood Lumber*. U.S. Forest Service Research Note CS-28. Central States Experiment Station, Columbus, Ohio.

11. U.S. PUBLIC HEALTH SERVICE. 1962. *Manual of Individual Water Supply Systems*. Public Health Service Publication No. 24. U.S. Department of Health, Education, and Welfare, Washington, D.C. 121 pages.

12. U.S. PUBLIC HEALTH SERVICE. 1965. *Environmental Health Practice in Recreational Areas*. P.H.S. Publication No. 1195. U.S. Department of Health, Education, and Welfare, Washington, D.C.

CHAPTER 10

Organization Camps

INTRODUCTION

Organization campsites are areas that are developed to serve an organized group of people having similar interests. The organization camp provides supervised activities, social and educational opportunities, meals, and lodging incidental to the forest recreation experience. Organization camps are designed and operated to provide for the existence needs of the user as well as to provide him with a full schedule of supervised activities. This type of camp generally caters to the young people from the ages of 8 to 16; however, this is not always the situation in that some organized camps provide for the wants of adult users or family groups. Communities, church organizations, large associations, and youth groups often sponsor organized camping on a non-profit basis.

Historically, the organization camp traces its roots to the private summer-camps-for-children idea that still thrives throughout the country.[1] Especially in the Northeast, summer camps are serving a definite need for the children of urban areas whose parents can afford to pay the costs of room and board at the camps. The educational and character building organizations such as the YMCA and Boy Scouts of America were the next group of organizations to get into the camp business following the success of privately owned camps. As the organized camp idea caught on and spread to political units, lodges, and government sponsored groups, the character of the camp itself began to change.

Generally, the early organization camps were based on fun, enjoyment, and relaxation. Unfortunately, this casual air did not last after the professional educators and frustrated military officer-type of individuals took charge of the organized camp movement. Camp-life evolved into a nightmarish mixture of "Boot Camp" and reform school with bugle calls, company streets, and a packed schedule of formal activities. This misguided approach to physical activities and recreation lead to rebellion and overfatique.[1] It was this era in organization camp history that soured many children and parents on this form of forest recreation; thereby leading to jokes about packing the screaming kids off for the summer.

Today, the organized camps have matured in their outlook and purpose. The educators now realize that their 1930 approach is not in keeping with modern theories on child behavior and training. Military leadership principles remain the same but the techniques of leadership have changed markedly even within the army. Experience has taught the military that seven or eight persons is all that one man can effectively control. As a result of these changes, the organized camp has undergone a modification that influences its physical layout and is of importance to the recreation developer. Formal, pseudo-military camp arrangements are losing popularity and the informal camps made up of scattered units are now recommended to provide the best atmosphere for education, self-expression, and relaxed recreation.

The organization camp has a place in forest recreation.[6] From the user's standpoint, these camps fill a need that can not be satisfied by any other type of development. To the land manager, organization camps provide a way of relieving some of the pressure on the regular camping and day-use facilities. By providing special areas for organization camping, the manager will be able to keep the organized groups from overrunning facilities that were designed for family camping groups.

The U.S. Forest Service makes every effort possible to provide opportunities for this type of recreation. Although its federally supplied funds are not used to build, to operate, or to maintain the highly developed organization camps, the

Forest Service does list the organization camp fourth on its priority list for available sites. Public campgrounds, picnicking areas, and water-sport sites take precedence over organization camps for available sites on the national forests. [6]

SITE SELECTION

The principles of recreation site selection that are outlined in Chapter 5 are applicable for locating organization camps as well as any other popular type of forest recreation area. On the other hand, requirements for the general location of the site are different than for any other type of recreation because of the nature of the user group. Privacy, size, accessibility, and topography all present problems unique to organized camps.

Privacy

Privacy is an important ingredient of site selection for an organization camp. The activities performed in many camps require the feeling of complete isolation from civilization for enthusiastic involvement by the participants. The feeling of complete isolation is not achieved only at a large federal wilderness area or a similarly large place. It can be achieved by screening the camp from the outside world's activity with vegetation or topographic features.

Also, intruders are unwelcome in organization camps where activity programs are being carried on; therefore, the isolation technique of external security plays a large part. That is, people will be less likely to intrude into an area if it is not readily accessible or is not visible from regularly traveled roads. Privacy is difficult to ensure in sites that are divided by public roads or are crossed by easements; therefore, one contiguous tract of land located off a forest or township road offers the ideal situation for privacy. By constructing only one access road into the organization camp site, the developer will make the job of excluding trespassers easier than if he opens several entrance points.

Organization Camps

Size

The requirement for size is related to the general environment and ownership of the surrounding lands. When the adjacent lands are in private ownership or are public lands that are not managed with recreation as a major factor, a large area of ownership is needed to provide protection from the impacts of activities that would have adverse affects on the organization camp. Organization camps that are surrounded by or located in state parks or on national forests do not require as much acreage because the quality of the general environment is protected. Also, those areas will always be open for use by the participants.

Land is needed within the campsite area to provide room between each of the individual camp units, to permit separation of the camping areas and the administrative buildings, and to allow for some roaming and activities within the boundaries of the camp. One rule of thumb for the amount of land required for a privately owned organization camp calls for one acre of usable land for each camperspace available.[5] This rule of thumb will give a rough approximation for determining the required size based on capacity. Space must be available for play, nature study, crafts, and group activities as well as for the existence needs of sleeping, eating, and sanitation.

Accessibility

The accessibility requirements for organized camps will vary somewhat according to the type of camp that it is. Camps serving one select group such as the Boy Scouts must be located so as to be near the troops using it. The closer the camp is to the municipality or council sponsoring it, the more it will be used. It may be necessary to encourage short-term use throughout most of the year in order to justify the high cost of establishing the camp. Long-term summer camp planners can be more independent of distance while selecting a site; however, they should keep the round trip short enough to be completed during the daylight hours.

Location within an area served by good highways is a must even though the camp itself should be away from the main roads. Long or difficult access will cut down on use, raise the cost of construction, and make operation costly and inconvenient. Good roads and nearby communities enable camp personnel to obtain the necessary supplies for camp operation without great inconvenience or cost.

Accessibility also has a bearing on the type of caretaker staff that will stay in the camp over the winter. Directors and owners of isolated camps state that they have difficulty in hiring competent caretakers to live at their facilities through the winter.[4]

Topography

The topography or configuration of the land should be as varied as possible in the vicinity of the organization campsite. Variations in the landscape increase the value of the setting and offer more opportunities for different activities.[2] Nearly level spots are necessary for living, play, and administrative areas while streams, ponds, or lakes add considerable value to the area. Water for recreational purposes is very important for the success of organizational camps; therefore, every effort should be made to include some usable body of water nearby the camp. For user-safety, site protection, and administrative control, a buffer area should be left between the camp and the water's edge. Organization camps can be located on relatively rough terrain because they do not require the large flat athletic field play areas that are needed in cities. Organization camps located within the forests should be designed to encourage participation in activities that are not available in towns and playgrounds. Hiking, nature study, and water-based activities should be some of the major forms of recreation activities included when planning such camps.

Swamps, marshes, and other low spots can be both disadvantages and advantages. They breed mosquitoes and restrict passage without special modifications. On the other hand, swamps and marshes provide the habitat for much unusual

167

and interesting flora and fauna. These wetlands make outstanding nature study areas when developed for the purpose.

Natural features in the topography make the best boundary lines. Ridgelines and bodies of water give dimensions to property that painted boundary lines can never impart. Besides being easily located, they provide natural barriers against intruders and they convey a feeling of ownership.

The roughness of the topography will have a marked affect upon campground layout. Gently rolling terrain permits the camp to be developed with the minimum consideration for topographic advantages and limitations. The structures, trails, and service facilities can be dispersed or concentrated where they are most suitable to the users and the administrators. However, rugged topography inflicts severe limitations on the layout. Because of the lack of large areas with gentle slopes, the facilities must be spread out over a large area to take advantage of the existing sites or else the facilities must be concentrated into a few of the available spots. The ideal situation lies somewhere between the two extremes. The terrain should be irregular enough to provide variations in scenery and in activities but not rugged enough to prevent the proper dispersal of facilities.

LAYOUT

The organization camps of today are generally based upon the dispersed unit theory or "dice-throw" arrangement where small subcamps are scattered around a common administrative site. [1, 6] Besides the sub-camps that meet the needs of living, sanitation, and limited activities, an organized camp must include dining facilities, infirmary, administration buildings, and both extensive and intensive forest recreation opportunities.

Sub-Camps

The sub-camps are scattered around the developed area in such a way as to break the overall camp population into several smaller units. These smaller units each occupy their own area where their users live and partake in limited group activities. The sub-camp theory fits in well with unorganized groups because it organizes the campers into small groups with which the individual camper can identify himself as a part. This immediately gives him common ground with his fellow unit members and sets the stage for the establishment of an *esprit de corps* as the season progresses. Each sub-camp should accommodate between sixteen and thirty-two people. The smaller number is best for the camper; but, the higher number will reduce overall camp development costs. Twenty-four persons to each sub-camp provides a good compromise figure.

Fig. 10.1. Sketch of organization camp employing sub-camp layout.

Participating groups that are already organized into units such as the Boy Scout type organizations fit right into the sub-camp layout. Each troop can have its own sub-camp to operate without friction from other troops. Generally, these groups have between sixteen and thirty-two members so that they can fill one unit. Also, the troops are broken down into patrols that can each fill one housing unit.

The sub-camp provides for all of the living requirements of the camper except for eating. This means that besides the group play area and housing facilities, the sub-camp must contain a washhouse and a latrine. The trails that connect the sub-camps together and to the administrative site should be 8 feet wide and suitable for light-haul maintenance and operation vehicles.

Housing

Usually, living quarters should be large enough to accommodate eight persons in each structure.[6] Organized groups that do not rely upon paid counselors prefer to use cabins accommodating four or six persons.[5] Local ordinances often govern the size of cabins; but a good minimum to follow is to reserve 30 to 40 square feet of floor space for each occupant of the cabins.[7] The U.S. Forest Service states that 500 cubic feet of space within the building is adequate when there is adequate ventilation.[6] Wide eaves overhanging the building walls permit the windows and doors to be left open during rainstorms and when the occupants are temporarily away when rain threatens.

The three basic forms of housing that are used in organization camps are the cabin, the tent, and combination of the two called tentalow or tent-cabin. The choice of shelters will depend upon available funds, desires of the user groups, and permanence of the individual units.

The housing units should be placed approximately 50 feet apart when some supervision of the campers is required.[4] When supervision is not required such as in family organization camps, the distance can be much greater between units. In part, the distance between sub-camps of the organization camp will have some bearing on the distance between the cabins within one sub-camp. The organization camp with enough land to permit a wide dispersal of the sub-camps can have greater spacing within the scattered units without losing each sub-camp's identity. Conversely, camps that do not have enough space to disperse the sub-camps should not have such a wide spacing of the housing. Wide spacing between housing units under the latter conditions could mean a loss of the individual sub-camp's integrity because of diffusion with adjacent sub-camps.

Each cabin or tent should be situated so that it receives sunlight during the morning hours and shade during late afternoon. Morning sunlight will warm the cabin and dry off the pre-dawn moisture that will accumulate within the cabin. Sunlight will also make the morning seem more pleasant to those arising. The afternoon shade will permit the cabin to cool off before bedtime.

Sanitary Facilities

Each sub-camp should have its own washhouse and its own toilet facilities. Because of the dispersed location of the sub-camps, flush toilets will be impractical in all but the most highly financed camps. The light use of the sub-camp toilets will also help to justify the use of a non-water carriage sewage disposal system. Not only is the number of campers in each sub-camp small but much of the time those occupants will be off to other parts of the camp where central sanitary facilities will be located. Since most states are developing camp sanitation codes, the local board of health should be consulted during the early planning stages.[3]

The pump-out vault privy is probably the most suitable type of toilet facility under these conditions. It has more permanence than do simple pit toilets; therefore, more elaborate efforts can be put into making it a satisfactory sewage disposal set-up. The problems associated with pumping-out of the accumulated excreta should not prove to be a problem in most rural areas since commercial operators are present to service septic-tanks and similar systems. Details on sewage disposal systems are presented in Chapter 12.

171

The unit washhouse should be a separate structure from the toilet facilities with an underground sump located nearby to catch the waste water and leach it into the soil. A porch-like shelter with a concrete floor, a central row of sinks, and self-closing faucets is a simple and commonly used design for a washhouse. Hot water is a luxury that might prove to be uneconomical at sub-camp washhouses. For this reason, one or more central washhouses that are supplied with hot water and equipped with showers should be constructed at strategic locations so as to serve campers in many sub-camps. These central washhouses should also contain flush type toilets to handle the concentration of use.

Dining Facilities

One large dining hall is usually employed to feed all of the campers and the staff of an organization camp. This enables the camp to furnish the proper meals that are prepared in an adequate kitchen area. The large dining hall area can also be used as a meeting place for camp activities.

The kitchen must be enclosed and it must be adequately screened to exclude insects and rodents. At least 12 square feet of floor space is required for each diner. [7] Also, it is desirable to have the kitchen connected to a screened dining area. [6] Massive log construction is now out of favor for dining halls because of its expense and its dark and dreary atmosphere. Open, airy, and light structures offer more pleasant and more practical buildings for dining halls.

Although dining halls should occupy good sites within the camp, they should not dominate the scene by being placed on the spot with the best view or along the water's edge. These locations satisfy adult values but do not make the best sites for dining halls. The dining hall should be located so that it is easily accessible from all of the sub-units, where the soil and terrain conditions are suitable, and where the access road construction costs will be kept at a minimum.

Administration areas are favorite places for dining halls.

172

This is a satisfactory location only when the administration area is centrally located. If the dining hall is part of the administration area, it must be kept separate from the other administration buildings. It should not be attached to any other structures and it should not be modified for use as anything but a dining hall and a meeting place for the campers and staff.[5]

Campfire Circles

The campfire circle, or council ring, is a very popular part of most organization camps. As are many other facets of the organization camp, the campfire ring is oriented to indian lore in that it represents the council fires of by-gone tribal gatherings. Singing, games, and other social activities dominate today's council ring fires. These campfire circles should be centrally located within the camp so as to provide the easiest access from all parts of the camp. In that much use will be made of the council ring after dark, the trails leading to it should be well marked and well maintained.

The campfire fireplace should be circular and ringed by a low wall of stones to retain the fire and ashes. Circles or semicircles of rough benches around the fire will add to the convenience of the user, and make the group placement more orderly. If the fireplace is located on a flat spot next to a gently sloping hill, the benches can be placed on the slope so that they are higher than the fireplace and the stage area surrounding it. When a sloping area is not available, the fireplace should be raised above the ground level so that the fire will be visible to those persons in the rear of the audience. The fireplace should be raised above the ground level by a stone platform that is approximately 24 inches high. The stage area between the fireplace and the benches should be raised approximately 12 inches.

Administration Area

The administration area contains all of the structures and facilities that are needed to administer and manage the organ-

173

ized camp along with certain other facilities that will improve the general quality of the camp. This area contains the administrative offices, infirmary, equipment storage sheds, service personnel living accommodations, and camp store. A central washhouse is generally included in this area.

The best location for the administration area is at the end of the public access road. This is the logical point to supply information and to greet incoming campers. In that the road terminus is the major concern in locating an administration area, the area might not be centrally located within the camp. This is probably a good situation since it would be undesirable to have public access all of the way to the camp's interior.

It is the administration area that the visitors and campers will see first upon arrival at the camp and last when departing. Therefore, that area should present a good picture of the camp. The public road should pass in front of the buildings where there is adequate parking facilities and avoid such necessary eyesores as the garbage can racks behind the dining hall.[1]

Water-oriented Sports

Although organization camp structures should not be built right along the water's edge, the camp should be oriented so that the campers have easy access to the water. Swimming and boating play a large role in organization camping and should be considered in the camp's layout. In so far as possible, the sub-camps should be located in such a way that all have equal access to the water frontage. Also, the layout should provide trails to guide the movement of campers from their sub-units to the water sports area without taking them through other sub-camps.

The beach improvements and requirements for swimming and boating are discussed in Chapter 13. A qualified life guard is usually required at organization camps and non-swimmer areas must be marked off.

174

Extensive Recreation Activities

Extensive recreation activities take place over large areas and require the minimum of facilities. Hiking, nature study, fishing, and horse back riding are some of the extensive recreation activities enjoyed by organization campers. A system of hiking trails should be developed to provide the camp with access to points of interest within the area. Those camps located on or adjacent to state or national forests have the advantage of being able to use the state or federally maintained trails for riding or hiking. The trails should be accessible from all the sub-camps; but they should not pass through them.

Certain stream improvement projects could be undertaken to increase the recreation potential of any suitable streams flowing through the camp's property. Fishing is the second most popular activity at privately owned recreation areas and should not be overlooked when developing an organization camp.[4]

REFERENCES

1. NATIONAL PARK SERVICE. 1938. *Park and Recreation Structures*. U.S. Department of the Interior. Government Printing Office, Washington, D.C.
2. NEEF, P. 1965. Applied Silviculture in Managing Outdoor Recreation Sites. *Proceedings of the Society of American Foresters*. Detroit, Michigan.
3. OHIO DEPARTMENT OF HEALTH. 1964. Camp Sanitation-Laws, Regulations, and Recommendations. Columbus, Ohio.
4. OUTDOOR RECREATION RESOURCES REVIEW COMMISSION. 1962. *Private Outdoor Recreation Facilities*. Study Report No. 11. Government Printing Office, Washington, D.C. 154 pages.
5. SALOMON, J.H. 1959. *Campsite Development*. Council Administrative Series, No. 5B. Girl Scouts of the United States of America, New York, N.Y.
6. U.S. FOREST SERVICE. 1963. *Recreation Management*. Handbook Title 2300. U.S. Department of Agriculture, Washington, D.C.
7. YOUNG MEN'S CHRISTIAN ASSOCIATION. 1960. *Developing Camp Sites and Facilities*. National Commission on YMCA Camp Layouts, Buildings, and Facilities. Associated Press, New York, N.Y.

CHAPTER 11

Water Supply

INTRODUCTION

What are the water needs of a picnicker or a camper? What constitutes usable water? What determines water quality? How can it be made safe? Where can it be found and in what quantities? For what will the water be used? How many users will occupy an area and when will they be there? How should the water be distributed? These are questions that soon come to the mind of people attempting to plan a water supply system. They deal with problems of quality and quantity requirements, sources, treatment, and distribution. The answers to these questions will aid a recreation area planner to develop a water system that is both safe and adequate for the uses intended.

Water is an essential ingredient for most forest recreation activities. It is important from two views in that water is needed for existence requirements and is desirable for the recreation wants of the user. The comfort level of recreationists is highly dependent upon water. Intensive forest recreation areas are in demand near ponds, lakes, streams, rivers, and oceans. Private picnic and campground developers generally include nearby recreational water as a must for success. This view is substantiated by the heavy development of recreation sites along lake shores and river banks. The development of swimming and boating facilities is covered in Chapter 13 and the supply of water required for the existence needs of recreationists is discussed in this chapter.

QUANTITY OF WATER

Demand

The quantity of water required for a recreation area depends upon the number and types of facilities and upon the intensity of use of those facilities. By investigating the probable uses that people will have for water, the planner will have a start in determining how much water he needs to supply. Average figures of water volumes used with various types of recreation facilities have been published by the United States Public Health Service.[12] Recreation area users need water for drinking, cooking, washing, laundering, and sanitation. Table 11.1 gives a planning guide for water use that is based upon the Public Health Service estimations.

TABLE 11.1
UNITED STATES PUBLIC HEALTH SERVICE ESTIMATES OF WATER
REQUIREMENTS[a]

	gallons per day
Campground with flush toilets each camper	25
Trailer with bath unit each camper	50
Picnic areas with flush toilets each picnicker	10
Showers and bathhouse each person	10
Laundry—self-service per customer	50
Horse drinking	12

[a] U.S. Public Health Service Manual of Individual Water Supply Systems.

The use of water in recreation areas fluctuates widely throughout the day; therefore, a planner must consider the average daily water use as well as the peak demands that occur at certain times during the day. The peak demands must be anticipated in order to determine the pipe sizes, pressure losses, and storage requirements necessary to provide sufficient water during these periods.[12]

Certain patterns of peak-use of water occur with each type of activity. The peak use in a picnic-swimming area will vary

177

directly with the use of the facilities. As the numbers of users increase at a beach area through the afternoon, the bathhouse use becomes heavy and the water demand rises. Camping areas probably tend to follow the more familar water demand patterns found in rural and suburban areas where water use rates are highest during mealtimes, at midmorning, laundry times, and at bedtime.[12]

Using the figures in Table 11.1 as a guide, one can determine that a picnicker or camper uses an average range of 10 to 50 gallons of water per day when there is running water available. The planner must realize that the availability of water is an invitation to its use. Therefore, the more readily available water is, the more it will be used. The very fact that water is under pressure stimulates its use.[14] The problems of heavy water use must be weighed against the benefits of user satisfaction when deciding for or against a pressure water system.

Campgrounds are generally organized around the basic camping unit which is designed to accommodate a family sized group. When investigating the water requirements within a campground, the planner should think in terms of water demand per unit rather than per person. Cooking, dishwashing, and laundrying are group functions that use the water for the entire family. By using the following five-step method, a planner can approximate the quantity of water that will be required for a planned campground.

The five-step method of approximating the quantity of water needed to supply a planned campground is:

Step 1. *Number of units.* The number of units must be decided upon in the early planning stages. The figure arrived at does not need to be the final size of the campground because expansion may take place at a later date; however, a fixed number of units must be decided upon as a basis for initial planning. Factors influencing the number of camping units are discussed in Chapter 4.

Step 2. *Number of people per unit.* The number of people occupying each camping unit will have an overall affect on the total water consumption. Therefore, some ground managers in the nearby areas probably will be willing to pass on their experiences. Some state or federal recreation areas will produce complete records concerning the size of user groups. The research that has been done to determine figures for user groups indicates that the average camping party consists of four or five people.[3, 5]

Quite often the recreation area being planned will have unique attractions that make its appeal different from any development operating nearby. In this case, intuitive reasoning of the planner will be needed to estimate the probable size, age distribution, and wants of the user groups. Deductive reasoning based on experience, attractions, facilities, and expected clientele should give estimates of sufficient precision for use here. Many campground managers limit the size of a party occupying a given camping unit. This practice does aid both the planner and the manager in their duties; however, it may alienate certain users.

Step 3. *Percent occupancy.* Most campgrounds are developed on the premise that a certain percentage of the camping units will be occupied at all times during the season. Actual percent occupancy figures are generally prone to be much lower than the original estimates. Fifty percent is the maximum figure that should be used in estimating seasonal occupancy.

Having estimated the number of units occupied each day, the planner will have an estimate of the continuing minimum water requirements during the season. Next, he must determine the peak load requirements that must be met periodically on such occasions as holidays and weekends. The difference

179

between the minimum occupancy requirements and the peakload demands will be the volume of water that must be stored throughout the weekdays and before holidays.

Step 4. *Special use.* Irrigation of lawns and shrubbery requires additional water above that needed for peak loads. Sprinklers should spread approximately 300 gallons per hour over 100 sqaure feet. This amounts to 5 gallons per minute or $\frac{1}{2}$ inch of water. The water system should be capable of supplying this volume once per week in addition to meeting the regular demands. Adequate fire protection will require a much larger flow rate than most campgrounds need for normal use; however, the larger water system capability will provide users with more conveniences. The U.S. Public Health Service recommends that a capacity of 500 gallons per hour be specified for new water systems.[12] This is probably beyond the requirements of most campgrounds.

Step 5. *Making estimates.* After the planner has taken the first four steps, he can apply simple mathematics to ascertain the campground needs. For example, consider a campground with one hundred units that is expected to have a predicted occupancy of 40 percent on weekdays and 100 percent on weekends. This means that forty units will be drawing water on a daily basis during the five weekdays; however, one hundred units will be used on Friday and Saturday nights. Step number two indicated that the average group occupying the camping units will probably be composed of five persons and will require approximately 200 gallons per day. Two acres of play area will be irrigated at the rate of $\frac{1}{2}$ inch per week through the summer months.

In this case, the water supply must be capable of supplying a minimum of 341,360 gallons per week throughout the season. Large storage areas for retention of water are an alternative to continuous flow; however, costs for such structures are generally prohibitive for recreation area water supply.

Requirements	Gallons
Normal occupancy/day $= 40 \times 200 \times 5$ week-days	40,000
Irrigation $\dfrac{43,560}{100} \times 2$ acres $\times 300$ gal/day	261,360
Peakload $100 \times 200 \times 2$	40,000
Weekly requirement	341,360

Source of Water

After making the estimate, a planner must consider the water supply available to determine whether or not it is adequate to meet the volume demanded by the proposed project. The obvious step to take here is to compare the anticipated demand with the quantity available at the source. Does the source supply sufficient flow to satisfy the need? The effects of prolonged dry seasons must be considered when evaluating the source. Some water sources may be adequate during the fall, winter, and spring seasons when much of the planning is done; however, they fail during the long dry periods of late summer. Even if the source does not completely fail, it will be at its low point while the recreational load is at its highest.

Aside from personal observation, the planner has many recourses for determining the reliability of the water source. In a few cases, the hydrological records for specific water sources are maintained by the U.S. Geological Survey, the U.S. Army Corps of Engineers, the U.S. Bureau of Sports Fisheries and Wildlife, or some interested state agencies. The use of witness evidence is probably the easiest and often the most reliable way of determining the dependability and fluctuations of a water

181

source in the past. A little investigation will often turn up several "old-timers" who have been familiar with that specific water source for many years back. True, the reliability of the witness's statement could be questioned; but that is a problem for the investigator to weigh. Certainly, the statements of several witnesses would carry more weight than the statement of one witness. One specific reading reference recommended is the U.S. Department of Agriculture's *Climate and Man*.[11] This Yearbook of Agriculture discusses seasonal variations in rainfall for each state over a long period. The historic rainfall variations should give the planner an idea of what to expect in the future.

If the continued flow of the source is inadequate for direct usage, an alternate solution must be sought. Three choices are available for the planner. One, the size of the recreation area can be reduced until it is in line with what the water source can supply. Two, additional sources can be found to meet the continuous use. Three, a storage system can be developed to store enough water during periods of low demand to satisfy the total need. The use of one or more of these choices might be necessary to bring the water supply into balance with the proposed demands.

Occasionally, a forest recreation area is situated where it can hook onto a municipal water system that has pipelines passing nearby. In many cases, the costs of this connection will be money well spent when balanced against the expense and inconvenience of maintaining a safe and adequate water system. Some parks take water from municipal water systems during the periods of low demand that occur from late evening until early morning. This water is placed in storage for use within the park during the following day.

Unfortunately, municipal water lines seldom run through or near to forest recreation areas. Therefore, the planner must look elsewhere for his source of water. Water is available as it flows over the surface or in the aquifers underground. Surface water is that water on the surface of the earth that makes up the rivers, streams, lakes, and ponds. It is the result of direct runoff or of the surfacing of ground waters. Ground water is the water that has infiltrated into the soil and has percolated downward until reaching an impervious layer. This ground water moves laterally and downward as a result of gravity.In areas of deep soils accumulation, the ground water table establishes a huge underground reservoir.

Certain strata of bedrock, usually sandstones, permit water to move through them. If the next lower bedrock strata is impermeable, it blocks the downward movement of the water. The sandstone strata then becomes both an aquifer which serves as a storage area and a pipeline for the trapped water. Hydrostatic pressure built up as the sandstone strata dips down provides the force for flowing artesian wells. A well tapped into this aquifer will provide water that might have entered the ground many miles away.

When the impermeable rock strata or the impervious soil horizon contacts the earth's surface, the trapped water flows out onto the surface as springs or seeps. Figure 11.1 shows a stylized concept of the perpetual circulation of water from the ocean to the land and back again. This circulation of water is known as the hydrologic cycle.

SURFACE WATER. Some areas of the United States still contain lakes that are pure enough to use for drinking water. The campground operator who can use such a lake is very fortunate indeed. Some operators use the water directly from adjacent lakes while others treat it in one or more ways. Maine's Lake Sabago State Park has a water system to supply over two hundred camp units. This installation has a chlorination system that handles more than 70,000 gallons of water per day without filtration. Campgrounds on the heavily used Lake Winnipesaukee in New Hampshire pump the water directly from the lake to the user. As the lakes occur further from population centers, they have a better chance of remaining free from contamination.

WELLS. Depending upon locality and need, wells may be made by digging, drilling, boring, or driving. [2] Dug and bored wells are usually shallow wells that utilize the ground water

183

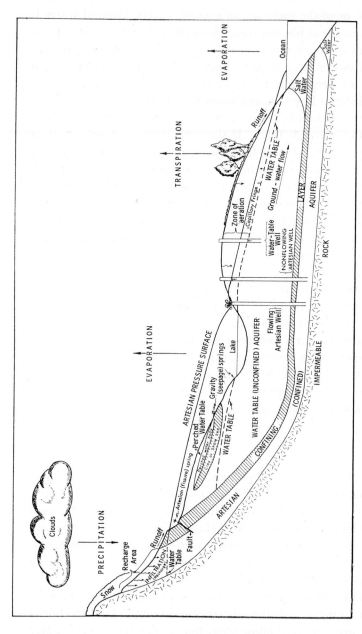

FIG. 11.1. A sketch of the hydrologic cycle showing the various routes of water movement from and toward the ocean. (U.S. Public Health Service.)

table. Drilled and driver wells are usually narrow and deep. Some states require the special approval of the health officer for dug wells and other types that are less than 25 feet deep. [7] Pumping of the water from the underground water table lowers the water table around the pump. It is possible to pump a well dry for periods by pumping water out faster than it can be replaced by the water-bearing strata. Aquifers can also be depleted of their water supply by well outlets. However, the results of a depleted aquifer can be more serious than just the occurrence of dry wells. The presence of drinkable water in the aquifer may have been keeping out undesirable salt water. With the water pressure depleted the aquifer can accept the flow of salt water from the ocean or saline deposits. [12]

Any well should meet with the minimum specifications listed below. [2, 8, 9, 12]

1. The well opening should be higher than adjacent ground so as to prevent the flow of surface water into the well.
2. Wells should be placed at a minimum of 100 feet from any possible source of contamination.
3. The upper 10 feet of any well should be cased to prevent seepage of polluted water into the well.
4. Every well must be covered with a waterproof cover or seal.
5. Artesian wells should be cased down to unfissured bedrock so as to prevent loss of pressure.
6. All newly constructed wells should be decontaminated before use to neutralize contamination caused by construction. Usually household bleach will suffice if mixed as two parts water and one part bleach. This mixture should be added to the well at the rate of two quarts for each estimated 100 gallons. This is not necessary for a free flowing artesian well.

A well must be tested for capacity to determine the amount of water that it can supply. This is done by pumping out water at a given rate per hour and then determining the recovery rate after pumping is stopped. The testing techniques used and the pumps required might differ with the standards of each state health department. In many areas, dug or drilled wells are not possible because of the shallow soil mantle. The deep drilled wells are quite common in the eastern rural areas. However, without the costs of casing included, a drilled well represents an investment of approximately two to three and a half dollars for each foot of depth. In forested areas where a history of successful wells is lacking, investment in a drilled well becomes speculatory. On the other hand, the location of a well near the use area might mean a considerable saving in transmission costs required to move water from an existing surface supply.

Springs. Springs offer an excellent water source for forest recreation areas. Quite often one or more springs providing the proper quality and quantity of water can be found uphill from the recreation area. Gravity feed from these uphill springs will greatly simplify the water storage and distribution system. Springs occur where water-bearing rock strata or impervious soil horizons contact the surface and allow trapped water to flow out of its confinement.

Unfortunately, all springs do not produce pure drinking water. The entrapment areas may be so close to the outlet as to permit insufficient filtration. Also, fissured limestone may provide open channels for water to flow through without the benefits of filtration. Glaciated areas have a similar problem to the limestone areas in that contaminated water can seep into underground channels remaining in the glacial drift. As with deep artesian wells, pollution can enter the aquifer at a far distant point and be carried to the spring. Placing an outhouse on the reverse side of the knob from a lower spring will not prevent contamination from entering the spring. Figure 11.2 shows how contamination is believed to have entered a spring by flowing through or along rock strata on the Monongahela National Forest in West Virginia. The spring had been a producer of good water for a long period of years until two privy type toilets were built on the reverse slope of the hill to accommodate visitors to the fire tower located there.

Any spring should be checked by state health authorities before it is used for drinking purposes. The occurrence of turbidity after a rainstorm is an indication that surface runoff is reaching the spring. The spring should be enclosed to protect the water from contamination from outside sources. Also, the

Fig. 11.2. Probable source of contamination of a mountain spring from reverse slope recreation area.

water should not be stored at the spring house but moved to a storage area where any pumping is to take place. Overflow pipes should be at least 6 inches above the ground and should be screened to prevent entrance of rodents and insects.

The minimum precautions for protecting a spring are as follows.[2, 12]

1. An open bottomed, watertight basin should be constructed on bedrock or into the impervious layer trapping the water. Allowance must be made for expansion and contraction of the concrete.
2. A tight fitting, heavy cover should close the top of the spring-box. It should overlap the edge of the opening by approximately 4 inches with downward edges and it should be locked in place.
3. A clean-out drain that is separate from the distribution system should be provided.

4. Provision should be made to permit water to flow into a separate storage facility for eventual distribution.

5. Overflow precautions must be taken. This is generally accomplished by placing an outlet pipe at the maximum desirable water height. This pipe should carry the extra water far enough away from the spring-box to prevent it from undermining the structure.

Fig. 11.3. Sketch of spring house enclosing and protecting a spring.

Measuring Quantity

How can the quantity of flow be measured to determine whether or not a source is adequate? The solution is quite simple if the planner remembers that all he must do is measure the water flowing by a given point each second. This is a three-step problem. Step one is to determine the square feet of area in a vertical cross-section of the stream. The second step is to ascertain how fast the water is flowing through that cross-section. The third step is a simple multiplication of the cross-section area in square feet by the stream velocity in feet per second. Generally, the stream or spring flow serving as a source for drinking water will be small and easily waded. The cross-section should be established on a reach of the stream where the water is flowing smoothly because this technique is not applicable to turbulent flow.

A simple, but effective, way to obtain an approximation of flow in a small stream can be made by using a string, a yardstick, and a piece of cork. A point should be placed on each stream bank and a string stretched between them. The points must be placed so that the string is perpendicular to the streamflow. At one foot intervals along the string, the water depth is measured by placing a yardstick vertically into the stream. These depth measurements and the width measurements are used to find the cross-section area. Directly plotting the cross-section on graph or cross-section paper to scale will provide sufficient precision for finding the area in square feet.

Stream velocity is usually measured slightly below the surface; however, surface measurements are very satisfactory for this technique of stream gauging. Simply place a cork in the water and record the time it takes to float over a premeasured distance. If the cork moves downstream 10 feet in 20 seconds, its velocity can be determined by the following formula:

$$\frac{\text{distance in feet}}{\text{time in seconds}} \times 60 \text{ seconds per minute} = \text{answer in}$$

feet per minute.

EXAMPLE:

$$\frac{10 \text{ feet}}{20 \text{ seconds}} \times 60 \text{ seconds} = 30 \text{ feet per minute.}$$

The cross-section area in square feet is multiplied by the velocity of the water flow in feet per minute. The answer is given in cubic feet per minute. Since each cubic foot contains 7.48 gallons, a simple conversion gives the answer in gallons per minute.

189

Water Supply

Example:

$$\underset{\substack{\text{stream cross-section}\\ \text{(square feet)}}}{} \times \underset{\substack{\text{velocity (feet}\\ \text{per minute)}}}{} \times \underset{\substack{\text{7.48 gallons}\\ \text{per cubic foot}}}{} = \underset{\substack{\text{flow in}\\ \text{gallons}\\ \text{per minute}}}{}$$

$1.5 \times 30 \times 7.48 = 337$ (approx.) gallons per minute.

Stream or spring flow may vary greatly during the year; therefore, it should be checked for its potential during the periods that it will be receiving use. In much of the United States, heavy forest recreation use takes place during July and August when the stream-flow is characteristically at its lowest.

Elaborate measuring stations are constructed for the purpose of measuring stream flow where the need justifies the expenditure of thousands of dollars. However, recreational planners are basing their needs on educated guesses that are justified by approximations and intuitive reasoning. The expensive and precisely constructed measuring dams, or weirs as they are technically termed, would be unnecessary in all but the largest recreation areas.

If the streamflow is turbulent or if the quantity measurement is critical, a small weir can be constructed and the stream flow computed by mathematics. A 90° V-notch weir with a sharpedge blade will best serve the purpose for this project. Although several designs of weirs have been developed for measuring stream flow under various conditions, the 90° V-notch weir provides the greatest sensitivity at low flow and is best suited for small watershed areas of between 5 and 50 acres. They are generally designed to handle a maximum crest of 2 feet.[10]

A simple V-notch weir can be constructed from a half inch thick sheet of exterior or marine plywood. It should be embedded into the bottom and in the banks of the streambed so that it effectively dams up the stream flow. Four-inch baffles should be fastened to the plywood below the soil line with resorcinal glue and screws to prevent seepage.[15] The 90° notch should be centered on the top edge of the board. It should be

190

cut to a depth of 1 or 2 feet and edged with metal to form a sharp crest. Since the principle of the V-notch weir relies on the water breaking away from the lip of the weir, the crest

FIG. 11.4. Schematic view from upstream side of installed plywood cut-off wall as developed by R. Z. Whipkey.

FIG. 11.5. Sketch of low cost homemade V-notch weir in operation.

191

must be sharp enough to produce this break-away action. Galvanized metal is used for the blade in the larger and permanent structures; however, any sheet metal will serve the purpose for this operatoin if it can be cut accurately to form a 90° V-notch.

Placement of the weir is important. The bottom of the notch must be at least twice the height of the maximum stream flow.[11] This is to prevent drowning of the notch during high-flow periods. In cases where the stream gradient is so steep that it will interfere with the operation of the weir, a small ponding basin should be scooped out to hold the pool behind the weir. Precautions must be taken in areas having coarse soils to prevent by-pass of the weir by leakage.

TABLE 11.2
APPROXIMATE FLOW OVER 90° V-NOTCH WEIRS
FOR EACH TENTH FOOT OF HEAD[a]

Height of head	Discharge	
	cubic feet/second	gallons/minute
0.1	0.008	0.060
0.2	0.047	0.352
0.3	0.129	0.965
0.4	0.262	1.960
0.5	0.455	3.404
0.6	0.714	5.341
0.7	1.044	7.810
0.8	1.452	10.862
0.9	1.943	14.535
1.0	2.520	18.852
1.1	3.189	23.857
1.2	3.954	29.579
1.3	4.818	36.043
1.4	5.785	43.278
1.5	6.860	51.320
2.0	13.96	104.435

[a] By formula: $Q = 2.54H^{2.47}$ (King, 1954).

The amount of flow can be determined by measuring the head of water behind the notch and using a formula developed by King for this purpose.[6] A measuring stick should be firmly mounted in a vertical position upstream from the weir. The distance between the weir and the measuring stick should be at least twice the depth of the notch. Calibration of the measuring post should be done in tenths of feet with the zero point level with the bottom of the notch. For convenience and accuracy, the calibration should take place after the stick is implaced. If an engineer's level is not available to locate the zero point, the water level can be used with sufficient precision. At the instant the water level reaches the point of the notch, it will mark the zero point on the post. The calibrations should be measured upward from that point. The flow over the blade cannot be used to determine height of head because of the downward curve of the water. Table 11.2 gives flow values over the weirs described here as they would be determined by King's formula for computing flow over sharp-crested 90° V-notch weirs.[6]

STORAGE OF WATER

The storage of water becomes a consideration if the source does not supply a continuous and sufficient quantity to assure uninterupted usage or if the source is not elevated to provide the proper pressure for usage. The problem of water pressure can be solved as part of the storage for sufficient quantity. Elevated tanks and ground level cisterns provide the best solution to recreation area water storage problems. The pneumatic pumps and tanks used in home water systems generally lack sufficient volume or require too large an investment and upkeep for use in recreation areas.

Above ground storage tanks can be made of wood, metal, concrete, or brick; however, redwood or cypress wood is the most commonly used material. Redwood and cypress will probably produce the cheapest tank and will remain watertight while the tank contains water. Generally, a two-day peak supply of water is planned for an elevated storage tank.[12] Water can be moved into the tank by gravity or raised by pumping. Whenever the terrain will permit it, gravity flow frees the recreation area manager from the worry of pump operation and maintenance.

The ground-level cistern or reservoir is the best facility for storing large quantities of water for recreation area use. The ground-level reservoir is a large water-proof container that is set down into the ground and covered to prevent the contamination if its contents. The reservoir should not be placed where high water or surface run-off could enter. The overlapping cover should be raised at least 4 inches above the ground surface and locked into place. The floor should slope toward the drain to permit complete drainage and all openings should be screened to exclude rodents.[12] Overflow systems must be independent of any sewage system.[2]

The concrete and brick reservoirs can be made watertight by an interior coating of rich cement. The U.S. Public Health Service objects to the use of asphalt or tar for waterproofing because of the objectionable taste it can give to the water and because it might react chemically with some of the chemicals used later for treatment.[12]

As with wells, the reservoir should be disinfected before use and after repairs that could pollute the water supply. The system should be flushed clean of any dirt and particles resulting from construction. Next, a disinfecting solution of calcium hypochlorite should be added and allowed to stand for 24 hours. The American Water Works Association recommends that the 1.2 pounds of high-test 70 percent calcium hypochlorite be used for each 1000 gallons of water in the reservoir. If no chroline is present at the end of the 24 hour period, the process should be repeated.[1] Flush out the disinfecting solution before putting the reservoir into operation.

The size of the storage facility required will depend upon the quantity of water demanded at peak usage and the system's ability to replenish the supply during the dry season. The problem of water quantity requirements were discussed earlier

PLAN

ELEVATION

Fig. 11.6. Typical ground level reservoir. (U.S. Public Health Service.)

195

in this chapter. As mentioned earlier, water-use generally is confined to the half-day beginning at breakfast and ending at evening. Because of this onesided distribution of use, the water supply or storage must be larger than it would if the use was spread evenly over the recharge period. The peakload expectation is used to determine the minimum storage facility required. This is done as shown in the steps below:

1. Estimate daily water requirement during peak use of campground.
2. Determine hourly recharge rate.
3. Subtract twelve times hourly recharge rate from maximum water requirement.
4. The remainder is the minimum size of storage required. Example of method for determining minimum water storage requirement:
   Estimated daily water use during full capacity
   $$= 40,000 \text{ gallons.}$$
   Recharge capacity of spring during lowest flow
   $$= 2000 \text{ gal/hr.}$$
   $$40,000 - (12 \times 2000) = 16,000 \text{ gal (approx.) to be stored.}$$

This example is based on the assumption that the water supply is capable of producing enough water over a 24 hour period to supply the peakload requirements. If it cannot do this, additonal storage must be built in order to collect water during low-use days or supplementary sources must be developed. The size limitations caused by costs or space may preclude too large a storage space. The reservoir needed to hold 16,000 gallons as would be approximately large enough to fulfill the requirements in the example would have to contain 2120 cubic feet of space. Such a reservoir would require inside dimensions of $12 \times 12 \times 12$ feet.

Distribution System

The distribution system must accomplish two objectives. First, it must transport water from the source and storage area to the point of use in the most efficient manner possible. Second, the distribution system must protect the water from contamination during transit. No water quality reductions should occur as a result of the distribution system. Most state health departments have regulations and guidelines for water supply systems. These are available without charge upon request and should be consulted prior to construction of the system.

Pipelines for small distribution systems are usually made from the standard galvanized pipe and fittings although pipes of many other materials are suitable. Plastic pipe material is often used for cold water transmission because of its lower cost and convenience of installation; however, plastic pipe requires more protection from crushing than does galvanized pipe and it is susceptible to rodent damage. All plastic pipe should be certified by the National Sanitation Foundation, or similar testing laboratory, as being non-toxic or non-taste-producing.[12] The transmission lines should be as straight as possible and deep enough to avoid danger from freezing if they are to be used during cold weather. The expense of deep burial of the water lines can be avoided if the lines are drained prior to the danger of freezing. Air vents should be placed at high points to bleed air out of the lines, and valves should be placed in convenient locations for line drainage or repairs. A standard "T" connection can be used instead of the valves that are to be used for drainage. The open end can be capped during normal use periods. Besides providing for a saving in the capital investment, the "T" connections can permit future expansion of the system with a minimum of effort.

Although state regulations may vary somewhat, they generally agree that water lines must always pass above any sewage lines and that the two kinds of pipelines must remain 10 feet apart when parallel. Also, no connections of any kind can be tolerated between the drinking water system and a contaminated source. Decontamination of a pipeline with a 40 to 60 ml solution of chlorine for 24 hours is necessary after its construction or any repairs that could contaminate it.

Water Supply

Self-closing non-threaded faucets cost more initially. However, they will save money in the long run by conserving water and reducing the muddy mess that can be associated with a water tap. Occasional threaded faucets should be available for irrigation or fire control.

The question of the pipeline construction need not be difficult to solve. The line should be laid as straight as possible in a trench for efficiency and safety. Although most reliable textbooks and consultants will advise that the pipes be buried in trenches, many recreation areas have surface lines. In certain situations, the surface lines have proved satisfactory. They save digging in the very rocky areas that are often associated with forest or mountain land. Also, leaks are easily detected and repaired. Surface lines have three problems that are not as serious with sub-surface lines. (a) They must be drained to prevent freezing. (b) The pipe material can not be plastic because of possible rodent damage. (c) The pipeline should be inaccessible to the public so as to guard against accidental damage or vandalism.

Determining the proper diameter pipe is a problem facing the developer. The three variables that must be used in order to calculate the pipe size are: (a) the water pressure, (b) the hydraulic gradient, and (c) the flow per minute.

Water pressure is measured in pounds per square inch (psi). A column of water that is 2.31 feet high will produce 1 psi of downward pressure. Therefore, the normal domestic water pressure of 15 to 60 psi will require a head, or column of water, that is 35 to 140 feet high.[12]

Table 11.3 gives the pipe size that is required to obtain a given quantity of water at a given headloss per foot. The term headloss refers to the head or column height in excess of that required to give the required water pressure. In order to obtain the average domestic pressure of 30 psi, a head of 2.3×30, or 69 feet, is required. If the reservoir is 200 feet above the outlet, a headloss of 200—69, or 131 feet, occurs within the distribution system. The headloss per foot is calculated by dividing the headloss by the length of the pipeline in feet:

$$\text{hydraulic gradient (headloss/foot)} = \frac{\text{headloss}}{\text{length of line in feet}}.$$

If the reservoir is 1000 feet from the point of use, the headloss per foot is equal to the headloss (H) of 131 divided by the length (L) of 1000 $\cdot$ $H/L = \dfrac{131}{1000} = 0.131$.

Now that the pressure and hydraulic gradient have been determined the only remaining factor to be resolved is that of quantity of water required at the distribution point. The U.S. Department of Health, Education, and Welfare recommends that any new system be designed to supply at least 8.5 gallons per minute.[12] Although this may be excessive for some recreation areas, it provides fire protection for a slightly higher development cost than for a smaller water system. Also, with the increasing use of outdoor recreation facilities has come the need for more complete sanitation facilities that include flush toilets, showers, and laundries. All of these facilities require large quantities of water. In general, the recreation area that will continue to satisfy its users must be able to provide these facilities and be ready to expand or enlarge them.

After the desired water pressure, the hydraulic gradient, and the flow per minute have been determined, the pipe diameter can be obtained from Fig. 11.7. By entering the calculated values into the table, one determines that the required pipe diameter for galvanized iron pipes in the example is approximately $1\frac{7}{16}$ inches.

EXAMPLE:
$$H = 200 - 2.3 \times 30 = 131 \text{ (feet)}$$

$$H/L = 0.131 \text{ (headloss in feet/foot of line)}$$

$$\text{Flow} = 8.5 \text{ (gpm)}$$

Therefore, $1\frac{7}{16}$ inch diameter pipe is required (Fig. 11.7). Because galvanized iron pipe comes in inch and half-inch sizes, the next larger size above the calculated value must be chosen to meet the desired specifications.

199

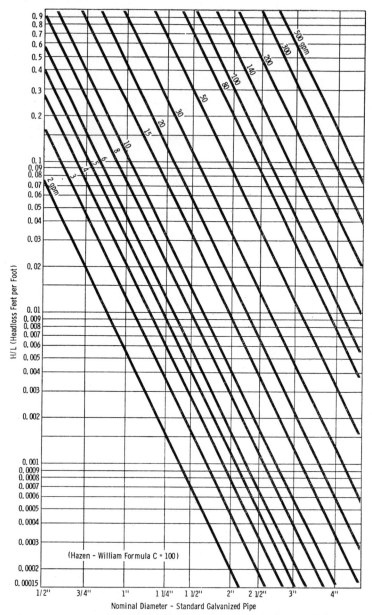

FIG. 11.7. Required pipe diameter is dependent upon headloss and desired flow.

The distribution system should be thoroughly flushed out and disinfected prior to use. Also, no outlets should be placed down in bowls, sinks, or other containers that could fill up to the outlet. This is to protect against back-syphoning through a flooded outlet.

QUALITY OF WATER

The U.S. Public Health Service published standards for drinking water in 1962. [13] Many of the states are now following with similar standards that will assist the campground planner in his development plan. A check with the state health service is advisable right at the beginning of the recreation area planning stage and will determine if an insurmountable stumbling block exists. Some states have drinking water standards, but they do not require any testing for purity. Many recreation area operators have the drinking water tested as a matter of safety to their customers and a safeguard for themselves against lawsuits that might develop as a result of providing contaminated water.

What does the term water quality mean? It is the relative bacteriological, physical, radiological, and chemical characteristics of water in relation to its safe and desirable use by humans. [12] The bacteriological or biologic quality is probably the most serious and widespread problem concerning water quality. It is the biologic quality that is considered when the term "purity" is used among laymen. The other facets of water quality are locally limiting but not universally troublesome.

The bacteriological characteristic is determined by counting the number of coliform bacteria present in a water sample. Although the coliform group of bacteria are non-pathogenic, they are used to measure pollution of water for two reasons. First, they dwell in human intestines and have life cycles that are similar to pathogenic bacteria. Second, they are more numerous and easier to detect than the pathogenic bacteria. Techniques for sampling the water are available from the health departments of each state. The U.S. Public Health Service standards permit only one coliform organism for each 100 ml of water.[12, 13] This amounts to about two bacteria in each cup of water.

The use of the coliform count gives only an indication of the pathogenic bacteria present in the water. It does not measure the enteric viruses present. However, evidence points out that water supplies are not frequently guilty of carrying viral infections. Fortunately, virus organisms are far less numerous than are the coliform bacteria; therefore, if the virus count were too high, the coliform count probably would be proportionally higher, thereby drawing attention to the pollution.

The physical characteristics of water are turbidity, taste, and odor. Turbidity refers to the presence of suspended mineral and organic material in the water. When the suspended particles are readily visible in a glass of water the turbidity level is too high. Even though the water is biologically safe, it is aesthetically undesirable.

The dark color often seen in woodland streams is generally caused by organic acids given off by decaying vegetation. The local terms of "pine-water" and "cedar water" aptly describe the appearance of organically colored water. This phenomenon is generally associated with water that has collected in a bog area. Coloration of water also can be caused by dissolved inorganic substances and by algae. Coloration caused by organic acids or dissolved minerals is often accompanied by a taste. Tastes in water are very objectional to the consumer and should be avoided if possible. Certain treatment can be done to lessen or eliminate some offending tastes.

Turbidity, color, and taste may cause the user to seek an alternate source of water. In the case of forest recreation, the user might not remain in the recreation area.

The chemical characteristics of water in an area are closely tied to the geology of the area. Limestone valleys generally have hard water springs and streams while the coal-bearing sediments of the carboniferous era produce very acid water. When water falls as precipitation, it is relatively free from dissolved chemicals. As it flows over, around, and through the rocks and soil, the water dissolves and carries away chemicals inherent in the geology of the area. The usual chemical analysis of water determines the total hardness, alkalinity, acidity, and the presence of sulfates and chlorides. However, there are local problem areas where water contains an excessive amount of toxic chemicals and cannot be used. Tests for these chemicals should be made in areas where they are commonly found.

Water Treatment

Water that is destined for human consumption should be of the highest possible quality. It should be technically safe from bacteriologic pollution, free of suspended particles, colorless, and without odor or taste. Some recreation areas supply water that meets these standards and do not need to treat the water in any way. Others are not so fortunate and must be involved in extensive water treatment. The majority of forest recreation areas probably are in an intermediate position. That is, they have a water supply from wells, springs, streams, or lakes that meets most minimal standards but are near enough to the danger point for concern. The possibility of pollution is something to be considered by a private operator from a business standpoint. Even a temporary closure because of poor water quality could have a disastrous affect on a private business establishment. Many large developments chlorinate water as a general practice for protection against possible pollution even though the water is biologically safe for drinking.

The treatment that water gets will vary according to the conditions of the water. There are several treatment processes used in preparing water for drinking. Any one or more may be required in any specific instance. These processes and their purposes are given in Table 11.3. ·

The most important treatment process is that of disinfecting the water. Chlorine-bearing compounds serve this purpose

TABLE 11.3.
WATER TREATMENT PROCESSES AND THEIR PURPOSE

Process	Purpose	Technique
Sedimentation	Removal of heavy suspended particles	Gravity settling in quiescent pond or tank
Coagulation	Removal of very fine suspended particles	Flocculation of solids by adding alum in still water
Filtration	Removal of suspended particles	Passage of water through sand or diatomaceous earth. Sometimes used with sedimentation when water is very turbid
Disinfection	Destroy pathogenic organisms	Addition of chemical disinfectant with high germicidal power

quite well and are easy to administer. The most popular form of chlorine is calcium hypochlorite which is commercially available in tablet and powder form. Sodium hypochlorite solutions are commonly used in small water systems where the household bleaches are available at local stores. The available chlorine in the sodium hypochlorite solutions vary in strength from 3 to 15 percent.

The chlorination of the water should be done by one of the many commercially designed systems on the market. The equipment should be installed and operated so that the water is treated and rapidly mixed with the chlorine continuously. The U.S. Public Health Service states that, "At least two parts per million of free residual chlorine should be in contact with the water for not less than twenty minutes before the treated water reaches the first consumer".[14]

State health authorities should be consulted during the early stages of development planning. Their advice early in the planning might help to prevent their wrath later on. Most state health authorities are quite willing to help an operator get off to a good start; but it is their responsibility to protect the citizens that will be using the facility. If the water supply system is going to be disapproved, it is better to have it happen before hundreds of dollars are invested in it.

REFERENCES

1. AMERICAN WATER WORKS ASSOCIATION. 1954. *Procedure for Disinfecting Water Mains*. Report C601–54. Park Avenue, New York, N.Y.
2. ELHERS, V. and STEELE, E. 1965. *Municipal and Rural Sanitation*. 6th edition. McGraw-Hill, New York. 643 pages.
3. FINE, I. and WERNER, E. 1960. *Camping in State Parks and Forests in Wisconsin*, vol. 1, No. 3. University of Wisconsin. 18 pages.
4. FORBES, R. and MEYER, A.B. 1961. *Forestry Handbook*. Ronald Press Company, New York.
5. JAMES, G. and RIPLEY, T. 1963. *Instructions for Using Traffic Counters to Establish Recreation Visits and Use*. Southeast Experiment Station Paper SE-3. Asheville, North Carolina.
6. KING, H. 1954. *Handbook of Hydraulics*. 4th edition. McGraw-Hill, New York. 556 pages.
7. MICHIGAN DEPARTMENT OF HEALTH. 1965. *Regulations for Certain Water Supplies in Michigan*. Act No. 146, Public Acts of 1919 as Amended.
8. OHIO DEPARTMENT OF HEALTH. 1964. *Camp Sanitation-Laws, Regulations, and Recommendations*. Columbus, Ohio.
9. ORT, DON R. 1963. *Recommended Campground Sanitation Requirements. In Guidelines for Developing Land for Outdoor Recreational Uses*. Cooperative Extension Service. Purdue University, West Lafayette, Ind.
10. REINHART K. and PIERCE, R. 1964. *Stream–Gaging Stations for Research on Small Watersheds*. Agriculture Handbook No. 268. U.S. Forest Service NE Experiment Station, Upper Darby, Pa.
11. U.S. DEPARTMENT OF AGRICULTURE. 1941. *Climate and Man Yearbook of Agriculture*, Government Printing Office, Washington, D.C.
12. U.S. PUBLIC HEALTH SERVICE. 1962. *Manual of Individual Water Supply Systems*. Publication No. 24. U.S. Department of Health, Education, and Welfare, Washington, D.C.
13. U.S. PUBLIC HEALTH SERVICE. 1962. *Drinking Water Standards*. Publication No. 956. U.S. Department of Health, Education, and Welfare, Washington, D.C.
14. U.S. PUBLIC HEALTH SERVICE. 1965. *Environmental Health Practice in Recreation Areas*. Publication No. 1195. U.S. Department of Health, Education, and Welfare, Washington, D.C.
15. WHIPKEY, R.Z. 1961. *Plywood Cutoff Walls for Temporary Weirs*. Central States Forest Experiment Station Note 150. U.S. Forest Service, Columbus, Ohio.

CHAPTER 12

Sanitation

INTRODUCTION

Sanitation, as it is covered in this chapter, refers to the collection, treatment, or processing of sewage, refuse, and wash water. Sanitation facilities are necessary for the protection of the visiting public, of the employees, and of the nearby communities from diseases.[13] Although sewage and refuse are menaces to health, they are to a much greater extent creators of esthetic nuisances. They are offensive to both the senses of smell and sight and cause esthetic devaluation that is far out of proportion with their danger to human health.[1]

Adequate sanitary facilities at forest recreation areas are of the utmost importance. The user will often judge the recreational quality of the area by the sanitation facilities. In fact, research has shown that the sanitary facilities are more often criticized than any other part of camping.[3] By definition, the U.S. Forest Service considers sanitary facilities a part of any of its developed recreation areas.[9] Of course, user reaction is just one reason, and perhaps not the most important one, for providing sanitary facilities at such areas.

SEWAGE

Sewage is, by definition, human excreta that has been mixed with water; however, in the field of forest recreation where water systems are not always used sewage has become a synonym for excreta.[2] This change has probably occurred because of the social acceptance of the word sewage and not of excreta. In this book, we shall consider sewage to be any human waste products.

The recreation area manager or planner needs to have an understanding of the basic principles involved in sewage treatment so that he can sensibly investigate the available systems or analyze troubles in existing systems. In other words, knowledge of the capabilities and limitations of the various sewage systems will aid the manager in giving the best service to the public for the money that he has at his disposal.

Characteristics and Biology of Sewage

Solids make up only 800 parts per million of water-borne sewage, so that the actual volume of solids is very small for the problems it creates. Furthermore, only half of the solids are organic matter and therefore decomposable. Why should the reader be concerned over such a small amount of solids since the solids themselves are not pathogenic? Why not simply be concerned with killing the disease-bearing organisms? The reason for being so concerned about the organic solids is that it is the decomposing organic matter that produces the offensive odors and dark colors that are associated with sewage. The organic matter must be decomposed before the sewage effluent is put into the soil or run into streams, or else serious problems occur. Organic matter will plug up the pores in the soil mantle and prevent the infiltration of the effluent. Also, the aquatic structure of the stream will be changed because of the presence of the undecomposed organic matter.

The decomposition of organic matter is a result of bacteriological processes that take place either in the presence or in the absence of free oxygen. Organic matter is decomposed by aerobic bacteria when sufficient free oxygen is present and by anaerobic bacteria when free oxygen is not present.

The aerobic bacteria carry on their life processes in the presence of free oxygen that occurs in the air or dissolved in the water. The aerobic process is odorless and relatively rapid in that it takes a matter of hours. Nitrates and sulfates are produced through the oxidation of nitrites and sulfur compounds

207

occurring in the organic matter. These products are available for use as plant fertilizer.

Anaerobic bacteria act on the organic compounds in the absence of free oxygen. Since the bacteria require oxygen to survive, they take it from oxygen-containing compounds within the sewage. This is a reduction technique that occurs commonly in nature. Swamp gases such as methane are products of anaerobic activity occurring in the wet areas. The grey mottling that is associated with poorly drained soils is a result of the reduction of the iron compounds in the mineral soil by anaerobic bacteria.

Decomposition by the anaerobic action is very slow and the organic matter may require many weeks to completely stabilize into the dark and almost odorless humus.[2] Ammonia and hydrogen sulfide are two very odorous products of this process. In cases where the free oxygen supply is limited, the aerobic action might use up all of the free oxygen supply and the decomposition process will switch to an anaerobic action.

Decomposition of organic matter dumped into streams will occur if the water temperature is above 40 °F. If the quantity of sewage is sufficient, the stream's supply of free oxygen will be depleted, setting the stage for anaerobic processes to begin with its accompanying odors and colors. Fish cannot live in streams that do not contain dissolved free oxygen. With the use of its open streams for sewers, society has created widespread channels of esthetic degradation through the countryside. Fortunately, all is not lost because nature has the ability to correct some of man-created sewage problems.

The streams can "cleanse" themselves to a certain degree if the pollution is not overwhelming. As the stream water moves along, it absorbs oxygen through the surface and ripple action. Algae growing in the water use carbon dioxide and produce oxygen which greatly adds to the recovery rate of the dissolved oxygen. As the stream recovers and the oxygen approaches saturation, aerobic bacteria again take over the decomposition of organic matter. Although pathogenic organisms die off as time passes, some survive for a very long time. These surviving pathogens make the danger of disease too great to ever consider once polluted water safe for drinking purposes without treatment.

Neither aerobic nor anaerobic bacteria are associated with disease; they are naturally occurring bacteria that function when the conditions are favorable for growth of such organisms. If the conditions of food, temperature, and moisture are favorable, the bacteria will grow. On the other hand, anaerobic and areobic action does not remove infectious agents from the sewage. [11] It simply decomposes the organic solids within the sewage without having any great effect on pathogenic organisms.

Pathogenic organisms contained within sewage are relatively small in number and they meet a hostile environment immediately upon leaving the human body. Within 5 days most of the typhoid and typhus bacteria are dead. [2] A much more common group of bacteria organisms are the coliforms. Although these coliform bacteria are not pathogenic, they do have a life cycle that parallels the pathogens. Therefore, the coliforms are used as indicators of water contamination. [10]

Sewage Disposal

Sewage disposal at forest recreation developments will generally be less elaborate than that in municipal areas; however, to the user, it is every bit as important. Of course, there are the wilderness seekers who do not want to see any signs of sewage disposal systems other than a shovel. This chapter confines its interest to the developed forest recreation areas and leaves the wilderness user to his own digging.

Many different methods of disposing of sewage are being used in developed forest recreation areas. Basically, these systems either store the human waste in some sort of container or they move it in water through a treatment process. Therefore, the fundamental classification of the disposal system is made on the basis of whether or not the system uses water for carrying the sewage.

209

Sanitation

The decision to use water carriage or non-water carriage systems will depend largely upon available capital, expected use, soil conditions, and water quantity. Non-water carriage systems are considerably cheaper to build than water carriage systems. However, they are the less desirable of the two classes of sewage disposal from maintenance costs and user satisfaction standpoints. The public favors the flush toilet systems at the present time. For this reason, private campground owners who must cater to the will of the customers should make an effort to install a water carriage system.[8]

State sanitary codes in many states are just beginning to be written up for forest recreation developments. In the absence of specific legislation, many states have made trailer park or tourist accommodation regulations apply to campgrounds. Picnic and other day-use areas have been ignored except that they are controlled and guided by local ordinances. Some states are presently attempting to pass laws for state licensing of campgrounds in addition to establishing sanitary codes.[1]

In all cases, the best arrangement for sewage disposal is the tying into a municipal type sewage disposal system. Although the initial costs may be higher than for a separate system, the problems will be fewer. Most of the problems concerning soil and water pollution from disposal of sewage are solved when a municipal system is used. Unfortunately, most forest recreation areas are not situated near a municipal sewer and must be served by some other sewage disposal system.

Non-water Carriage Sewage Systems

There are four types of non-water carriage sewage systems that can be used in recreation areas. They are listed as:

1. Pump-out vault privy.
2. Simple pit privy.
3. Chemical tanks.
4. Incinerator vaults.

Of these four, the simple pit privy and the pump-out vault are the types usually employed in forest recreation areas. They are the cheapest to construct and the easiest to maintain.

Non-water carriage disposal systems are not as desirable as water carriage systems, but they are adequate under certain situations and used under almost any conditions. [13] Light use, insufficient water, or unsuitable soil conditions for water carriage systems are three valid reasons for the use of non-water carriage disposal of sewage. The cost factor is often used as a reason to avoid flush toilets; however, this argument does not always hold up in heavily used recreation areas. Temporary-use areas that are not designed for continuous use and therefore do not warrant a large investment would be a place where costs could be held down by less elaborate sanitary facilities. Overflow, or peakload, areas for campgrounds are not intended to give the user more than adequate facilities; therefore, privy toilets would satisfy the short-term use and the minimal facility requirements.

Although water carriage systems are best from the sanitation and user satisfaction standpoints, they do not preclude the use of other systems. Many large and heavily used picnic and campgrounds in some states are still using privies with no adverse affect. However, this is because of excellent construction and maintenance techniques such as used at Point Beach State Park in Wisconsin where pump-out vault toilets are proving satisfactory. Whether because of poor planning or insufficient maintenance, privy type toilets are generally not satisfactory in heavy use areas.

PUMP-OUT VAULT PRIVY. The pump-out vault privy has proved to be the best non-water carriage system in places where use is moderately heavy. The pit is lined with concrete so that it is waterproof and prevents the escape of any liquids into the soil or water table. Periodically, the contents of the tank are pumped out by a contractor with the appropriate equipment. In order to facilitate the emptying of the pit, a tightly sealed exterior pump-out opening should be built. The state sanitary codes may vary on pump-out vault size requirements and

211

should be checked in advance of building. Figure 12.1 shows a pump-out vault toilet built in accordance with Forest Service designs. The land should slope away from the structure in order to carry away surface run-off. The Forest Service recommends a 12:1 slope away from the building to accomplish satisfactory run-off.

FIG. 12.1. Diagram of pump-out vault toilet.

SIMPLE PIT PRIVY. The oldest and still very common type of sewage disposal system is the simple pit-toilet. This is little more than a small building placed over a hole in the ground. For safety, the sides are often shored with lumber or stone and the floor is made from a precast reinforced concrete slab. [9] A 50-foot safety zone is needed between a privy and water sources; however, some states require as much as 100 feet between the privy and the water source. [2]

212

As with pump-out pits, it is desirable to keep out surface runoff water. This can be done by maintaining at least a 12:1 slope away from the privy.[9] The pit privy functions better if the contents are dry; therefore, if the area is situated where there is a danger of high water some other system should be considered. Also, the rising water table would increase the danger of subsurface water pollution and make the pit privy undesirable. Any water that has collected in the pit will be a breeding place for mosquitoes unless treated. A cup of kerosine added to the contents each week will control their breeding.

Any biologic action taking place in the pit will be impeded by disinfectants; therefore, care should be taken to prevent their introduction. Also, screening and a self-closing toilet seat will help to exclude rodents and insects from the pit.

Odors and pit toilets have appeared to be inseparable over the years. Some odors can be reduced by the application of burnt lime; however, this has proved to be of limited value. In recent years, the Forest Service has come up with a satisfactory technique for controlling these bad odors. Wagar has developed a convection stack device to move air currents down through the seat opening and out through a ventilating stack.[14]

Simple ventilation stacks have proved to be satisfactory only when the pit contents were warm enough to permit the air to rise through the stack. The convection stack developed by Wagar uses a gas or kerosine burner in the stack to create convection currents. Besides causing the desired movement of air, the flame in the stack burns and modifies some of the offensive gases as they move upward through the stack.

A flash barrier is needed with this convection system to prevent ignition of volatile fuels that might be dumped into the pit. These flash barriers can be fabricated from wire mesh scouring pads that have been unrolled and repacked until they are packed so densely as to block all but pinpoint spots of light, the theory here being that any flash originating at the flame would be cooled below ignition when passing through the copper strand barrier.

Completely prepared convection stack units can now be purchased from the commercial forest supply companies for approximately 20 dollars. If this system of odor control is to be installed, the developer should obtain Wagar's research note from the USFS Northeastern Forest Experiment Station.

Fig. 12.2. Diagram of pit toilet showing air circulation caused by convection stack. (U.S. Forest Service.)

Unfortunately, the effectiveness and simplicity of this system of odor control does have a drawback. It has encouraged the use of pit toilets in some eastern state parks where the use is much too heavy to warrant such a method of sewage disposal.

Toilet buildings need all the help that they can get to be appealing to most users. Large central washhouses with tile floors and electric lights require an enormous investment and do not fit in small recreation areas. Two very important steps have been taken in recent years to improve the lot of privy users. First, the homemade toilet risers are being replaced by

214

the commercially sold stainless steel risers with plastic seats.[9] The size and shape of these risers make cleaning up easier and reduces horrifying thoughts in the minds of parents of young children. Second, public agencies are abandoning the strict policy of constructing dark and dreary buildings just to avoid using "unnatural" building materials. The use of corrugated translucent fiber glass roofing has done a lot to brighten up the privy and make its interior more attractive. The translucent fiber glass roofing should be used whenever possible.

Some attempts have been made to use prefabricated light-gauge corrugated metal buildings for privies. The author's observations indicate that these are unsuitable for forest recreation areas. The metal does not withstand the beating that it receives and the entire structure is very susceptible to severe damage by vandalism.

Water Carriage Sewage Systems

There are two types of individual water carriage sewage systems that are satisfactory for use in a recreation area. The underground distribution system employing a septic tank and a leaching field is very commonly used in areas that are not serviced by municipal sewage systems. The surface distribution into a stabilization pond is a less common system that is ideally suited for many forest recreation areas. Many regulations governing use and many prejudices based upon misuse of these systems exist at all levels of government. Local sanitation codes should be consulted prior to construction. On-the-ground investigation and rigid engineering standards are necessary to ensure that these systems will perform satisfactorily.

The investment is too large and the dangers are too numerous to leave the sewage disposal system at the mercy of a contractor. The developer should either plan the system himself or have it done by a qualified person for his approval. Most important, the developer should oversee every step of the construction to ensure proper installation.

SEPTIC-TANK SYSTEMS. The septic-tank system probably is the most economical and practical method of sewage disposal where the quantities of sewage are small and the soils are suitable for dispersing the effluent. [13] Proper planning and installation are critical for the satisfactory functioning of a septic-tank system. Improper construction or indiscriminate use of septic-tank systems has created many serious economic and health problems.

A septic-tank system is made up of a buried waterproof tank, a distribution box, and a tile drainfield all connected together by continuous iron or terracotta pipes. The purpose of this system is to get the sewage effluent dispersed into the soil mantle. This purpose is accomplished by passing the sewage through the septic tank where it is conditioned by anaerobic bacteria. When the conditioned effluent passes from the tank, it moves through the distribution box and into the porous leaching lines where it infiltrates into the soil.

The success of a septic tank depends upon the soil's ability to absorb the effluent rapidly enough to prevent the fluid from breaking out onto the ground surface or backing up into the plumbing fixtures. Some soils are loose enough to handle large quantities of liquid, while others are not suited for effluent disposal. A percolation test should be run to rate the soil for effluent disposal.

The percolation test measures the rate that water will infiltrate and percolate into moist soil. At least six test holes must be drilled or dug on the proposed absorption site. The holes can be from 4 to 12 inches in diameter and should reach as deeply as the proposed absorption trenches. The sides of the holes should be roughened slightly and all loose material removed. A 2-inch layer of pebbles or gravel on the bottom of each hole is needed to protect the soil from "puddling" when the water is poured into the hole. The test holes should be kept filled with water for at least 4 hours. Overnight soaking of the holes is often recommended to be certain that the soil will be as wet as it will be during the wettest part of the year. Do not overdo this part by waiting for the soil to soak more than 24 hours. [6, 11]

To measure the percolation rate, adjust the water level to 6 inches above the gravel layer. Measure the drop in water level for a 30 minute period. This drop determines the suitability of the soil for septic-tank absorption or leaching fields. If the water requires more than 60 minutes to drop 1 inch, the soil is unsuited for a septic-tank system.

In order to determine the size of the absorption field required, the developer must correlate the soil's percolation rate with the amount of effluent produced by the facility. An estimate of the amounts of sewage flow that can be expected from park facilities during use is listed in Table 12.1. By multiplying the quantity of sewage from each type of fixture by the number of each fixture, the total flow of effluent can be estimated.

TABLE 12.1

ESTIMATE OF SEWAGE FLOW AT PUBLIC PARKS DURING PARK USE HOURS

Type of fixture	Gallons per hour	Type of fixture	Gallons per hour
Flush toilets	36	Showers	150
Urinals	10	Faucets	15

U.S. Public Health Service.

TABLE 12.2

ALLOWABLE RATE OF SEWAGE APPLICATION TO A SOIL ABSORPTION SYSTEM

Percolation rate (minutes for 1 inch drop in water level)	Maximum sewage application rate (gallons per square foot each day)
2	3.5
3	2.9
4	2.5
5	2.2
10	1.6
15	1.3
30	0.9
45	0.6

U.S. Public Health Service.

217

Sanitation

Using the information in Table 12.1, a developer can obtain an estimate of what volumes of sewage he will need to dispose of. The example following Table 12.2 will show how to use this information in determining the size of the absorption field. Table 12.2 gives the maximum rate of sewage that can be applied per square foot of trench bottom. Always plan on a minimum of 225 square feet of area or 114 linear feet of 24 inch wide trench.[6] This is the minimum that is to be used in lieu of local ordinances that require more minimum area.

EXAMPLE 1

Determine length of line required for a washhouse containing four flush toilets, two showers, and four faucets in area that has a percolation rate of 5 minutes. The campground is expected to operate at peak capacity on holidays.

Step 1. Number of each facility × estimated flow in gallons:

4 toilets × 35 each	144 gallons
2 showers × 150 each	300 gallons
2 faucets × 15 each	30 gallons
Total	474 gallons per hour

Step 2. Assume 12 hours of use for each facility:
$474 \times 12 = 5688$ gal/day.

Step 3. Determine number of square feet of trench required to absorb a day's total sewage:
5688 gal/day ÷ 2.2 gal/sq.ft. = 2585 square feet of absorption area required.

Step 4. Compute the length of 2 foot wide trench required:
2585 ÷ 2 sq.ft./linear foot
= 1293 linear feet.

Nearly 1300 feet of absorption trench might appear to be excessive for one washhouse. The percolation rate of the soil can not be changed by different calculations; but perhaps the sewage flow as estimated from Table 12.1 appears too high.

Fig. 12.3. Diagramatic sketch of septic tank disposal system. (U.S. Public Health Service.)

Fig. 12.4. Longitudinal section of the septic tank. (U.S. Public Health Service.)

Fig. 12.5. Diagram of devices for measuring sludge and scum within a septic tank. (U.S. Public Health Service.)

Fig. 12.6. Septic tank and dosing tank.

Another approach to the estimate of sewage can be made by basing the estimate on the expected use of the area as described in the following paragraphs.

The ideal situation is to have one toilet for each sex for every ten camping units. This is not widely followed and some states use a recommended minimum of one toilet for each sex for every thirty camping units.[5] It would be safe to assume that the example used above would apply to a thirty unit campground.

The average camping group consists of four or five persons who will each produce approximately 35 gallons of sewage daily.[3,11] Example 2 computes length of trench required using the figures for water requirements per camper for the same area that was used in Example 1.

EXAMPLE 2

Step 1. Determine daily volume of sewage produced at the washhouse when the campground is at capacity and all thirty units are using the washhouse facilities:
35 gal/person/day × 5 persons/unit
= 175 gal/unit/day.
30 units × 175 gal/day = 5250 gal/day of sewage.

Step 2. Determine the length of 2 foot wide trench needed to absorb a day's sewage from thirty campgrounds when the soil percolation rate is 5 minutes per inch:
5250 gal/day ÷ 2.2 gal/sq. ft./day
= 2386 sq.ft. of absorption area required.
2386 ÷ 2 sq.ft./linear foot = 1193 linear feet of 2 foot wide absorbton trench required.

Most tables that list recommended absorption trench areas are designed for the private residential dwelling and not for a recreation area. Table 12.1 listing the sewage flow at public parks can be used to compute the absorption area. These figures will work well for most day-use areas.[11] Table 12.3 presents the length of absorption trench required for each campground as determined by the percolation rate. The computations for Table 12.3 are based upon U.S. Public Health Service data concerning percolation rates.

TABLE 12.3
LINEAR FOOTAGE OF ABSORPTION TRENCH REQUIRED
FOR EACH CAMPING UNIT AS RELATED TO PERCOLATION RATE

Percolation rate (minutes per 1 inch drop)	Recommended linear feet of absorption trench[a] per camping unit[b] (approx.)[c]
2	25
4	35
5	40
10	55
15	70
30	100

[a] 24 inch wide absorption trench.
[b] Based on average of five persons per unit.
[c] Rounded up to nearest 5 feet.

Septic tank. The purpose of a septic tank is to condition the sewage so that it will infiltrate into the ground more readily than the unfiltered sewage would do.[13] The effluent from the septic tank is nearly as polluted with bacteria as that which flowed into the tank. Also, while in the tank the organic solids are attacked by anaerobic bacteria causing the effluent to be "septic" and therefore bad smelling. In accomplishing its purpose of conditioning the sewage, the septic tank removes the solids, permits anaerobic bacterial action on the organic solids, and stores the sludge and scum accumulations.

The solid matter settles to the bottom of the tank where it remains quietly while the anaerobic bacteria work upon it. This bacterial action changes some of the solids into liquids or gases.[1] The anerobic action is very important in the treatmet of the sewage and in decreasing the amount of sludge and scum that must be disposed of. No additives are necessary to make the septic tank function properly. Actually, the many additives sold on the open market to improve septic tank operation will not improve its functioning.[13, 2]

Most normal household wastes will have no adverse affects upon the septic system. Common types of detergents and cleaning fluids in normal amounts will not interfere with proper functioning; however, the introduction of large quantities of disinfectants will kill the bacteria and interfere with the anaerobic action. Surface drainage water should not be piped into the septic tank because a large flow of water will flush sludge from the tank and into the dispersal field. Sludge passing through the drain tiles will clog up the soil pores and cause the system to malfunction.

The accumulated sludge and scum must be cleaned from the tank to prevent its being moved out into the drain field when too much collects within the tank. Definite intervals for cleaning are difficult to recommend; however, yearly inspections are probably wise in order to protect the large capital investment and to avoid the inconvenience of having trouble with the sewage system right in the middle of the recreation season. Once the field becomes blocked it might never function properly again and will probably need replacement. Generally, only one tank out of twenty will reach the danger point within three years.[11]

A white towel wrapped around a stick will serve to measure the sludge accumulation if it is placed down through a break in the surface scum and forced to the bottom of the sludge. The scum that floats upon the surface between the baffles will block the field if it is carried out through the outlet device. If the scum is 3 inches or less from the bottom of the outlet device the tank should be pumped out.

No part of the septic tank system should be closer than 50 feet to a water source in order to ensure against pollution. Some state codes require that the minimum distance to be 100 feet. Also, the U.S. Public Health Service recommends that the septic tank be at least 5 feet from any building while some states require an 8 foot spacing.[6] The pipes that are used to carry the sewage to the tank and then from the tank to the distribution box should be of durable material with the joints tightly sealed. Cast iron pipe is often recommended for this purpose; however, vitrified clay, concrete, bituminized fibers, plastic, and asbestos cement can also be used. Local ordinances will probably require the use of cast iron pipe within 5 feet of a building, 50 feet of a water system, or underneath a road.

Septic tanks can be constructed in place with non-corrosive waterproof materials or purchased as a prefabricated unit. The latter method probably eliminates the problems of sealing and of health authority approval; however, it is limited to the smaller tanks. Many tanks are built in place from reinforced concrete. It is recommended that a sloping bottom be built into a septic tank to aid in cleaning.[2]

It is difficult and probably unnecessary to determine the exact septic tank size required; however, the trend is towards larger septic tanks that require less cleaning. Also, the difference in price between a 750 gallon capacity tank and a 1000 gallon tank is relatively small and many local ordinances require a minimum capacity of 750 gallons. For an effective septic system, the tank volume should have a one day's retention capacity. That is, the tank should have a large enough useable volume to store one day's sewage output. When sewage flows are expected to be greater than 1500 gallons each day, the tank capacity should equal 1125 gallons plus 75 percent of the daily expected flow.

EXAMPLE

Anticipated sewage $= 5250$ gal/day.
Formula for determining required tank volume:

$$V = 1125 + 0.75 \text{ quantity/day.}$$
$$V = 1125 + 3937.$$
$$V = 5062 \text{ gallons.}$$

Two compartment tanks are more effective that single ones and are recommended for large flow establishments. The relative absence of solids in the second compartment serves as an indication of how successfully the first tank is functioning. Two tanks in series will serve as a two compartment tank which may be difficult to purchase. The capacity of the first tank should be twice that of the second or outlet tank.

Distribution boxes. The distribution box is necessary to ensure equal distribution of the effluent into all parts of the absorption trenches. It prevents the overloading of one line while the rest remain underused. There is nothing complicated about distribution boxes in that they are just concrete boxes that receive the effluent from the septic tank and let it flow out through outlets that lead to the absorption trenches. To insure equal flow through all absorption trenches the outlets from the distribution box must be at the exact same level and at least 4 inches from the bottom of the box. The flow into the distribution box should be baffled to prevent a direct flow-through situation.

Absorption field. The purpose of the absorption field or leaching field is to distribute the septic-tank effluent into the soil mantle. The effluent moves through 4-inch diameter cement tiles that are placed loosely end to end so that approximately $\frac{1}{4}$-inch spacings occur between tiles. As the effluent moves along down a grade of 2 to 4 inches per hundred linear feet, it leaks out of the tile pipe and into the absorption trench where it infiltrates into the soil. The lines should follow the contours if necessary to keep the proper grade since the top of the tile should be 1 to 2 feet below the ground surface.[6] Each open joint between tiles should be covered with a piece of roofing paper to exclude water from above. Sharp turns in the line are exceptions to this arrangement of the tiles in that all joints on the turns should be sealed.

The tile should be set down within an aggregate-filled trench that is between 18 and 36 inches deep and between 12 and 36 inches wide. At least 6 inches of $\frac{1}{2}$ to $1\frac{1}{2}$ inch size aggregate stone material should lie below the tile pipe and at least 2 inches of aggregate depth should cover the pipe. The absorption trench should then be covered over with roofing paper and then approximately 1 foot of soil.

Drainage lines should not exceed 500 feet in length and should not be placed within 6 feet of the septic tank. Parallel lines should be at least 7 feet apart to provide sufficient space for lateral movement of the effluent in the soil. Whenever the total line length is greater than 750 feet, a dosing tank should be used in conjunction with the septic tank. [6] A single dosing tank set-up will permit the operation of two 500 foot lines for 1000 foot long field.

The dosing tank is a concrete box that has a capacity equal to one-third that of the septic tank. The septic tank effluent empties into the dosing tank where it is stored until enough effluent has accumulated to fill 75 percent of the drain-field's capacity. An automatic siphon functions every 2 or 3 hours to discharge the dosing tank contents through the distribution box and into the lines. This system has three advantages over one without a dosing tank. First, it gives the field periodic rests to that it gets an opportunity to dry out between uses. Second, proper distribution of the effluent throughout the absorption trenches is achieved by the use of the dosing tank. Third, alternating halves of the absorption field can be used by incorporationg two siphons and two distribution boxes to handle lines requiring more than a thousand feet of total line.

Automatic dosing siphons do not contain any moving parts; therefore, they give satisfactory service over long periods of time. Prefabricated dosing boxes with automatic siphons are available on the open market from plumbing supply houses or builder supplier corporations.

STABILIZATION POND. The stabilization pond is a shallow pool of sewage that is being worked on by aerobic bacteria which use the dissolved oxygen in the water. The biochemical oxygen will be satisfied in the pond; therefore, the pond is sometimes called an oxidation pond. [2] The dissolved oxygen is replenished from the atmosphere and from the algae growing in the water. The pond should have a regular perimeter and be approximately 3 feet deep. This depth is shallow enough to permit the penetration of sunlight to all parts of the liquid and thereby encourage algae growth; however, it is deep enough to discourage some rooted aquatic plants. Two to 5 feet is the range of depth acceptable in a stabilization pond.

The pond should be formed from constructed dikes in order to eliminate the collection of surface runoff. The pond site should be located at a practical distance away from the recreation developments to prevent its becoming a nuisance. The oxidation process in itself does not cause unfavorable odors; however, large concentrations of sewage in parts of the pond can cause anaerobic activity with its odors. The Michigan State Park System is using stabilization ponds with success at such large parks as Harrisonville State Park. Two hundred yards appears to be a satisfactory distance from the developed recreation sites for a properly functioning pond. More than one inlet to the pond will help to solve the problem of large concentration of unstable sewage in the pond. If only one inlet pipe is provided, it is usually placed near the pond's center.

The stabilization pond does not require daily maintenance and is relatively free from operation problems other than the switching of input pipes to prevent sewage concentrations. The grass and weeds must be mowed, the mosquitoes eradicated, and unauthorized people excluded. The exclusion of trespassers will require a high fence and warning signs. Weeds and willows can be controlled by soil sterilants and by mowing. Also, the dikes must be protected from erosion and from tunneling by burrowing rodents.

The local health authorities should be contacted in order to ascertain what design criteria exist within their jurisdiction. For a rough estimation, one can plan on one surface acre of pond for every one thousand users.

Refuse

Refuse collection and disposal is becoming a monstrous problem in forest recreation areas. The average camper produces approximately $\frac{4}{10}$ cubic foot of refuse every day.[13] In 1964, there were 70 million campers in the United States. In that year, campers alone produced 28 million cubic feet of garbage and rubbish. After the picnicker, hiker, water skier, and fisherman has piled on his refuse, there is quite a heap. Things are getting worse from the standpoint of litter. Even the beer bottles are disposable nowadays and aluminum soft drink cans never rust away. Although the picnicker produces less than a tenth of a cubic foot per day, his numbers make up for his small contributions. The Bureau of Outdoor Recreation has estimated that there will be 700 million picnic visit per year by the year 2000.[7]

Refuse, as used here, means both garbage and rubbish. The recreation area manager must face three major problems connected with refuse. He must decide how to keep it stored on site, how to get it collected, and how to dispose of it after collection.

Storage and Collection of Refuse

The on site refuse container should be watertight and made of 26 to 30 gage galvanized metal. Thirty gallon capacity cans are the maximum that workmen should be expected to handle when collecting refuse. The 55 gallon oil drums that are used in some recreation areas might be less expensive than a properly designed refuse can; however, they are also unsatisfactory in the long run and should not be used. Each can should have a tight fitting lid to keep out insects and rats. A pair of handles to facilitate lifting should be attached to each can.

Refuse cans must be kept clean or else they will become a nuisance as well as a health hazard. The refuse containers can be collected and washed periodically to prevent odors and breeding of flies. Approximately 6 days are required for the complete development of the fly adult; however, cleaning will be necessary much more often than every 6 days. Some progressive recreation areas combine a daily pick-up with a double set of cans so that one set of containers can be in use while the other set is being washed and dried. The use of plastic bag liners for refuse cans has become common practice in recent years. Thirty gallon bags are available for approximately 8 cents apiece. They will more than pay for themselves in convenience, in work saved, and in can protection. Refuse can be collected simply by picking up the plastic bag and setting it in a truck.

The proper containers for storage of refuse at the point of origin will minimize health hazards and odor nuisances as well as speed up the collection process. [12] The containers should be located so that they are convenient to the user as well as being readily accessible to the collector. Special storage containers may be required in most forest recreation areas in order to thwart scavenging bears, dogs, and racoons. In addition to being durable, these containers should have some way of being firmly anchored in order to minimize the scattering of refuse by the scavengers. Buried cans with foot-petal lids, special flap-top locked lids, or anchoring pipes can be used to help overcome spillage of refuse by animals.

The scheduling of refuse collection in intensive recreation areas is a simple matter. It should be collected daily in most areas. In situations of very light use, the collection interval can be stretched to 2- or 3-day intervals. However, this longer period is probably not much of a money saver in any but the more isolated areas since the manager or work crews will be traveling through the area each day anyway. Frequently, heavy-use picnic areas need more than one pickup on busy days.

A contractual arrangement between the campground manager and a reputable collection firm is the most advantageous arrangement when large quantities of refuse are involved. A contract stating definite collection means, times, equipment, and routes of travel should be signed by both parties involved. Unfortunately, all forest recreation areas are not conveniently located in an area serviced by a commercial refuse collector and therefore the managers must find other means of collecting refuse.

227

Sanitation

Any truck can be used to haul refuse that remains in the cans or plastic liners; however, trucks with waterproof beds should be used if the refuse is to be dumped into the truck bed. The dumping of refuse into open bed trucks is generally the less desirable collection method. This method permits spillage, causes odors, and makes the truck dirty. If the quantity is too great to pick up the individual bags or cans, an enclosed packer truck should be considered. Refuse packing trucks reduce the cost per trip by carrying refuse compacted into two thirds of its original volume. They permit low loading levels that make dumping easier on the man lifting the can and lessen the spillage that accompanies high lifting of the refuse cans. Also, refuse packers reduce odors and spillage along the road because all refuse is enclosed within the truck body.

Disposal

Once the mountain of refuse has been collected it must be put somewhere or treated so that it will not become a health problem or a public nuisance. Open dumping, sanitary land fill, and incineration along with modifications of each are methods that are suited for recreation area refuse disposal. Separate collection of rubbish and garbage along with hog feeding are often mentioned in publications but are not practical for use in disposing of recreation refuse.

OPEN DUMPING. Open dumping of refuse in some out-of-the-way place is a very common, perhaps the most common, of the refuse disposal methods. Publications on sanitation generally avoid admitting that open dumping does occur and concentrate their efforts on more desirable refuse disposal techniques. Fortunately, many local governments have ordinances prohibiting open dumping. Odors, fire danger, windblown debris, rats, and mosquitoes are some of the problems that accompany open dumping.[2] Some managers have stayed with this undesirable practice because at first inspection it is the cheapest and most convenient method of disposing of refuse. In some areas open dumps even provide a form of off-beat recreation.

Rat hunting and depraved bear watching attract visitors to many dumps. However, in consideration for public health and general esthetics, the enlightened manager will avoid the open dumping method of refuse disposal.

SANITARY LANDFILL. If the recreation area manager can not work out a satisfactory contract for the collection and the removal of the refuse from his area, he should then investigate the next best method of refuse disposal which is the sanitary landfill method. The sanitary landfill method is just an elaborate way of burying the refuse. The refuse is placed into a predug trench, compacted by a crawler tractor, and buried under a six inch layer of soil each day. This is a very good method of refuse disposal that lends itself to use at forest recreation areas. Sanitary landfill provides an economical way of refuse disposal where the proper sites can be selected. A sufficient unforested land area must be available at the proper distance from the recreation site. The disposal site should be close enough to make hauling economical but far enough away so as not to be a public nuisance. Very deep, well-drained loams and sandy loams make the most desirable soil for sanitary landfill sites. Soils with impeded drainage can hinder the operation in wet weather and can cause the fill to become a health hazard through seepage. Also, the landfill areas should be located more than 50 feet from any surface water and in areas that are not subjected to high water tables or to flooding.

Approximately one half acre of 6 foot deep landfill would be needed for an all year operation servicing five thousand people.[12] Very few forest recreation areas serve that large number of users so that the required area would be proportionally smaller.

The steps in operating a sanitary landfill are relatively simple. First a 8 foot deep trench that is one and a half times wider than the dozer blade is dug out of a flat or gently sloping area. A 30 degree slope is graded at one end of the trench to serve as a base for the first layer of refuse. The refuse should be spread over the base slope to a vertical height of 6 feet from

229

the trench bottom and compacted by the crawler tractor. After the compacted layer of refuse becomes 2 feet thick, it should be covered with at least 6 inches of packed earth. The top two vertical feet should be used to form a soil plug over each layer.

FIG. 12.7. Diagram of sanitary landfill operation. (Texas State Department of Health.)

Small developments must make some modifications to fit their economic situation. Most forest recreation areas can not afford to keep a crawler tractor standing by the refuse dump. Therefore, it is most advantageous for them to have the required capacity trench dug all at one time and the soil stockpiled for use during the season. Mechanical equipment can be brought in twice a week to cover the refuse. Some small recreation areas have been adequately served by a daily burning of mixed refuse in a prepared trench followed every couple of weeks by burial.[12] This system has been stretched by many campground operators who bury the refuse only at the end of the season. This practise favors the breeding of rats, flies, and mosquitous and is not to be recommended.

230

Hand-dug trenches can serve some very small forest recreation areas where mechanical equipment is not available. A 1 foot deep layer of refuse is spread in a 2 foot deep trench and burned. After the burning is completed, the trench should be filled with soil.

INCINERATION. The complete burning of all refuse to ashes eliminates breeding of rats, flies, and mosquitous. It removes the material that attracts bears, dogs, racoons, and other animals to refuse dumps. This process of burning refuse at high temperatures in specially designed enclosures is called incineration.[12] Incinerators have been used for many years to aid in the disposal of municipal refuse; however, they have been used only to a limited extent in forest recreation areas. Incinerators are expensive to build and to operate and can compete with sanitary landfill only where use is extremely heavy and landfill sites are scarce. Neither of these situations really exist in forest recreation sites in spite of the crowded conditions of some areas. Some U.S. Forest Service personnel in the Northern Rocky Mountain Area now are considering the increased use of incinerators because of the piles of debris that will need to be disposed of when the projected figure of 86 million visits a year is reached on those national forests alone.[4]

For most situations, the initial cost of approximately 5000 dollars per ton of rated 24 hour capacity is too high.[2] The smallest incinerators, capable of burning 50 pounds of refuse per hour, has a rated 24 hour capacity of 1200 pounds and will cost approximately 3000 dollars to build. The need for skilled operators and maintenance people to operate incinerators, the operation cost of 3 to more than 7 dollars per ton burned, and the high initial costs of the incinerator make the incineration method unsuited for most forest recreation areas. Publications on the subject of incinerators are available from the U.S. Public Health Service for those persons wishing to investigate the subject further.

Sanitation

REFERENCES

1. BABBIT, H.E. 1947. *Sewage and Sewage Treatment*. John Wiley, New York. 691 pages.

2. ELHERS, V. and STEEL, E. 1965. *Municipal and Rural Sanitation*. 6th edition. McGraw-Hill. 643 pages.

3. FINE, I. and WERNER, E. 1960. *Camping in State Parks and Forests in Wisconsin*, vol. 1, No. 3. University of Wisconsin, Madison, Wisc.

4. HUTCHISON, S. 1962. *Recreation Opportunities and Problems in the National Forests of the Intermountain Region*. Research Paper 66. Intermountain Forest and Range Experiment Station, Ogden, Utah.

5. ORT, D.R. 1963. Recommended Campground Sanitation Requirements. In *Guidelines for Developing Land for Outdoor Recreational Uses*. Cooperative Extensive Service, Purdue University, West Lafayette, Ind.

6. SHEPHARD, W. *et. al.* 1958. *Questions and Answers about Home Sewage Disposal*. Joint Public Circular E-9. Cooperative Extensive Service, Michigan State University.

7. SULLIVAN, J. 1965. *Northeast Outdoor Memorandum* 5-65. Northeastern Region Bureau of Outdoor Recreation, Philadelphia, Pa.

8. U.S. FOREST SERVICE. 1962. Forest Recreation for Profit. *Agriculture Information Bulletin* No. 265. Washington, D.C.

9. U.S. FOREST SERVICE. 1963. *Recreation Management–Manual and Handbook* Title 2300. U.S. Department of Agriculture, Washington, D.C.

10. U.S. PUBLIC HEALTH SERVICE. 1962. *Drinking Water Standards*. Publication No. 956. Department of Health, Education, and Welfare, Washington, D.C.

11. U.S. PUBLIC HEALTH SERVICE. 1963. *Manual of Septic Tank Practice*. Publication No. 526. Department of Health, Education, and Welfare, Washington, D.C.

12. U.S. PUBLIC HEALTH SERVICE. 1963. *Suggested Design Criteria for Refuse Storage, Collection, and Disposal*. Pacific Southwest Inter-agency Committee and Columbia Basin Inter-agency Committee, Department of Health, Education, and Welfare, Washington, D.C.

13. U.S. PUBLIC HEALTH SERVICE. 1965. *Environmental Health Practice in Recreational Areas*. Publication. No. 1195. Department of Health, Education, and Welfare, Washington, D.C.

14. WAGAR, J.A. 1962. *The Convection Stack—A Device for Ridding Pit Toilets of Bad Odor*. NE 133. U.S. Forest Service Northeast Experiment Station, Upper Darby, Pa.

CHAPTER 13

Water-oriented
Recreation Development

INTRODUCTION

Water plays a major role in forest recreation by providing either the primary purpose for the visit or by supplementing some other activity. Many people come to the forest solely to participate in water-based activities. To them, any other recreation activity is secondary. Almost half of the national population prefers water-based activities to any other type of outdoor recreation. [11] Even land-based activities are enhanced by nearby water that provides a secondary activity or improves the setting.

Most participants engage in more than one activity on each forest recreation visit; therefore, the primary purpose of the visit generates use of supplementary facilities. People who travel into the forest to swim often combine that activity with picnicking for one or two meals. Campers prefer to have swimming, fishing, or boating opportunities available to them in order to supplement their primary activity. Here again, the forest manager must not be too concerned about exact descriptions. Too much can be made of whether the activity is primary or supplementary because more of the user's total time might be spent in supplementary activities than in the primary activity.

As with forest recreation in general, water-oriented recreation is developed and managed according to type of use. Activities that require developed facilities to handle a concentration of use on a limited area are intensive-use activities. Swimming epitomizes the intensive-use type of water-oriented recreation. Conversely, an extensive-use recreation activity takes place over a relatively large area and requires a minimum of developed facilities. Fishing and downstream canoeing characterize extensive-use recreation activities.

Intensive Water-oriented Recreation

Swimming

By the year 2000, swimming will be the most popular of the outdoor recreation activities. It now makes the difference between success and failure for most types of private forest recreation businesses. Areas where swimming is the primary activity are used mostly by local people. Studies made in Ohio indicate that the majority of people travel less than 5 miles to go swimming. This means swimming by itself should be developed in the high land value areas near population centers. This criteria does not include most forest recreation land; therefore, swimming alone does not have a major role in intensive-use forest recreation development. The same study shows that most picnickers in Ohio travel about 15 miles in one direction while campers go 60 miles.[15] Picnicking and swimming are supplemental activities that rely upon each other for mutual success.[25] Swimming, wading, and sunbathing are very important supplementary activities for camping, as is borne out by the emphasis placed on available swimming areas in camping advertising. In most cases, swimming becomes an intensive-use forest recreation activity when it is supplemental with another type of forest activity.

Swimming sites. Swimming sites can be located on either natural bodies of water or at swimming pools. Much literature is available concerning the design and operation of a swimming pool; however, the swimming pool is not favored by the forest recreation user. Good, natural waterfront areas are superior to manmade structures.[17] Even the U.S. Forest Service Handbook on recreation discourages the use of manmade pools.[23] In this text, the term "natural water bodies" is meant to include ponds, lakes, streams, rivers, and oceans. Reservoirs are included as lakes in this chapter because they have most of the shoreline characteristics and limnological characteristics of lakes.

SAFETY. The safety of the user is the prime obligation of any recreation manager. Therefore, he must supply the user with a swimming area that is bacteriologically safe and physically free from unreasonable hazards. Water pollution or physical hazards can be limiting factors when selecting a swimming site on a natural body of water. That is, the pollution or the physical hazard eliminates the site from consideration.

Quality. The bacteriological quality of the water must be sufficiently high so as to be considered safe for swimming by the local health code. The safe range for the bacteriological quality of swimming water is generally listed as that water having less than 1000 coliform organisms per 100 ml of water.[16] This is approximately one thousand times more coliform organisms than are permissible in public drinking water.[24] The permissible rate of pollution varies widely between states. There is so much disagreement on this point that some states permit nine times the number of coliforms in swimming water than do other states. These accepted figures range from 250 to 2400 coliforms per 100 ml of water.[25, 21]

The volume of water present will have some bearing on water quality. Some pollution of the water will occur as a result of human bathing; therefore, a sufficient quantity of water should be available to keep the pollution diluted to less than the permissible coliform count. Streams, creeks, and rivers should have a flow through rate of more than 500 gallons for each user-day.[28] This turnover rate of water must occur during every day that the area is in use to prevent pollution. The rate of flow can easily be estimated by following the simple stream guaging procedures described in Chapter 11.

Bodies of standing water are more susceptible to contamination from bacteria introduced into the water by bathers. Small ponds with little or no flow through will soon become polluted with heavy use; therefore, they will satisfy the demand generated at small campgrounds or similar light-use developments. Each user requires 50 square feet of water surface in small ponds and lakes. In the larger bodies of water where surface area is obviously sufficient, the area for standing in the water can be as small as 10 square feet per person.[17]

Disinfection of natural water bodies has not been satisfactory except under research conditions and does not hold any immediate solution to the pollution problem. The elimination of the pollution cause is the best control over natural pollution.[17]

Physical hazards. Physical hazards are the second limiting factor associated with user safety. They occur as submerged, water-edge, and in-water hazards. All hazards should be removed from improved swimming areas when possible. Warning signs and barriers should be erected to protect the public from hazards that can not be removed.

The submerged hazards are the most common and probably the most dangerous forms of hazards. Beaches should have a gentle, even underwater slope that extends to a depth of approximately 6 feet.[23] Drop-offs, escarpments, and underwater rocks must be considered as submerged hazards. Snags, logs, metal, and glass are common hazards that must be removed from under the water in the improved swimming sites.

The depth of the water itself constitutes a form of hazard and must be considered in designing and managing the site. It is advisable to erect markers in the water to denote depth. The U.S Forest Service has done an effective job of depth marking on unprotected bathing beaches such as the improved beach on Lac Vieux Desert where they have placed two rows of vertical posts out from the shore. Each post has calibrations marked on it to indicate the actual depth of water at that point. In natural water bodies, this method is better than simply giving the depth on a sign because it automatically indicates fluctuating water depth.

The water-edge hazards are easier to eliminate or to compensate for than are the submerged hazards. Cliffs, overhanging banks, snags, rocks, metal, and glass are common water-edge hazards. Overhanging banks can be bulldozed down and rocky ground can be covered with sand or soil. Cliffs usually are desirable for scenery but dangerous as climbing or diving spots. Fencing or signs might be necessary to keep swimmers from climbing around on the cliff. General cleanup techniques will eliminate many other water-edge hazards.

FIG. 13.2. Sketch of self-reading depth rods that are recommended for use in areas with fluctuating water depth.

Poison ivy, wasps, and spiders are water-edge nuisances found around stream banks and muddy spots. Poison ivy eradication needs more management attention than it gets in most recreation areas. An intensive noxious plant eradication program is very important to user safety although the sad effects of these plants is not as spectacular as that of a broken bottle or similar hazards. Wasps and other stinging insects can be controlled by a direct assault on their nests with insecticide and by the elimination of the muddy conditions that attract them. Spiders present more fright value than danger; however, the spider population should be kept under control by the judicious use of insecticides.

The depth and velocity of mountain streams can vary widely

throughout the swimming season. This fluctuation must be considered when the site is being selected and when the swimming area is being designed. Low flow can prevent swimming completely or cause a pollution hazard while very high flows will combine with higher water velocities to flood over the banks, tear out improvements, and alter the stream bottom. Some of the depth fluctuations can be compensated for by the use of the self-reading depth rods that are mentioned earlier in this chapter. These rods will keep the user-public informed of the actual depths. Flood waters will necessitate closure of the swimming area.

Stream water should be flowing at less than 2 miles per hour when passing through the swimming area. High velocities in the stream create a hazard to those who could be pulled downstream by the flowing water and to small non-swimming youngsters. Low dams can be used to pool stream water and thereby reduce its velocity as it moves through the swimming area. Some water movement is desirable to prevent pollution and to give the swimmer a chance to swim without going too far from shore by swimming upstream.

Low water dams can be made by lining large boulders across the stream. Concrete low water dams are rather expensive and not necessary in most cases. A rather recent development in stream improvement work has been the introduction into this country of the gabions. Gabions are one cubic meter or larger wire baskets that are set up in place and filled with local stone material. A detailed description of gabions is given later in this chapter under extensive water-oriented recreation developments. Since gabions are porous, they permit water to flow through them and thereby do not cause stagnant pools during periods of low flow.

The placement of low dams both downstream and upstream may be necessary to create a permanent and safe pool in the stream. The downstream dam will form the pool and reduce the velocity of flow through the swimming area. The low dam on the upstream side will protect the bottom of the swimming area by reducing the velocity of the inflowing water before it damages any improvements. The energy of the downward flowing water is dissipated in the drop over the first dam and not in tearing through the swimming area. This is much as if the water were being let down a ladder rather than flowing down a chute. Sedimentation takes place in the upper pond and does not fill up the main swimming zone. The scenic value of the water falling over the low water dams is an added bonus for the area.

Safety equipment. Some states require lifeguards to be stationed at any paid swimming area. Even where the law does not require their presence, lifeguards should be employed to protect swimmers in heavy-use areas. Often, forest recreation areas do not have enough use to warrant the cost of a lifeguard so other methods of bather protection must be utilized. Life saving equipment such as floating rings, ropes, and long poles should be readily accessible at the beach. Concise and clear descriptions of water rescue techniques employing the available equipment should be posted on a conspicuous display board next to the equipment. Ropes with floats are often used to mark certain depths. The floating ropes restrict the bather and provide a safe place for him to reach for if he gets into difficulty in the water. A non-swimmer area is usually roped off at a depth of $3\frac{1}{2}$ feet. An outside rope at the 7 foot depth will mark off the swimmers area and tend to set the outside limit even when restrictions are not posted.

BEACH DEVELOPMENT. The bottom of the swimming area should have a uniform and gentle slope into a water depth of 6 feet. In order to be safe for children this slope should have a 1 foot drop for every 12 or 15 feet of horizontal distance.[7] When sand or gravel bottoms exist as they do in New England lakes and ponds, they are both firm and comfortable to walk on. A minimum of grading and underwater work usually will be required to make a good beach.

Coarse sand or fine gravel makes the best bottom for swimming areas. It is too heavy to remain suspended in the water and fine enough to walk on with unprotected feet. Firm bottoms can be covered directly with 12 inches of coarse sand to

239

achieve the desired results; however, muddy or soft bottom soil will not remain beneath the sand. Muck, clay, and silt loam mud will work its way up through the sand as a result of trampling by the bathers. Soft bottom areas will have to be stabilized with a crushed rock base that is overlaid with coarse gravel and then 6 to 12 inches of sand. One problem besides cost that arises with the use of crushed stone is that of exposed stones. It is advisable to keep the base material well below the water's edge so that the rocks do not get uncovered and become safety hazards or missiles.

Stream flow will remove sand from the bottom and wash it downstream. This downstream movement of sand will be speeded up by the churning action of the user's feet. The particle size that a stream will move increases exponentially with the increase in stream velocity. The actual effect of velocity on the movement of sand particles will vary with channel and flow characteristics; however, empirical data indicate that a $\frac{1}{2}$ mile per hour flow will carry 1 mm size sand. A flow of 1 mile per hour or 1.46 feet per second will transport bean-sized gravel.[22]

TABLE 13.1

VELOCITY OF FLOWING WATER REQUIRED
TO MOVE PARTICLES OF VARIOUS SIZE CLASSES[a]

Particle size class	Water velocity required to start movement(ft/sec)
Clay	0.27–0.35
Angular sand	0.70–1.10
Pea-sized gravel	0.62–0.70
Bean-sized gravel	1.10–1.55[b]
Half-inch gravel	2.30–3.20
One and a half-inch angular gravel	3.20–4.0

[a] U.S. Forest Service.
[b] 1 mile per hour equals 1.49 ft/sec.

In order to prevent the erosion of the beach bottom, the developer should use a coarse gravel and reduce the velocity of the water where necessary on fast moving streams. The problem of bottom erosion should be considered during the site selection process. Since the size of particle movement is dependent upon water velocity, it makes sense to choose spots where the stream gradient is low or where low water dams can be employed. Erosion is most damaging in stream sections where steep gradients occur in that the stream velocity will double with every 4 percent increase in gradient. [22]

A beach-play area should be constructed at the swimming area when one does not exist naturally. The size of the beach depends upon the use that it is expected to receive. The Bureau of Outdoor Recreation plans on 75 square feet of beach for each man-day of use.†[2] The beach should have at least a 12-inch layer of sand or pea-sized gravel on it to serve both as a play area for children and as a sunbathing spot for adults. [7] For protection of bare feet, the beach area should be kept clean of rocks, glass, and pieces of metal. In areas where grass will grow well, it can be used to improve the quality of the water-front area. A grass-covered strip with scattered shade trees will provide a place for relaxation near the water without being on the sand or in the sun. Some limited research indicates that grass covered beaches are preferred to sand beaches by sunbathers. [18] A portion of this grass area could be designated as a play area that would serve to keep ballgames off the beach.

Except for mass bathing areas in high-use locations, the beaches should provide some privacy from non-users. A little space and some screening should separate the beach area from the picnic grounds and from the parking lot. Camping areas are generally situated more than 200 or 300 yards from the beach so that day-use visitors do not intrude in the camp-grounds.

REQUIRED SUPPORTING FACILITIES. The development of a swimming area involves more than just the improvement of the waterfront area. It also includes the building, the maintenance, and the operation of sanitation, drinking, dressing, and

† A man-day of use means a full day's use by one individual.

parking facilities. Here again, these supporting facilities accomplish a dual objective. First, they provide conveniences to
the user and thereby make his visit more pleasant. Second,
they keep the user's activities controlled to specific spots and
thereby protect the site from damage.

The sanitation facilities should be constructed near the beach
to permit ready access to the swimmers. Every effort should be
made to construct the best possible toilet facilities in a convenient location so as to encourage their use. At least one toilet
per sex is needed at all swimming areas. The U.S. Public
Health Service recommends that one toilet be constructed for
every 50 man-days of use that the swimming area is designed
to handle. [25]

One drinking fountain should be located next to the beach
area where it is accessible to the swimmers. The drinking fountain is not to be placed in the toilet rooms. If the fountain is
not located on very porous soil such as sand or gravel, it should
be placed on a paved pad that has a water collecting drain and
sump. This will help to prevent the muddy spots that are
associated with so many drinking fountains in poorly designed recreations areas. When people are walking around the
beach without shoes on, they are not inclined to walk in the
mud or upon mud-gathering wasps in order to get a drink of
water.

Refuse containers should be placed at the entrances to the
beach and at convenient locations on the beach. These containers should meet the standards for refuse cans that are given
in Chapter 12. Even though picnicking on the beach area
should be discouraged, people will still produce some litter
from snacks, newspapers, and enough other sources to require
a trash collection and a regularly scheduled cleanup of the
beach area.

Bath houses will be necessary for the changing of clothes.
There should be at least one bathhouse, or dressing room, for
each sex except when the swimming area is used exclusively
by campers from a nearby campground. In this case the additional cost of dressing rooms can be avoided. Bathhouses should

be placed near the beach but on the route from the parking lot so as to make their use convenient.

A central parking lot designed to serve the swimming area should be located approximately 50 to 100 yards from the beach. Surfaced trails should connect the two areas so as to provide good access and to channel the use along the designated route of travel. The parking lot can serve as a control on the amount of use the beach receives by limiting access to the area. Each parking spot will require 300 square feet of area and will probably account for four people when occupied.[1, 2] A central parking lot with a usable area of 30,000 square feet will hold 100 cars which will probably mean 400 visitors. The Bureau of Outdoor Recreation estimates that a gravel parking lot costs approximately 100 dollars for each parking place while paved lots are approximately 135 dollars for each parking place.[1]

SUPPLEMENTAL FACILITIES. Swimming often attracts day-users to the area. These day-users will combine other activities with swimming so that additional facilities will be required to satisfy the demand and to protect the site from misuse. Facilities for play, picnicking, and food purchase are the common supplemental facilities associated with forest recreation swimming areas. These facilities should be located away from the beach area so that their use is a separate activity from swimming and sun bathing.[23]

Play fields that are improved for use with swimming and picnic areas should be level, cleared areas that are suitable for impromtu games of tag, volley ball, softball, and other "pick-up" games. No improvements are necessary other than what is required for clearing and leveling the area to make it safe and suitable for play. Occasionally, local demand will justify the construction of playground equipment for the children's use. Private operators often include playground equipment in the development to encourage the use of the facility by family groups.

Picnic grounds should be near to the beach area but separate from it. This type of picnic area should be of the general use

243

design that is described in Chapter 8. Some planners believe that a separate parking lot should be constructed to serve the picnic areas in order to handle those persons who are going to picnic but not to swim. Another advantage of the second central parking lot is that it does spread the users out. At least, it gives them a choice of which lot they want to use. Since picnickers generally do not want to walk very far from the cars, they will be closer to the tables if a special lot is placed at the picnic area.

Hotdogs, hamburgers, soda, ice cream, and such foods traditionally have been part of a day at the beach. The sale of prepared foods is both a convenience to the user and a method of making a profit for the operator. In recreation areas, the place of business where food and sundry items are sold is commonly called the "concession stand" although the business might or might not be operated under a true concession agreement as is described in Chapter 4. Private operators claim that the concession stands supply much of their profit.[14]

The concession stand should be placed off the beach but convenient to both the beach and the picnic area. A couple of bars, stand-up counters, or tables should be clustered around the concession stand to encourage the bathers to eat the food there and not take it back to the beach. Several trash containers should be placed around the concession stand and along the trails leading to the picnic and beach areas in order to help keep the trash from being discarded along the way or carried into the beach or picnic areas.

Boating

Boating for pleasure has more than kept pace with the outdoor recreation boom. It is probably responsible for the tremendous upsurge in visits to the Corps of Engineer Reservoirs where recreation visits have soared from 16 million in 1950 to 106 million by 1960.[11] The Bureau of Reclamation showed approximately a fivefold increase in the number of visitors within a 14-year period as more than 34 million visits were made to its reservoirs in 1963.[5]

There is a wide variation in the types of boats used by the American public. The user's choice or financial limitations include everything from large sonar equipped cabin cruisers down to fold boats that are tucked into the automobile trunk. By 1962, Americans owned more than 8 million pleasure boats.[25] Forest recreation is normally concerned with the smaller types of craft that are associated with users of forest recreation facilities. Small power craft and outboard motorboats that can be moved by the family car, sailboats, rowboats, and canoes are the major concern of the forest recreation developer or manager.

WATER QUALITY. Water to be used for boating should meet certain quality limitations. Bacteriological pollution in itself is not a limiting factor to prevent boating. However, many of the symptoms associated with bacteriological pollution do downgrade the water's usefulness for pleasure boating.

Odor. Offensive odor probably is the biggest detracting factor in boating water quality. Since a person is obliged to smell the odors in the air that he breathes, he will be affected by odors before any other degrading factor of the water. Most people can make the association between certain odors and organic pollution of water; therefore, those people lose a certain sense of enjoyment with the first smell. Anaerobic bacteria action causes both bad odors and dark colors which is a second degrading factor.

Color. Much of the dark color in water is caused by the decomposition of organic matter in the absence of dissolved oxygen. Decomposing organic matter uses up free oxygen by the aerobic process and then switches to the anaerobic process which does not require free oxygen. Anaerobic action is a slow process that produces a foul odor and forms dark colored products. As long as there is enough dissolved oxygen in the water to maintain the aerobic process, organic solids will not cause dark colored water or offensive odors. Chemical pollutants are a different matter and must be controlled at their source. Coloration caused by suspended clay and silt particles

245

is not too great a degrading factor for boating water if people do not object to their craft having a dirty hull.

Reaction. The acidity and alkalinity measurements are often listed as being an important criteria for boating water; however, there are indications that it is overplayed. A suggested limit for the pH values are from pH of 6.0 on the acid side of neutral to a pH of 8.5 on the alkaline side. [12] Water that is any more acid or alkaline than these suggested limits could cause some corrosion of the craft's surfaces. Usually, the local problems are known to the users who can take precautionary measures to protect the surfaces of their boats whenever such conditions exist.

SUPPORTING FACILITIES. Points of access are needed to permit the public to put its boats into the water. If unlimited access to the water exists, the danger of indiscriminate boat launching also exists. Indiscriminate launching destroys the vegetative cover, breaks down banks, and causes widespread litter and sanitation problems. Unloading of boats along highways creates a serious safety problem to the boat owners as well as to the general motoring public. Since the cars and trailers have to be left somewhere, they are just pulled off the road wherever it is convenient to the driver. This parking causes increased damage to the waterfront zone. Management and cleanup of such an area can become an impossible task when more than the lightest use takes place.

Boat landings should be built along bodies of water that have recreational boating value to meet the public demand, as a site protection technique, and as a management aid. In very heavy-use areas of California, one boat launching site is recommended for every 160 surface acres of boating water. [3] Under normal conditions fewer launching points will be adequate. This does not mean that launching sites should be built only on lakes and reservoirs. Relatively small streams can provide some very enjoyable, and sometimes exciting, experiences for canoists. The Tennessee State Planning Commission recommends that "float streams" be established as part of the state's total recreation plan. [20]

246

A formal boat landing area usually consists of a loading ramp, a turn about area, a parking lot, and adequate sanitary facilities. Certain supplemental facilities such as picnicgrounds and campgrounds are often developed adjacent to the boat launching facilities. Since most people participate in more than one activity on each recreational visit, they enjoy the flexibility that supplemental facilities provide. Swimming beaches are often accompanied by a boat launching ramp as shown in Fig. 13.4. Quite often, these supplemental facilities are necessary just to improve the comfort and safety of those people who are going to participate in the activity anyway. Therefore, the construction of the supplemental facilities at boat landing sites is justified by the same reasons used to justify the landings themselves. That is, they are justified on the basis of public demand, site protection, and area management requirements.

Launching ramp. A launching ramp is used to back the boat trailer down into the water so that the boat can be floated off or onto it. Concrete is the recommended material for the ramp construction. A minimum ramp width of 10 feet is required in order to allow some manoeuverability for the backing automobiles.[25] The Bureau of Outdoor Recreation specifications call for 12-foot wide ramps to give an added measure of safety.[1] Twenty-foot wide ramps are recommended by the U.S. Public Health Service; however, the costs for such structures probably would be prohibitive for any establishment except the federal and some state governments. The launching ramp must cross the soft shoreline or beach and protrude into the water far enough to permit its use at any expected water level. Also, the ramp should be built with a maximum grade of 10 percent.

Approach road. A two-way road ending in a paved or gravel circle at the shore end of the loading ramp will provide normal head-on driving for the maximum distance toward the water. The circle should have a sufficiently large diameter to permit the car to manoeuver into position for backing the trailer down the ramp. The two-lane approach road should pass next to the

247

parking lot that is located within a short walking distance of the ramp.

Parking. Since many of the cars will be towing trailers, they will need approximately twice as much room for parking and manoeuvering as do cars without trailers. One solution to the problem of moving and parking trailer-pulling cars is to provide special drive-through parking stalls instead of the double rows of head-in stalls commonly used in central parking lots. The drive-through stalls will enable the driver to head into the stall when parking and to drive straight ahead to get out of the stall. By driving forward, the driver avoids the hazardous practice of backing up with a trailer attached to the car. Cars without trailers can be parked in a separate section of the lot where the normal head-in stalls are provided.

Water and sanitation. Some form of outlet should be constructed to provide drinking water. A well and pump with a built-in fountain is very satisfactory where the use is relatively low or no central water supply system can be developed. The sanitation facilities are also dependent upon amount of use and the water system. An out-of-the-way and lightly used area can be adequately serviced by water pumps and pump-out pit toilets if flooding is not a problem. Pit toilets are not recommended in areas that lie on low terraces, flood plains, or other such areas that are susceptible to periodic flooding. As in any other recreation development, flush toilets and drinking water under pressure should be provided when the use becomes heavy.

EXTENSIVE WATER-ORIENTED RECREATION

Water provides recreation opportunities far in excess of those occuring at developed facilities. Millions of recreationists range over the country's streams, rivers, lakes, and ponds in search of pleasure in one form or another without requiring many developed facilities. Inland fresh water, exclusive of the Great Lakes, covers more than 25 million acres within the contiguous 48 states.[13] Twenty percent of that surface area is formed by streams, another 50 percent is made up of natural lakes and ponds, and the remaining 30 percent have been produced by man-made reservoirs. Extensive use of fresh water includes the activities of fishing, hunting, and boating.

Fishing

In large areas such national forests and national wildlife refuges where fishing is available, it is the leading recreation activity.[13] Almost half of the adults in the United States engage in fishing; however, their impact on recreation is difficult to measure.[19] This is largely because of the extensive nature of fishing. Fishermen spread out along the streams and on the lakes to engage in their selected sport without much concern about developed facilities. Regulation of fishing practices and stocking of fish in streams and in large lakes are usually not the concern of land managers except where local restrictions on trespass or conflict are needed.

Land managers should be concerned with increasing the man-hours of fishing use to meet the carrying capacity of the water for fish. Wildlife biologists state that fish and game are a renewable resource that must be harvested or wasted. Each stream has a limit to the number of fish that it can support; therefore, any number of fish above the capacity of the stream to support them will die if they are not harvested.

DEVELOPED FACILITIES. Some of the most significant actions that land managers can take in encouraging fishing visits deal with the fisherman's access to the streams. Parking clearings should be provided at ends of trails leading to the streams. The combination of well-identified trails and parking spaces provide the fisherman with a positive access point, spreads use away from congested and overfished roadside points, and keeps the automobiles within defined locations so as to protect the roadside vegetation.

Footbridges provide the fisherman access to both banks where streams are too deep to wade. Bridges can be made from trees growing along the stream. All that is required is to fell the tree across the stream, limb off all the branches and top, and anchor both ends to the banks. The banks must be high enough to suspend the log well above the high water level so that it does not block floating debris and dam up the stream. Also the log must be placed so that it reaches far enough back onto the shore so as to cause the banks to crumble. An adze can be used to flatten the top of the log for safe walking and a handrail will greatly decrease any danger in using the bridge. The U.S. Forest Service has earned much user goodwill by the installation of footbridges.

Forest type campgrounds should be provided at the places where fishermen already have been staying for overnight fishing trips or at locations where the fishing pressure could be increased. These camps provide camping units, water, and sanitation facilities for the fisherman and makes outdoor life somewhat easier on the family if it goes along on the fishing trip. Here, as in most recreation developments, the campground will concentrate the wear into one place and protect the surrounding vegetation. True, the developed campground might encourage more visitors who will cause more wear. For that matter, some fisherman probably do not want their families to go with them and will not be able to use the primative conditions as an excuse to go fishing with the "Boys".

Sanitary facilities, refuse cans, and even picnic tables have their place at locations of relatively heavy use. If road access is convenient for the general public, these fisherman-oriented developments also can serve as general purpose picnicking grounds for day-use visitors. Such areas are ideally suited for families with young children who want to combine some fishing with a day's outing.

INCREASING THE CARRYING CAPACITIES OF STREAMS AND PONDS. Most hunters want to do more than hunt wild game; they want to find some once in a while. The same is true for fishermen. Much has been made concerning the recreation values of fishing. The fact is that fishermen want to catch fish not just fish for them. As a result of this obvious fact, efforts are being made by trained biologists and others to find ways of providing better fishing by manipulating the habitat. Some of these efforts have

FIG. 13.1. The crowd at this isolated lake on Spruce Knob in West Virginia points out the popularity of water-based recreation activities. (U. S. Forest Service.)

FIG. 13.3. Photograph of central parking lot serving high density use facility at Warren Dunes State Park, Michigan.

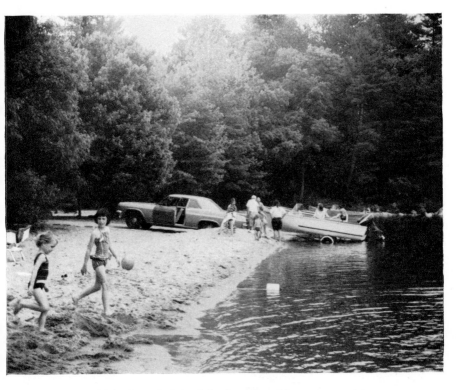

FIG. 13.4. A typical back-in boat launching ramp next to a
bathing beach at Sabago Lake State Park, Maine.

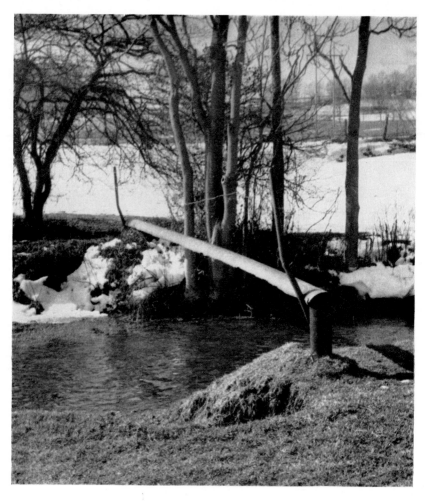

FIG. 13.5. Photograph of a small footbridge over a deep fishing
stream.

paid off in better fish yields while others remain of doubtful use. Rehabilitating or stocking of ponds and the modification of stream flow are the two major methods of producing more catchable fish that were investigated by the researchers.

Pond stocking and rehabilitation. Trout pond rehabilitation programs have been a success in that they actually have produced more fish for the angler to catch.[10] Ponds have proved to be highly successful in the production of trout and bass and can provide fisherman with a great number of recreation hours. The construction and management of fishing ponds is well outlined in a publication by Wingard and Heiney at The Pennsylvania State University.[27] Warmer water ponds are more suited to bass while the cool water ponds will support trout. The species are generally not mixed even in waters where they both can survive because trout can not compete with other fish for available food.

Ponds that are less than 6 feet deep should be stocked with fish only when there is a constant inflow of water from a stream or a spring. Approximately 600 trout or 100 bass can survive for each surface acre of water. However, since natural mortality is high, the originally stocked fish will die off in two or three years if they are not caught. Trout do not reproduce well in pond waters but bass do; therefore, many people who want the pond for light fishing use prefer to raise bass.

A larger population of trout than the natural carrying capacity can be raised in a small pond by supplement feeding. Bass lakes can be fertilized with an inorganic 10-10-10 fertilizer to produce more plankton for the food chain; however, trout lakes should not be fertilized. There is no point in fertilizing ponds that have a high flow-through rate because the effort is wasted by downstream dilution.

Stream management and improvement. Every effort should be made to avoid heavy stream siltation as a result of improperly constructed roads, poor logging practices, or overgrazing. Excess runoff should be controlled in an effort to stabilize the stream flow and thereby lessen the extremes in flow between flooding and no flow periods. In the North where rainfall is

251

relatively adequate, the riparian vegetation should be encouraged so that it will stabilize the bank and shade the water. In the Southwest, riparian vegetation draws off enough water to cause a significant lowering of stream flow.

The building of structures to improve the carrying capacity of streams might turn out to have been an enormous waste of money throughout the United States if their only purpose was to raise catchable fish. Although the construction of such structures as groins, low dams, and V-deflectors appear as structures recommended in handbooks on stream improvement, there is no research that indicates that the structures produce additional fish.[10] The arguments favoring the use of so called stream improvement structures are based on intuitive reasoning that have a very strong emotional appeal, but no scientific backing.

There are some limited situations in which local application of structures will speed up the recovery of a reach of stream that has been damaged by construction. However, even where creel limits supposedly have increased, the issue is cloudy. The findings of one study indicated that the increase in trout catch over five years cost $16.68 per pound as a result of construction cost.[10] At this rate, even successful stream improvement projects are losers since stocked fish cost $2.00 per pound of catch.

Fish biology researchers can not see much value in using structures to increase the number of catchable fish. The structures are strongly favored by sportsman's clubs, magazine article authors, politicians, and manufacturers of the materials used in constructing the structures.[8] State fish commissions are often pressured into giving their auspices to structure projects out of the necessity to do something to make the fishermen and therefore the politicians happy.[10]

Since fisherman like to fish the streams where structures are located, the structures do serve the purpose of increasing use. The increased use raises the harvest while providing more hours of recreational enjoyment.

Stream structures are very important for hydrologic purposes. They are needed to retard flows, to stop unravelling of stream beds, to keep the stream in the desired channel, and to stop bank erosion. These are measures that improve the stream but do not in themselves increase the carrying capacity of the stream.

Stream Floating

The preservation or the development of float streams has been given very little coverage in today's clamor for recreation activities. This is, in part, because of the nature of the stream floater. He is usually very enthusiastic about his water-oriented activity and eager to have friends join him; however, he does not want his favorite float area overrun or commercialized. So while he hopes the stream will remain protected from destructive change, the stream floater does not want to advertise his favored recreation pursuit. Although it presently is a matter of opinion, the reason for the lack of stream floating publicity probably is not only because the number of enthusiasts is small; but because they are reticent about the activity.

White-water canoists seek and get a great deal of publicity; however, many of the other stream floaters have personal interests to protect and therefore are satisfied with general anonymity. Much of the appeal of stream floating lies in solitude. The therapeutic effects that are often discussed in connection with fishing are certainly to be considered again when evaluating the enjoyment of stream floating. In some cases, the float is made as an end in itself for the enjoyment of floating down the stream; however, floating is often combined with other extensive recreation activities such as fishing and hunting.

Float fishing is very popular in much of the United States and some of the state planning commissions have included it in their recreation planning.[20] Hunting along the small tree lined streams has a relatively small number of very devoted adherents who regularly hunt waterfowl and squirrel from the bow of a canoe or on the stream banks.

STREAM DEVELOPMENT AND MANAGEMENT. The streams selected for floating should have adequate water flow through
all but the driest periods of the year. Within the limits of
practicability, there is very little that a land manager can do
to control the quantity of water-flow down the streams. Therefore, he must choose the reaches of the stream to be developed
on the basis of existing flow. A minimum depth of 12 inches
is desirable; however, canoe floats can have 8 inch minimum
depth over very short distances.

FIG. 13.6. V–deflector made from two gabion groins used to
concentrate stream flow and cut a deep channel.

Structures. Some stream improvements can be made by chan-
nelling the water through shallow spots by the use of water
deflectors. Many streams are not floatable because shallow
"riffles" block the boat passage at points along the stream
reach. Some of these riffle areas can be made passible by the
construction of a double deflector structure on the shallow
spot. Each water deflector in the pair is anchored to the bank
and to the stream bottom and angles down current at a
30 degree angle as shown in Fig. 13.6. Structures can be used
also to close off meander channels or to stop bank undercutting
where it will be detrimental to stream floating as illustrated in
Fig. 13.7.

The gabion is the recommended building block for making
stream improvement structures. The gabion is a rectangularly
shaped basket made out of heavy gauge galvanized wire. The
gabions are set up on a prepared spot and filled with small

Fig. 13.7 a. Gabion wall used to block off stream meander channel and concentrate low flows in one channel.

Fig. 13.7 b

rocks that are present at the site. The number of baskets needed to complete one part of the structure is assembled and wired together. As each gabion is filled, it is closed and wired shut. By wiring each gabion to an apron gabion on the stream bottom and then to every other gabion touching it, the builder forms a strong but flexible structure. Gabion structures have proved themselves superior to concrete or log structures because they do not crack or rot. Also, they are not left suspended in space if the stream bottom changes shape because they are flexible enough to conform to the shape of the stream bottom.

The manufacturer of gabions claims that litter, flotsam, and soil will gradually fill in the spaces that occur above the water level and permit the establishment of vegetation. [8] Maybe this will happen in certain localized spots after many years; however, on the basis of observations made on six-year-old gabion structures, it is just a claim and not a fact. This is really of very little importance anyway since the gabions usually are filled with stones from the creek bottom and blend into the scenery very well without a vegetative cover.

There is only one manufacturer of river gabions that produces a product acceptable to the U.S Forest Service. It is the Maccaferri Gabions of America, Incorporated which is an Italian corporation with offices in New York. Complete handbooks on the uses and the methods of installation of gabions are available through the manufacturer.

Riparian vegetation. In areas where sufficient rainfall occurs to permit the growth of vegetation along stream banks without an appreciable decrease in waterflow, the vegetation is a definite asset to the quality of the stream for floating. Trees, shrubs, and herbaceous vegetation provide food and cover for birds and animals, form a screen to provide privacy, stabilize the banks, and shades the water. In the East, woodduck hunting is confined largely to streams flowing through wooded bottomlands containing a lot of pin oak trees and streamside cover. Squirrels thrive among the hickory and black walnut trees found on the low terraces next to the stream. In the southwest, streamside or riparian vegetation is an enemy of stream floaters because it extracts large quantities of water from the stream. As a result, western forest landmanagers will be in step with other people concerned with water resources when they discourage the growth of riparian vegetation.

Safety. Periodic stream cleanups will be necessary to remove blockages and hazards caused by deposited debris. Any unusual hazards should be marked so that they are easily avoided. Warning signs and markers should be placed well upstream from such serious hazards as treacherous water or water falls. When access points are constructed, the serious dangers should be clearly indicated to the floating party prior to launching by signs describing the float area.

Access points. The people must be able to get to the stream by automobile in order float down it by boat. This means that all weather roads should reach to the stream bank at convenient points along the stream. In areas where roads cross or parallel the stream, boat landings can be established to permit the boater to "put-in" or "take out" of the stream. Usually, downstream floats require road connections between landing points; however, as any duck hunter will know, the connecting roads should not be anywhere near the stream.

Stream floats usually are made in small, car-top boats or canoes; therefore, an elaborate ramp and trailer space are unnecessary. All that is needed at a stream landing is a parking area and gently sloping spot cut out of the bank. Sanitation facilities might become necessary at points of heavy use; however, the use they would receive generally would not justify their cost.

Limnological Aspects of Recreational Water

Limnology, or the study of fresh water, is a science that is important to the field of forest recreation. As water-oriented recreation becomes more popular, as it surely will, it will necessitate a better understanding of the aquatic environment that is so often ignored by those who should have learned their lessons from land based studies of ecology. A fresh water lake is more than a slippery surface to ski on or a mysterious medium for growing sport fish. It is a dynamic and complex balance of many interacting physical, chemical, and biological forces.

Environment

The physical forces of temperature and light are very important factors in controlling the environment within a body of water. Thermal stratification takes place within the water of lakes and ponds as a result of heating. The character of the stratifications will vary according to the water depth, the climatic conditions, and the area of surface; however, the basic influence of the stratifications on the lake's internal environment remains the same. Thermal stratifications restrict circulation of oxygen and nutrient bearing water so that only the top layer is replenished by the wind mixed water.

During the early spring weeks, in the northern part of the country, the stratification breaks down so that there is the necessary circulation to raise the level of dissolved oxygen throughout the deep lakes. The amount of dissolved oxygen contained in fresh water is critical because fresh water fish require more than five parts of oxygen per million parts of water to survive.[12] If good fishing is to take place at varying depths as the fish retreat down to cooler water in the summer, the fish must have an adequate supply of oxygen at the deeper levels.

Oxygen is placed into the water directly from the air or as a result of aquatic plant functions. However, aquatic plants grow only as deep as light will penetrate through the water. The penetration zone of light, or the tropogenic zone, will vary from 5 feet to 90 feet in depth according to the amount of suspended materials and stains present in the water. Most plants live within the upper ten feet of water so that they do not add oxygen directly to the lower stata of water.[4]

Plant Pests Affecting Recreational Water Use

Plants have a dual role in their effect on the recreational quality of water. They are friends of the duck hunter, the

TABLE 13.2

SUMMARY TABLE OF AQUATIC PLANTS AND CONTROL MEASURES RECOMMENDED IN 1966[a]

Plant species	Mechanical methods	Environmental methods	Chemical and dosage[b]
Algae Green, blue–green, filamentous forms and other types.	In very small ponds rake or drag. This is only effective with the mat forming filamentous types.	Reduce nutrients in water. (ex. sewage effluent animal wastes, fertilizer runoff, fertilization, etc.)	All dosages are in terms of active ingredient: Copper sulfate $\frac{1}{2}$–1 ppm Diquat $\frac{1}{2}$–$1\frac{1}{2}$ ppm
Stonewort algae (*Charophyceae*)	None	None	Copper sulfate $\frac{1}{2}$–1 ppm Diquat $\frac{1}{2}$–$1\frac{1}{2}$ ppm
Submergents Coontails (*Ceratophyllum* sp.)	Mechanical harvesting machines of some use. Many species reproduce vegetatively from plant fragments and cutting may only make problems worse. This is true for most submergent plants.	Increased water depth, steeper sides.	2,4-D granules 20 lb/acre Endothall $\frac{1}{2}$–3 ppm
Pondweeds (*Potamogeton* sp.)	″	″	Endothall $\frac{1}{2}$–3 ppm Diquat $\frac{1}{2}$ ppm
Fanwort (*Cabomba* sp.)	″	″	Silvex 2 ppm
Bladderwort (*Utricularia* sp.)	″	″	Diquat $\frac{1}{4}$–$\frac{1}{2}$ ppm Silvex 2 ppm
Bushy pondweeds (*Najas* sp.)	″	″	Diquat $\frac{1}{4}$–$\frac{1}{2}$ ppm

Plant	Mechanical/Physical control	Water depth	Chemical control
Milfoil (*Myriophyllum* sp.)	Mechanical harvesting machines of some use. Many species reproduce vegetatively from plant fragments and cutting may only make problems worse. This is true for most submergent plants.	Increased water depth, steeper sides.	Diquat $\frac{1}{4}$–$\frac{1}{2}$ ppm Endothall 2–3 ppm 2,4-D granules 20 lb/acre
Waterweed (*Anacharis* sp.)	,,	,,	Diquat $\frac{1}{4}$–$\frac{1}{2}$ ppm Silvex 2 ppm
Floaters—attached Water lily (*Nymphaea* sp.)	For small ponds or limited areas repeated cutting and pulling can be successful.	Increased water depth and steeper sides will reduce the problem.	2,4-D granules 20 lb/acre Silvex 6–8 lb/acre as a foliage spray
Spatterdock (*Nuphar* sp.)	,,	,,	Silvex 6–8 lb/acre as a foliage spray
Floaters—free Duckweed (*Lemma* sp.) Watermeal (*Wolffia* sp.) Giant duckweed (*Spirodela* sp.)	None	None	Diquat $\frac{1}{4}$–$\frac{1}{2}$ ppm
Emergents Cattail (*Typha* sp.)	For small areas repeated cutting and pulling can be successful.	Increased water depth and steeper sides will reduce the problem.	2,4-D granules 20 lb/acre
Arrowarum (*Peltandra* sp.) Arrowhead (*Sagittaria* sp.) Bulrush (*Scirpus* sp.) Burreed (*Sparganium* sp.) Pickerel weed (*Pontederia* sp.)			2,4-D; 2,4,5-T liquid Silvex liquid
Rushes (*Juncus* sp.)			2,4-D; Silvex liquid

[a] Agricultural Extension Service, The Pennsylvania State University.
[b] Diquat may not be used in domestic water supplies.

bass fisherman, and even the sightseer; however, plants are enemies to the swimmer, the boater, and some fishermen. Excessive numbers of plants actually interfere with fish propagation.[4] Since plants migrate into water areas and become troublesome to the recreationists, this text will consider the plant pests that are commonly encountered. These plants are classified as algae, submergent weeds, or emergent weeds.

ALGAE. Algae are the simplest form of oxygen-producing plants.[26] Although algae grow in both fresh and salt water, this discussion will be confined to the blue–green and green algae that are found in fresh water. The blue–green algae, which is the most primitive form of plantlife on earth, forms a characteristic dark green scum on polluted or overfertilized water. Although the green algae occasionally form blooms upon the water surface, they are usually floating free or else attached to any solid object within the water.

The algae provide the basic building block in the food chain within and dependent upon the lake waters. All forms of suspended algae are part of a large collection of microscopic plants and animals known as plankton. A great number of algae blooms make the water undesirable for swimming or drinking because of the discoloration or slimy scum formed by the blooms. The odor of decomposing algae is another degrading factor that arises when the algae population gets too high.

Temperature, sunlight, water quality, and shape of the water basin are important factors affecting algae growth. Warm temperatures and direct sunlight encourage rapid growth of algae. Algae, as plants, need food in order to grow. Large concentrations of phosphates and nitrates in the water enable large masses of algae to develop. Nutrients are either washed into the water from the surrounding watershed or they are introduced by sewage disposal systems. Even well-treated sewage contains nitrates and phosphates.[4] Algae do not flourish far out to sea or in a large lake because the introduced nutrients can not get out that far.[26] This is why the shape and the size of the water basin are important factors in algae growth. Wind mixing of the water is most effective on lakes or ponds that are oriented so that the wind can regularly blow along the long axis. The orientation is especially important in areas of rough terrain where the water surface could be shielded from the wind.

Certain algae have toxic effects on birds, fish, and animals when present in concentrated quantity; however, no toxic effect on man has ever been proved. There are some cases where algae were the suspected cause of intestinal disorders but they could never be isolated as the causal agent.[9] Poor esthetic quality and obnoxious odors are the primary problems caused by algae.

Algae control. Algae can be controlled in lakes and ponds by treatment with either copper sulfate or diquat. Diquat is a relatively new aquatic herbicide that is effective in killing algae when used properly. However, water treated with diquat can not be used for domestic drinking water. Since diquat treated water can be used for recreation purposes 10 days after treatment, that herbicide can be used in recreational water that will not be used for drinking. It should be applied to the water surface at a rate of $\frac{1}{4}$ to $1\frac{1}{2}$ parts of active ingredient per million parts of water. Tables 13.3 and 13.4 give the quantities of chemical required to achieve certain treatment concentrations.

Copper sulfate has been the favored method of controlling algae since it was first used for this purpose in 1904.[9] Besides the fact that it can be conveniently purchased at agriculture supply stores, it is a relatively safe and effective chemical to use under most circumstances even though it does have some disadvantages. Copper sulfate will kill trout when applied in sufficient quantity to control the algae. Any application in excess of the amount prescribed to kill the algae will have an adverse effect on all species of fish. Therefore, if fishing is an activity, the results of the continued use of copper sulfate must be watched carefully. Also, copper sulfate solutions will corrode metal and the copper sulfate dust is very irritating to human eyes and nostrils.

TABLE 13.3

GALLONS OF LIQUID CHEMICAL NEEDED (BASED ON THE POUNDS OF ACTIVE INGREDIENT PER GALLON) TO TREAT ONE-ACRE FOOT OF WATER WITH 1 TO 10 PARTS PER MILLION CONCENTRATION[a]

Pounds of active ingredient per gallon	Parts per million									
	1	2	3	4	5	6	7	8	9	10
1	2.719	5.438	8.157	10.876	13.595	16.314	19.033	21.752	24.471	27.190
2	1.359	2.718	4.077	5.436	6.795	8.154	9.513	10.872	12.231	12.590
3	0.906	1.812	2.718	3.624	4.530	5.436	6.342	7.248	8.154	9.060
4	0.680	1.360	2.040	2.720	3.400	4.080	4.760	5.440	6.120	6.800
5	0.544	1.088	1.632	2.176	2.720	3.264	3.808	4.352	4.896	5.440
6	0.453	0.906	1.359	1.812	2.265	2.718	3.171	3.624	4.077	4.530
7	0.388	0.776	1.164	1.552	1.940	2.328	2.716	3.104	3.492	3.880
8	0.340	0.680	1.029	1.360	1.700	2.040	2.380	2.720	3.060	3.400
9	0.302	0.604	0.906	1.208	1.510	1.812	2.114	2.416	2.718	3.020
10	0.272	0.544	0.816	1.088	1.360	1.632	1.904	2.176	2.448	2.720

[a] Agriculture Extension Service, The Pennsylvania State University.

POUNDS OF CHEMICAL NEEDED (BASED ON THE PERCENT OF ...) OF WATER WITH 1 TO 10 PARTS PER MILLION CONCENTRATION[a]

Percent active ingredient	Parts per million									
	1	2	3	4	5	6	7	8	9	10
1	270.0	540.0	810.0	1080.0	1350.0	1620.0	1890.0	2160.0	2430.0	2700.0
2	135.0	270.0	405.0	540.0	675.0	810.0	945.0	1080.0	1215.0	1350.0
3	90.0	180.0	270.0	360.0	450.0	540.0	630.0	720.0	810.0	900.0
4	67.5	135.0	202.5	270.0	337.5	405.0	472.5	540.0	607.5	675.0
5	54.0	108.0	162.0	216.0	270.0	324.0	378.0	432.0	486.0	540.0
6	45.0	90.0	135.0	180.0	225.0	270.0	315.0	360.0	405.0	450.0
7	38.6	77.2	115.8	154.4	193.0	231.6	270.0	308.8	374.4	386.0
8	33.8	67.6	101.4	135.2	169.0	202.8	236.6	270.4	304.2	338.0
9	30.0	60.0	90.0	120.0	150.0	180.0	210.0	240.0	270.0	300.0
10	27.0	54.0	81.0	108.0	135.0	162.0	189.0	216.0	243.0	270.0
11	24.5	49.0	73.5	98.0	122.5	147.0	171.5	196.0	220.5	245.0
12	22.5	45.0	67.5	90.0	112.5	135.0	157.5	180.0	202.5	225.0
13	20.8	41.6	62.4	83.2	104.0	124.8	145.6	166.4	187.2	208.0
14	19.3	38.6	57.9	77.2	96.5	115.8	135.1	154.4	173.7	193.0
15	18.0	36.0	54.0	72.0	90.0	108.0	126.0	144.0	162.0	180.0
16	16.9	33.8	50.7	67.6	84.5	101.4	118.3	135.2	152.1	169.0
17	15.9	31.8	47.7	63.6	79.5	95.4	111.3	127.2	143.1	159.0
18	15.0	30.0	45.0	60.0	75.0	90.0	105.0	120.0	135.0	150.0
19	14.2	28.4	42.6	56.8	71.0	85.2	99.4	113.6	127.8	142.0
20	13.5	27.0	40.5	54.0	67.5	81.0	94.5	108.0	121.5	135.0
21	12.9	25.8	38.7	51.6	64.5	77.4	90.3	103.2	116.1	129.0
22	12.3	24.6	36.9	49.2	61.5	73.8	86.1	98.4	110.7	123.0
23	11.7	23.4	35.1	46.8	58.5	70.2	81.9	93.6	105.3	117.0
24	11.3	22.6	33.9	45.2	56.5	67.8	79.1	90.4	101.7	113.0
25	10.8	21.6	32.4	43.2	54.0	64.8	75.6	86.4	97.2	108.0
50	5.4	10.8	16.2	21.6	27.0	32.5	37.8	43.2	48.6	54.0
100	2.7	5.4	8.1	10.8	13.5	16.2	18.9	21.6	24.3	27.0

[a] Agriculture Extension Service, The Pennsylvania State University.

A concentration of $\frac{1}{2}$ part of copper sulfate per million parts of water should be a satisfactory application for most water; however, the concentration will have to be increased for hard water. If the kill is unsatisfactory after one week, a 50 percent stronger application should be made. [4]

The control of algae should begin before dense populations of algae form. The killing of a dense population will cause a severe strain on the dissolved oxygen supply within the water. If a dense population has built up, it should be divided and treated by sections so as not to make an overwhelming demand upon the oxygen needed in aerobic decomposition.

Copper sulfate can be spread by boat or airplane and applied as a solid or a liquid. Small ponds can be treated by dragging a bag of crystals off the stern of a rowboat until they have dissolved.

SUBMERGENT PLANTS. Submergent plants are higher forms of plant life that live in deep water. They are either attached to the bottom or they float freely. Nutrients are absorbed directly from the water and only anchorage is supplied by the roots. These weeds provide some cover for fish when not too plentiful; but they cause fish population problems when they are too dense. Submergent plants make swimming hazardous and fishing unpleasant; therefore, they must be controlled.

Submergent plant control. Mechanical methods of removal should not be used to control submergents. Many submergent water weeds will reproduce by vegetative propagation. Raking, dragging, or chopping will leave pieces behind to develop into full plants in a very short time. Mechanical attempts to remove submergents will only succeed in multiplying the plant's numbers and extending its coverage area.

Milford, some of the pondweeds, and other submergents can be controlled by modifying the environment. A lowering of the water level during early winter will permit some of the bottom areas to freeze and kill the submergents. Unfortunately, the oxygen supply is proportionally smaller and might have an adverse affect on the concentrated fish population. [26]

Ponds with a slow rate of water turnover can be fertilized to increase the plankton growth and thereby cutting down on sunlight penetration. The photosynthesis of the submergents is slowed down and their growth is inhibited. Fertilization with a 10-10-10 fertilizer should be done until visibility is limited to 15 to 20 inches of water depth by algae growth. Fertilization should not continue beyond September in locations where the pond will freeze in the winter, because of the problem of oxygen depletion. This technique of submergent weed control is not recommended in ponds that will be used for swimming.

The chemical control of submergents used to be done with arsenic compound; however, they are dangerous and have been replaced by herbicides.[9] Some of the herbicides used in the control of submergents today are 2,4-D; 2,4,5-T; simazine; silvex; diquat; and endothall. The note of caution that must be sounded here is that these materials have not been tested long enough to ascertain their long range effects. As a result of the uncertainties involved in applying these chemicals to water, some states require approval from the fish commission or health authorities prior to application. Table 13.2 lists some of the methods used to control various aquatic plants.

FLOATER PLANTS. Floaters are shallow water plants that have their foliage at or slightly above the water surface level. They generally obtain nutrients from the muddy bottom except for the unattached duckweeds of the North and the water hyacinth of the South.[26] These two floaters obtain their nutrients directly from the water and are not as dependent upon depth as are the other floaters.

The infamous water hyacinth was introduced into this country from Venezuela during the 1889 New Orleans Cotton Exposition. This showy water floater now clogs streams, ponds, and canals throughout Louisiana and Florida.[6] Spadderdock and the water lily are characteristic of the rooted floaters. The dense shade caused by the floater plants eliminates the submerged vegetative growth.

EMERGENT PLANTS. The aquatic plants that send their stems, leaves, and flowers well above the water surface are known as emergent plants. Cattails, bullrushes, and rice are good examples of emergents. Emergents are favored by shallow water, gently sloping shorelines, stable bottoms, cold water, and nutrient-poor water. [9] The emergents reproduce by seed, runners, and fragmentation.

Control of floater and emergents. Mechanical, environmental, biological, and chemical controls can be used effectively against floaters and emergents. Mechanical control of floaters and emergents is a common practice in both large and small bodies of water. However, care must be taken to remove the cut-up pieces of plants from the water so that each piece does not develop into a mature plant. If mechanic control is not done with care, the weed problem is intensified and not alleviated by the effort.

By manipulation of the factors that affect the shallow water environment, control of emergent plants can be established. If the shoreline can be altered so that it dips steeply to a depth of 10 feet, the emergent will be permanently eliminated. The placement of black plastic sheets on the bottom will block the light and thereby stop plant growth. The plastic sheets are available in most agriculture supply stores where they are usually sold for mulching gardens.

Biologic controls have been tried on many land plants with success; however, no practical biologic control is available to the private landowners in his battle with aquatic plants. Waterfowl and muskrats eat some plants; however, they probably contribute more to the plant's growth and spread than to their eradication. Manatees were introduced in an attempt to control the water hyacinth but so far they have not been able to do much. In the Congo River Basin of Africa where herbicides are not widely used, the manatee has proved to be a more effective biologic control than he has in this country.

Chemical controls offer the best solution to aquatic plant control. The common herbicides used to control submergents will also kill floaters and emergents. [9] Tens of thousands of acres of water surface have been freed of the strangling water hyacinths.

Herbicides can be spread in either liquid or granular form and can be applied from boats, airplane, or the shoreline. Even distribution of the chemical is the key to successful herbicide application. The quantity of chemical required and its application rate can be determined by using Tables 13.2, 13.3, and 13.4.

Animal Pests Affecting Recreational Water Use

Within the environment created by the fresh water and the factors affecting it, there is a natural balance of life. Small things eat smaller things so that they can be eaten in turn by larger things. Competition for light, oxygen, or nutrients keeps every species of living things battling with the other species for survival. Some of the animals that are part of this deadly fight for survival are also pests to humans and therefore undesirable creatures. However, to completely eradicate all the pests and their hosts will sometimes destroy the ecological balance within the entire body of water. Before a person sets out to destroy his enemies, he had better understand how much his friends need those enemies. He must realize that by killing off the populations of undesirable creatures, he might also eradicate the indigenous fish population or kill waterfowl at the same time. The common animal pests associated with the freshwater environment are mosquitoes, leeches, and swimmer's itch.

MOSQUITOES. The most important pest associated with fresh water is the mosquito. Besides being a vicious biting insect, it is the vector, or carrier, for encephalitis and malaria.[25] Mosquitoes breed best in shallow, still water where there is an abundance of cover and organic matter on the bottom of the water body. The amount of mosquitoes that an area produces is directly related to the amount of intersection of the water's surface by vegetation. The mosquito population increases when the amount of intersecting vegetation increases. An exception to this occurs when the vegetation becomes so dense that the vegetation is nearly packed solid. This situation actu-

267

ally cuts down on the intersection line formed by the vegetation protruding through the water's surface.[9]

Mosquito control. Good preparation of the shoreline and nearby land will greatly reduce the mosquito population. All of the vegetation should be removed from the water's edge. This strip should be kept clear to eliminate the intersection of the water surface by plants. All wet spots should be filled with soil or drained.

Chemical spraying is effective in reducing the land based adults; however, this only results in a temporary reduction of the population. Saturated hydrocarbons such as DDT have been used successfully in the past. Since its use has created some controversy and the mosquitoes are breeding a resistance to it, DDT is being replaced by an organophosphorous pesticide named Malathion. Malathion applications have been very effective when used as a fog application of slightly less than $\frac{1}{10}$ pound per acre.[25]

LEECHES. Leeches are flat, dark colored parasites that range in length from 1 to 5 inches. They prefer warm, shallow water where the water is usually calm. Stones, plants, and debris on the bottom provide shelter for the leeches during the daytime when they are the least active. As a result of this shelter requirement, leeches do not flourish where the bottom is made up of clay. During the winter, leeches burrow into the bottom and become dormant.[9]

Although leeches do not feed very often, they are a serious pest when present. Their presence can completely destroy the swimming value of a body of water. Even the sight of leeches that do not attack humans, ruins the swimming experience for many people. When they do feed, leeches attach to their victims by an oral suction device and painlessly penetrate the skin. As with other bloodsucking pests, the leeches inject a salivary anticoagulant into the wound in order to encourage a free flow of blood. It is the anticoagulant that causes the itching associated with leech bites.

Leech control. Leech control is possible by making environmental changes or by the application of chemicals; however, control is difficult and seldom becomes 100 percent effective. The control of leeches is difficult because of two reasons. The first reason is the leech's ability to swim over long distances in a short period of time. This means that local eradication of the leech population is only a temporary solution and must be repeated periodically. Second, the chemical applications needed to kill the leeches will also kill the fish. A large fish kill is undesirable in many places where fishing is a major attraction.

A technique of killing leeches by changing their environment has been employed successfully in northern lakes or ponds that can be drawn down. When the cold weather arrives and the leeches bury into the muddy bottoms they are protected from freezing by the shallow water above them. If the water is removed rapidly during freezing weather, the leeches will be killed. If the water level is lowered four feet and held there for two months during sub-freezing weather, the leeches in the frozen mud flats will be killed. Temperatures below 20°F are fatal to leeches.

Chemical applications are usually considered to be temporary because of rapid re-infestation by the leeches. However, complete elimination can be accomplished in small lakes if the danger of re-infestation is not great, the fish population is expendable, and the treated water is not released to flow downstream. A concentration of 5 parts of copper sulfate per million parts of water will kill the leeches, the fish, and a few other forms of aquatic life.

Temporary control around swimming beaches is a compromise measure that can be employed. One method of temporary control calls for a daily application of 100 pounds of powdered lime per acre each day. This is an expensive technique to get temporary control. Weekly treatments with 10 pounds of copper sulfate and 5 pounds of hydrated lime per acre have proved to be effective.

SWIMMER'S ITCH. The swimmer's itch is caused by a small free swimming worm larvae *(Schistosome cercariae)* which burrows into human skin where it dies. These larvae are not parasites of man; they attack man by accident after leaving certain

269

snails which act as alternate hosts to these bird and mammal parasites. The larvae are just visible to the naked eye when there is proper illumination.[9]

When the larvae burrow into human skin they die and their remains cause inflamation and itching. Each red spot is discrete, does not spread, and disappears after a couple of days. The swimmer's itch is most common in the North Central lake region of the United States where it has become a serious threat to lake swimming; however, it has been reported in nearly all regions of the country.

Control of swimmer's itch. The application of 5 parts per million of copper sulfate will kill the snails that act as the alternate hosts for the swimmer's itch causing larvae. Since this concentration of copper sulfate will be toxic to fish and other aquatic life, it should be applied only at the beach areas. The application is more successful when mixed with copper carbonate or hydrated lime. These chemicals should be applied at the rate of 2 pounds of snow grade copper sulfate and 2 pounds of copper carbonate for every thousand square feet of bottom surface to be treated.[9]

References

1. Bureau of Outdoor Recreation. 1966. *Wabash River Basin Comprehensive Study—Louisville Reservoir, Helm Reservoir.* BOR, Lake Central Region. U.S. Department of the Interior, Ann Arbor, Michigan.

2. Bureau of Outdoor Recreation. 1966. *Water Oriented Outdoor Recreation, Lake Erie Basin.* BOR, Lake Central Region. U.S. Department of the Interior, Ann Arbor, Michigan.

3. California Public Outdoor Recreation Plan Committee. 1960. California Public Outdoor Recreation Plan, Part II. Sacramento, California.

4. Cole, Wingard, Butler, and Bradford. 1966. *Aquatic Plants, Management and Control in Pennsylvania.* Natural Resource Series. Special Circular 79. The Pennsylvania State University Agriculture Extension Service, University Park, Pennsylvania.

5. Dominy, F. E. 1965. Multiple-purpose Reclaimation Projects Provide Public Recreation. *Proceedings of the Society of American Foresters*, Annual Meeting. Detroit, Michigan.

6. FARB, P. 1963. *Ecology.* Life Nature Library. Time Incorporated, New York, N.Y. 193 pages.

7. HUMPHERY, C. 1963. *Recreational Ponds and Beaches.* Guidelines for Developing Land for Outdoor Recreational Uses. Cooperative Extensive Service. Purdue University, W. Lafayette, Indiana.

8. MACCAFERI GABIONS OF AMERICA, Inc. 1966. *Stream Improvement Handbook.* Steller Press, Inc., New York, N.Y. 16 pages.

9. MACKENTHUN, INGRAM, and PORGES. 1964. *Limnological Aspects of Recreational Lakes.* U.S. Public Health Service Publication No. 1167. U.S. Department of Health, Education, and Welfare, Washington, D.C.

10. MULLEN, J.W. 1961. *Stream Improvement Prospectus for the Streams of the George Washington National Forests.* U.S. Forest Service, Washington, D.C.

11. OUTDOOR RECREATION RESOURCES REVIEW COMMISSION. 1962. *Outdoor Recreation for America.* Superintendent of Documents, Government Printing Office, Washington, D.C. 246 pages.

12. OUTDOOR RECREATION RESOURCES REVIEW COMMISSION. 1962. *Water for Recreation—Values and Opportunities.* Study Report No. 10. Washington, D.C. 130 pages.

13. OUTDOOR RECREATION RESOURCES REVIEW COMMISSION. 1962. *Sport Fishing—Today and Tomorrow.* Study Report No. 7. Washington, D.C. 130 pages.

14. OWENS, G.P. 1964. *Income Potential from Outdoor Recreation Enterprises in Rural Areas in Ohio.* Research Bull. No. 964. Ohio Agricultural Experiment Station, Wooster, Ohio.

15. OWENS, G.P. 1965. *Nature of Investment, Expense, and Income of Successful Outdoor Recreation Enterprises in Ohio.* Department Series AE 372. Ohio Agricultural Experiment Station, Wooster, Ohio.

16. PENNSYLVANIA DEPARTMENT OF HEALTH. 1957. *Regulations for Bathing Places.* Chapter IV, Article 442, Rules and Regulations. Harrisburg, Pennsylvania.

17. SALOMON, J.H. 1959. *Campsite Development.* Council Administrative Series No. 5B. Girl Scouts of the United States of America, New York, N.Y. 160 pages.

18. SHAFER, E.L., JR. 1967. Management Suggestions for Water-oriented Outdoor Recreation. Unpublished manuscript. NE Forest Experiment Station, U.S. Forest Service, Upper Darby, Pennsylvania.

19. STROUD, R. 1966. Key Values in Outdoor Recreation Planning. *Proceedings of the Northeast Fish and Wildlife Conference.* Boston, Massachusetts.

20. TENNESSEE PLANNING COMMISSION. 1962. *Public Outdoor Recreation Resources in Tennessee. Inventory and Plan for Development 1962.* Publication No. 323. Nashville, Tennessee.

21. TENNESSEE DEPARTMENT OF PUBLIC HEALTH. 1965. *Suggested Regulations Governing Organized Camps.* Chapter 65 of Public Acts 1965. Nashville, Tennessee.

271

22. U.S. FOREST SERVICE. 1961. *Handbook on Soils*. Category 2. Handbook Series 2512.2. Division of Administrative Management. USFS Department of Agriculture, Washington, D.C.

23. U.S. FOREST SERVICE. 1963. *Recreation Management*. Manual and Handbook, Title 2300. U.S. Department of Agriculture. Washington, D.C.

24. U.S. PUBLIC HEALTH SERVICE. 1962. *Manual of Individual Water Supply Systems*. Public Health Service Publication No. 24. U.S. Department of Health, Education, and Welfare, Washington, D.C.

25. U.S. PUBLIC HEALTH SERVICE. 1965. *Environmental Health Practice in Recreational Areas*. P.H.S. Publication No. 1195. U.S. Department of Health, Education, and Welfare, Washington, D.C.

26. WENT, F.W. 1963. *The Plants*. Life Nature Library. Time Incorporated, New York, N.Y. 193 pages.

27. WINGARD, R. and HEINEY, C. 1966. *Pond Construction and Management in Pennsylvania*. Special Circular No. 78. Natural Resource Series. Agriculture Extension Service, The Pennsylvania State University, University Park, Pa. 24 pages.

28. YOUNG MEN'S CHRISTIAN ASSOCIATION. 1960. *Developing Campsites and Facilities*. National Comm. on YMCA Camp Layouts. Building and Facilities Association Press, New York, 63 pages.

CHAPTER 14

Management of Forest Recreation Areas

INTRODUCTION

Management is defined by Webster as the, "judicious use of means to accomplish an end; skillful treatment". This implies that learned skills are applied to situations in such a way as to bring about an intended condition. In the management of a recreation area, the end product is user enjoyment. The skillful treatment used to obtain this end in a recreation area consists of techniques in planning, maintenance, and protection coupled with proper administration. The judicious use of each of these techniques must be dependent upon the desired end product. In that user enjoyment is the end product, the user's interests in the managed area must be analyzed. True, many areas have specific attractions and thereby can attract only those users interested in what the area has to offer.

Today the forest resources are used for recreation by everyone who comes in contact with them. One of the major pitfalls of the land manager, most notably the professional forester, has been his failure to recognize that almost everyone within the forested area is a recreationist of one kind or another. As a result, the public has become very vocal in its dissatisfaction of the forester's techniques of managing the nation's timbered lands. The land manager must recognize that the public should have more than campgrounds and picnic areas for recreation.

Forest recreation is loosely lumped into either intensive- or extensive-use activities. Intensive forest recreation activities are concentrated in a relatively centralized area that has been developed for use. Camping, swimming, boating, picnicking, and certain types of hiking are generally considered as intensive forest recreation activities. The fisherman, hunter, and overland hiker move about over large areas where the minimum of developments are required. These forest users are engaging in extensive forest recreation activities. One of the most important users of extensive forest recreation facilities is the sightseer who wants to be surrounded by as much natural beauty as the area can offer. Almost everyone who drives through forested areas is a user of extensive forest recreation facilities.

Many recreation users are involved in the combination of recreation activities. A camper is often a sightseer before, after, and during his camping. Although his primary use of the forest is in an intensive recreation area, he engages in extensive use of the forest. The intensive-extensive recreation area user, such as the camper, probably gets more attention from land managers than does his opposite number. In opposition to the intensive-extensive user is the person who comes to the forest to use its extensive facilities but also gets involved with intensive use areas such as roadside rests. Many sportsmen prefer to camp in the forest while fishing or hunting; but they came for the fishing or the hunting and not for the fun of camping.

The land manager would soon need psychiatric help if he tried to characterize each and every visitor to his area. He would do better to deal only in generalities and to compare those generalities to what his area can continuously produce. Often, the recreation area manager has nothing to say about planning of the layout, its implementation, its governing policy, or even its insect control program. Even when the manager has been placed squarely in the position of the technician, he must still be able to show ingenuity within the existing limitations. Many state park supervisors have done remarkable jobs of managing their parks in such a way as to make them better than other parks that have much better natural advantages. Even though he may not be permitted much freedom in planning the development of his area, the recreation area manager still has the other methods of treatment at his disposal. He can skillfully apply techniques of management, operation, and protection to provide an area that will continuously provide a given level of user enjoyment.

Management of Intensive-use Areas

Intensive-use areas provide facilities and services that are required for specific types of forest recreation. The range of intensive-use recreation areas extends from ski lifts and lodges to a developed swimming hole. Public agencies tend to give camping and picnic areas the highest priority and the most attention.[13] Whether private or public, these areas need a high priority. Such high investment ventures as ski lifts and lodges are operated by experienced operators and generally are not the direct concern of the forestland manager. The intensive-use development tends to concentrate use into the managed area thereby requiring more facilities and services. As the intensity of use increases, the need for increased management climbs. People control, site protection, maintenance, user safety and comfort, fire protection, and general esthetics are the major management concerns of a recreation area supervisor. These 6 items do not include the administrative problems of public relations, operation, personnel management, and policy.

The people who visit a forest area tend to destroy what they have come to admire. Their very presence in the forest has an impact upon the environment.[2, 4] Research has shown that even lightly used areas lose 50 to 99 percent of their original ground cover simply by trampling. This concentration of traffic wears out the vegetation, compacts the soil, accelerates erosion, kills the shade trees, and reduces the amount of barrier vegetation. Bare soil causes dust or mud problems and personal cleanliness becomes a full-time job for a family with small children. The summation of these affects is a deterioration of the site and a sharp decrease in user enjoyment.

Originally, wise planning can lessen some of these problems; however, to some extent, the problems will always remain for the manager to handle. The coarse granitic sands of southern Maine do not rise up as dust or turn into mudholes; therefore, they support good recreation sites with the minimum of paving. The limestone soils of West Virginia grow magnificent vegetation but they have the poorest possible trafficability characteristics. Roads and even trails on such soils need surfacing to be servicable in wet weather. Also, these limestone areas should be crossed in as short a route as possible.

All recreation areas cannot be located on the ideal soil. They must be developed where the need and the attractions are. As a result of putting the developments where the demand occurs, the recreation planners will have to put facilities in locations that do not have the best site characteristics. This means that recreation managers are going to inherit problems when they take charge of these new areas.

Site Protection

In order to maintain a given level of satisfactory use within an area, the manager can follow two courses. He can estimate the carrying capacity of the recreation area and provide administrative restrictions to limit use to that capacity. To a certain extent, the available facilities will limit the number of users; however, this is not satisfactory in all cases because people might not seek substitution areas or activities until the overuse of the area has done its damage. The second course of action is to apply land management techniques to the area. The supervisor can use various management techniques in order to maintain the attractiveness of the area.

Three interdependent tasks are required to lessen the long-term destructive impact of use. Those tasks are:

1. To concentrate the use to specific locales and channels whenever possible.
2. To modify or treat the ground surface at the concentrated use points to prevent wear.

3. To apply silvicultural techniques required to replace, repair, and care for vegetation and soil on the recreation site.

CONCENTRATION OF USE. Since carrying capacities are largely unknown for most sites, they can be used only in general terms or in arbitrary decrees. As more research is completed in this field, more weight can be applied to the carrying capacity theory. Although gross excesses in user loads are readily observable, the delicate balance between site quality and amount of use is difficult to achieve. It means that some limit of use must be established to prevent a reduction in site quality. It is very rare that a private operator will turn away income during peak use periods. It is probable that he would rather invest some time and money into repairing the damage from overuse.

The concentration of use to specific locales and channels is of the utmost importance. This can be done by judicious location of roads, trails, screening, barriers, and other developments. In campgrounds, this concentration of use technique should be applied to the camping unit interior as well as to the entire campground. The unit interior should be set up to facilitate direct movement among the car, table, and fireplace as well as direct routes out of the unit to the water supply and to the toilet facility. Some people object to a formal unit where the table is tied down, the vehicle is restricted, and the tent must be placed in a certain spot. In attempting to concentrate use, these steps might become necessary. If the tent pad is placed in the best location within the unit; if it is level; if it is high enough for good external drainage; and if it is made of coarse material for good internal drainage most people will use it. The use of the constructed tent pad also will help to eliminate the destructive practice of "tent-ditching" during rainy weather.

Concentration of use by itself will be self-defeating. It must be teamed with attractions and site modifications. People will go where the attractions are or where movement is most convenient. Forcing them to do otherwise would be a violation of the purpose of the managed recreation area and would invite disregard, ill feeling, and substitution. This does not imply that all people should be permitted to roam freely around the area; it simply underlines the need for judiciously placed facilities, trails, barriers, and roads.

Trails. Trails are the key to site protection in an intensive use area. When judiciously tied into the road system, trails facilitate movement of users to points of concentration. If properly located, the trails will channelize traffic into designated routes of travel. Even though people will not always walk where the manager wants them to, they will generally follow the easiest route to their objective. That is, if they know where their objective is located. Trails alone will not be effective. They must be identified by signs or sight. A trail without signs that leads to the pump is of limited value if all the picnickers do not know where the pump is located. Also, people will leave a worn dirt trail to avoid mud, steep grades, or unnecessary length. A 2 inch thick surface of gravel or black top stops wear and mud and makes the trail more attractive.

The trail opens up the forest to hiking, riding, and speciality purposes such as botanical walks. The best trail locations are on the ridges and along the contours of gentle slopes.[5] These positions lessen the danger of erosion, afford the best vistas, and provide more relaxed walking conditions. Most trails that are not paved will need water-bars to stop the erosive flow of water down their surfaces. Steps should be used on steep slopes and trails confined to more gentle slopes. The stairs will be easier on the user and will protect the trail surface from erosion or surface slippage. Surfacing material tends to work its way down hill below each barrier on steep slopes.[5] Steps must be properly employed and designed or they will be by-passed. The grade of trails can be lessened by using railroad ties or squared timbers. Two 18 inch long pieces of $\frac{1}{2}$-inch steel reinforcing rod placed through the wood and driven into the ground will hold the ties or timbers in place.

Shortcutting switchbacks is another unfavorable practice of trail users. They will shortcut to different levels of a trail if it

278

appears convenient. They will trample the vegetation on the steep slope and cause the soil to unravel. Barriers, screening, or signs will be needed to stop the shortcutting practice.

All trails should serve some purpose in order to justify their construction and maintenance costs. The problem in planning is how to design a trail system that is workable. Thoughtful planning is the best ingredient in trail layout; however, people do not always react in the way they are expected to react. Because of this, the manager quite often follows the practice of "path-paving" within recreation areas. That is, he lets the people wear a path and then he paves it. Path-paving has been quite common on large college campuses for decades. After all, the people will find the route of travel that is best for them. This technique has some drawbacks. First, the public might wreck the vegetation of the entire area before they wear out a satisfactory path. Second, the public-worn path may be located in such a way that it is objectionable for administrative or management reasons. For instance, it might cross the road at such a place as to cause a safety hazard. The third drawback to applying the path-paving technique is that all the people do not know where everything is located. This means that they must follow round-about existing trails and roads or go stumbling about the forest in search of the washhouse. On the other hand, planned trails might require more treatment than path-paved trails to keep users from wandering off them or from shortcutting.

Barriers. The word barrier is employed in a limited sense in recreation management. It does not mean an overwhelming wall that completely stops everything. Rather, a barrier in a recreation area should be subtle and suggestive. It should blend with the theme of the forested area so that it does not offend the recreationists. True, a high fence or similar barrier will be needed in some instances; however, they should be avoided when possible. Besides being used for controlling the movement of people, barriers can be used to screen unpleasant sights or to provide privacy. Generally, barriers are constructed from building materials or developed with vegetation.

279

Constructed barriers can be either permanently implaced or moveable. Fences, rows of short posts, and sleepers and rails are the common permanent barriers made from logs and lumber. Rocks and seeded soil piles can make use of native materials in very subtle ways for vehicle control. The judicious felling of trees and the piling of brush can form casual, but effective, barriers in locations where more elaborate efforts are not needed or not economically feasible. The stringing of barbed wire has no place in the field of outdoor recreation. The most unpleasant sight at the Indiana Dunes State Park is the barbed wire that is used to keep people off the sand-dunes.

Occasionally, the need arises to temporarily close a location to use. Moveable barriers should be used for this purpose rather than constructing a temporary in-place barrier. Moveable barriers can be tastefully constructed from durable materials and stored when not in use. Because of their flexibility and continued reusability, moveable barriers can justify larger cost per unit than can temporary barriers. Temporary barriers are usually thrift measures and end up looking "junky". Michigan State Parks use a moveable barrier that is simply made by fastening a poured concrete block to each end of a 6 foot long log.

Shrubbery and tree plantings make the esthetically ideal barrier. Vegetative plantings control movement of people, provide screening, and increase the scenic value of the setting. The loop roads that are so popular with recreation planners create a minor but irritating problem. Headlights of cars on the loop roads shine into half of the camping units as the vehicle moves along. Campground managers should consider the use of some shrubbery to shield campers from the headlight glare.

Generally, barrier plantings will take a beating from the users and will need replacement occasionally; however, all areas have not had the problem of replacement. Maine's Sabago Lake State Park finds itself in the happy position of too effective barrier plantings. Five years after white pine seedlings had been planted in great numbers throughout the expanding campground area, it became apparent that nearly all the trees were going to continue to grow in spite of very heavy use. The management is now undertaking a thinning and pruning operation to open up the overgrown areas of the campground. Unfortunately, all barrier plantings are not so durable and do not put the manager into such an enviable position.

The choice of species and the form of barrier planting offer a broad challenge to the manager. Will native vegetation withstand the abuse? Should new species be introduced to replace native plants? Quite often non-indigenous vegetation is more durable than native plants. Will a hedge be superior to a row of trees? Low hedges will channel traffic without blocking the view. Many recreation area managers have had great success with using low growing native junipers as barriers along paths. Junipers have been very successful in keeping bathers on the trails at Point Beach State Park in Wisconsin where extremely heavy use areas are strung along the strand. Beaked filbert (*Corylus carnuta*, Marsh.) is not only a very good barrier planting within its range but it provides two other functions. It is a tall, bushy shrub that screens the view and it produces a nutlike fruit that will attract wildlife. Although beaked filbert is not suited to every area, it is a good example of the species that managers should be considering for their areas. Rhododendron and azaleas generally prove to be the most durable shrub species in recreation areas. [10]

Screening has already been mentioned in regard to camping areas where it is planted to provide privacy within the units or to block the view of an unfavorable sight. Maintenance buildings, sewage plants, and parking lots should be screened from view by vegetation barriers. Not all campers desire to be completely screened in. Also, all campers do not desire to be widely separated from each other and that screening for privacy within campgrounds is not too important to them. [3] These people are usually content in a central campground where they have plenty of nearby neighbors. If the present trend continues, excessive vegetation will not trouble these people. Many, if not most, forest recreation areas have been so worn out that regular management programs will be of limited value. In these cases rehabilitation projects must be undertaken to raise the level of quality to the desired point.

SURFACE MODIFICATION. The thing to consider when concentrating use onto small areas is the increased need for better surfaces. Unprotected soil will quickly compact and wear away. Vegetation will be destroyed by trampling. A water faucet is a spot where use is definitely concentrated. Anyone who has waded around the muddy water faucets and fought the hornets there gathering mud will testify to the poor idea of user concentration. A paved apron with a water carry-off drain is usually needed to improve such a nuisance spot.

The trampling around a table quickly forms a circle of bare soil which becomes dirt on the children and dust on the food. Periodic movement of the table will spread the wear over a large area. This course of action might be satisfactory under certain conditions. However, in this period of heavy recreation demand, few managers can afford to donate enough land to one table to provide room for nature's healing hand. It may be better to tie the table down in one spot and treat the worn circle thus permitting the larger area to remain vegetated. One satisfactory technique that has been employed in very heavily used picnic areas such as roadside rests has been the construction of a concrete pad that is sufficiently large to hold the picnic table and to provide room for movement around the table. Near the center of the pad, a large eye-bolt is imbedded to hold a chain that fastens to the table.

The thought of paving within a picnic or camping site is repugnant to many land managers and recreationists upon first thought. This may go back to the roots of professional training or back to that urge to be Nathanial Bumpo or Daniel Boone. Interestingly, most of the indignant remarks over surfaced places within a campground or picnic area come from those who talk about or plan outdoor recreation but not from those who regularly use the overcrowded intensive-use areas.

Proper use of material can make surfacing less offensive to

Fig. 14.1. The careful adaptation of native materials and screening vegetation maintain the beauty of the setting at this picnic unit. (U.S. Forest Service photo.)

those who might object to it. Initial costs of concrete and black top material are high. Although they might save on maintenance in the long run, hard surfacing materials may be too much of a burden for many an operator's budget. Some natural mulching materials might be used to provide a more satisfactory surface. Entire camping units can be given a light coat of pine needles, wood chips, or sawdust at a very low investment. Parents of the family who have tried sitting around a fireplace on the dusty, worn-out ground would not complain about the reduction of dirt caused by a layer of wood chips. Besides producing the immediate benefit of less dust for the user, mulched surfaces provide an insulating cushion over the soil. The mulch cushion protects the soil from wear and compaction, the tree and shrubbery roots from exposure and trampling, and moisture loss through evaporation. One added benefit of mulch is that it will decompose over the years to build up the organic contents of the underlying soil.[7] The aging of mulching materials before they are applied will have two benefits. First, the material will lose its new and artificial look and will be less offensive in appearance. Second, it will have a chance to decompose slightly and not be such a great drain on the available nitrogen that it would be if it were used while fresh. The high demand for nitrogen by fresh mulching material can be countered by the addition of high nitrogen fertilizer when fresh mulching material is used.

SILVICULTURAL TECHNIQUES. All vegetation need not be considered as screening. In fact, complete screening of the recreationist from scenery is undesirable. People like to see things. They like views and variety; therefore, the forest might need some thinning to increase the viewing distance into it.[11]

The planting of trees and shrubs can provide other improvements to a recreation area. Tree and shrubs provide shade, enhance the area's beauty, and attract wildlife. Shade is an essential ingredient of the forest recreation area. It provides coolness for the user and contrast to the scenery. Shade alternated with sunshine provides part of the picture that forest

283

visitors desire to see. [11] Well-chosen tree and shrub species should be favored by the manager to add color to the forest picture. Redbud, flowering dogwood, wild cherries, and hawthorns are just examples of trees that provide pretty floral displays. Serious consideration should be given to using shrubbery that encourages the visits of birdlife. Species of trees, shrubs, vines, and grasses that the United States Forest Service recommends planting for area beautification, wildlife, and screening are given in the Appendix. [15]

Site damage does not increase in direct proportion to increasing use. Light use of an area destroys more than 80 percent of the ground cover and increased use over the following years will not cause enough additional damage equal to the extra use. [2] In fact, research has indicated that the vegetation will adapt to heavy-use as the years pass by a replacement of broadleafed species with fine-leafed grasses. Grasses provide the most durable living ground cover. Areas that were heavily worn during the first year showed some recovery during the second and third season of heavy use. [6] It is this natural recovery that should be encouraged whenever possible. Some researchers recommend a policy that they call "reverse silviculture". Reverse silviculture encourages ground cover at the expense of the overstory. This is accomplished simply by the removal of some codominate trees from the canopy. The openings will permit more sunlight to reach the herbaceous and shrub layer thereby stimulating their growth. [3]

The planting, irrigation, and fertilizing of grass is becoming a necessity for managers wishing to maintain a beautiful and clean site. Some recreation area managers seed durable grass on worn areas in the early fall as soon as the areas can be taken out of use. By keeping the seeded areas out of use until late spring or early summer, the manager can provide the area with the maximum percent of ground cover and the public with the minimum amount of dust.

Water is probably the most important ingredient in maintaining a durable recreation area. Most researchers agree that irrigation will do more to protect a site than any other cultural treatment.[4, 16] Wagar points out that watering helps to maintain the site quality in three ways:[16]

1. Watering permits establishment of durable species of grass where they would not otherwise exist.
2. Watering usually increases the total growth of vegetation.
3. Watering aids in the recovery of vegetation that has been bruised or trampled. Moist vegetation is more likely to recover after crushing then if it were subject to drying.

Certain problems occur when an area is irrigated. The soil is more subject to compaction when it is wet, and turgid vegetation is susceptible to damage by trampling. The caution here is to carry on irrigation projects after regular periods of heavy use rather than just before them. A heavy soaking on Monday will aid the trampled vegetation on its way to recovery. Also, the soil will be dry enough to better resist the trampling crowds that will arrive with the following weekend. Admittedly, some areas are recipient of continuous heavy use. These areas will need special schedules of watering, area closures, and more improved walk ways for the users.

Occasionally soils will need to be limed in order to get the soil reaction into the proper range of pH 6.3 to 6.9 that is best for grasses.[13] Several easy-to-use and inexpensive soil reaction test kits are available through the generally used supply houses. An investment of approximately 3 dollars will purchase an adequate soil reaction kit. By following simple directions and comparing colored reagents with a color chart, the manager can determine the soil reaction to the nearest half pH reading. This is precise enough to determine the proper year to lime. Liming is usually done in the fall with crushed limestone or in the spring with hydrated lime. County agents or local feed and grain cooperatives will gladly furnish assistance needed in determining the quantity of lime and fertilizers needed. The caution on liming of a recreation area is again a warning on timing. Lime should not be spread on the grass shortly prior to periods of public use. From this standpoint, late fall liming is advantageous in recreation areas. Spring liming should be done early enough in the year so that the lime will be washed into the soil before the users begin to arrive. It is unnecessary to lime during the summer when it will interfere with the visitors. If fall liming is impracticable, it is best to wait until the following year to lime. The loss of one year in liming is far less serious than the ill-feeling created among lime-coated picnickers.

Fertilizer has its place in forest recreation just as it does in agriculture and landscaping. Most home owners would not expect to maintain a lawn without the use of fertilizers. Why should recreation area managers attempt to do so? Many recreation sites receive more than enough use to wear out a well-established suburban lawn. "Complete" fertilizers contain nitrogen, phosphorus, potassium, and several trace elements that might be needed. Wagar points out that the fertilizer that is scattered around on the ground will be used by the understory and not benefit the larger trees.[16] In most cases, it is the understory and grass layers that need the most assistance in resisting wear. The fertilizer should be placed into small, drilled holes around the trees if it is to do the tree any good.

The rapid release of nitrogen from most fertilizers can "burn" the vegetation during dry periods. Urea formaldehyde fertilizers that are known as "slow release" fertilizers have come on to the market in recent years. These slow release fertilizers permit one application instead of many light ones and lessen the danger of "burning" the vegetation. Since urea formaldehyde fertilizers cost nearly twice as much as standard balanced fertilizers, their use is not likely to be rapidly accepted by cost conscious operators. However, their convenience and built-in safety for vegetation might prove to be a long-run saving to the manager who does not want to spend the time to spread several light applications of standard commercial fertilizer.

One problem with growing grass is that the grass must be mowed. Mowing gives the area a more pleasant appearance and permits more comfortable use of the grass covered areas. Most recreation managers mow much of their grass covered areas regularly without questioning the practice.

Research done in the Rocky Mountain areas indicates that watering will do more to help the vigor and growth of the overstory trees while fertilizing will do more to stimulate the growth of the ground cover.[16] This research is not complete; however, it does provide information that lends itself to the logical conclusion that trees are better able to utilize the added water while the more shallow rooted ground cover intercepts and utilizes the broadcast spread fertilizer.

Whatever treatments that will be necessary to maintain the level of recreation site quality will depend upon several factors. The cultural improvements required will vary with the type and intensity of use, the soil series, the topography, the vegetation, and other such factors. The most important ingredients in a well-managed recreation area are the manager's initiative, imagination, and interest in providing the users with a high quality site.

User Safety

The protection of the user's health and safety is of primary importance. To accomplish that end, the manager must provide the following:[14]

1. Satisfactory sanitary facilities.
2. Safe drinking water supply.
3. Elimination of hazards.
4. Fire protection.

Sanitary facilities and drinking water are each discussed in their individual chapters within this book. Hazard elimination and fire protection are problems that constantly vex the manager. It is the operator's obligation to protect the user within the bounds of common sense.

Existing hazards must be removed or nullified by means such as signs or barriers. Periodic inspections of the area should be made to check on specific hazards such as dying or damaged trees, snags, areas that threaten collapse, poison ivy, and yellow jackets. These periodic checks should be started just prior to the season's opening and carried on throughout its length. Monthly formal safety inspections will help to maintain the proper level of freedom from hazards. The administrative policy of making records of these formal inspections could prove to be helpful in the case of accidents in the area. Formal inspections and their follow-up are only part of the problem of hazard elimination.

Constant observation of the area and a sympathetic ear to complaints of the users will probably uncover more dangerous conditions than the formal inspections; however, the formal inspections accomplish three objectives. First, they turn up hazards. Second, they force a complete check of the entire area; not just where the inspector might happen to wander. Third, they emphasize the need for hazard reduction and set a standard of area safety.

Swimming areas are very touchy places when hazards are discussed. Policies governing use of swimming areas and the employment of life-guards are administrative matters that must be weighed carefully. Elimination of physical hazards, on the other hand, is a subject that can be dealt with easily by the manager. Cans, bottles, and other hazards should be removed from the water whenever necessary. The bottom of river and stream swimming areas should be checked in the spring after the high runoff passes to determine if any submerged rocks form hazards. A life-saving ring with attached rope should be located on a display board at the swimming area. A glass covered display case is an added expense; however, it will discourage the practice of using the life-saving ring for water sports. Directions on how to get assistance from the recreation area personnel, ambulance, and other emergency services should be prominently displayed throughout the recreation area.

As recreation areas become more common and more closely tied to population centers, they will attract more problems. Unwelcome visitors might be a problem in locations that are easily accessible. Theft has already become a major problem in some national parks. The manager must take steps to exclude intruders from the recreation area by administrative means as well as by management practices. Problems concerned with the exclusion of intruders will vary according to location, population, and size of the area.

The insulation of the recreation area by space or by barrier plantings and screening will lessen the interest of passers-by and make the separation of the users from the general public more distinct. Uncontrolled and unscreened access into a recreation area tends to invite trouble. Persons who are not interested in the type of recreation offered by the area can drift in and out as they desire and with little or no controls. The control of intruders is primarily an administration problem; however, this problem can be greatly eased by cultural improvements to the area.

Tawas City Park and Campground is located along the main highway in downtown Tawas City, Michigan. A 6 foot chain-link fence surrounds the park to exclude unregistered visitors. Campers generally dislike fences and especially chain-link fences. However, the fence at Tawas City Park has not affected the campers opinions of that area enough to lessen the crowds. The fence provides good security from unauthorized entry from a location with a heavy population; therefore, it is probably a desirable feature as far as most users are concerned.

Fire Protection

Most recreation areas have administrative policies concerning the building of fires. Some areas even exclude the use of fire within the intensive-use area. However, the campfire is inherently part of the great outdoor scene. Campers, picnickers, ice skaters, hunters, and others often feel that their outing would be enhanced by an evening campfire. The campfire is seldom used for cooking; however, it adds that flavor that the outdoor recreationist is seeking. The manager should try to favor the user's view on the matter of campfires and provide a safe place for the fire. The concrete rings that were originally used for charcoal disposal (Chapter 4) serve as ideal campfire enclosures.

It is cheaper to provide firewood for the fires than it is to permit the users to gather their own. Scrap wood or slabbing is always turning up during the maintenance work on the forest. This wood can be distributed to certain central points to be picked up by the camper. Some of the costs of this service can be recovered by selling measured racks of wood for a small sum. The practice of selling pre-cut wood for 25 cents an arm load or so, is well established in many large areas of intensive-use. Where the price is more for a control on excessive use than it is for profit, the user is asked to deposit a quarter in a container for each arm load that he takes from the pile. More formal arrangements can be developed by using a measuring rack which the buyer fills with the wood that he wants to buy. The choice between the honor system and regularly scheduled sales hours is an administrative decision that must be made as a result of conditions prevailing at each area.

Organic litter accumulation generally is not a problem in intensive-use areas; rather, the reverse is usually the case. However, the manager must guard against allowing dry leaves and other litter to accumulate under, against, or around structures where they would develop a hot spot and spread a ground fire to the structure. Also, some faucets within the area should be threaded so as to take hose for fire fighting.

The manager should organize into fire crews and train whatever manpower that he has available. In line with fire training, the manager should have enough specialized forest fighting tools on hand to supply his trained personnel. Even one man with the proper tools can do a great deal to contain most forest fires when they are small. The investment of time and money for forest fire protection is quite small when compared with the investment that would be destroyed by a wildfire. Most state forestry agencies will gladly assist any interested land manager in protecting his land against fire. Also, the State and Private Division of the United States Forest

Service can give some advice to land owners in the preparation of fire suppression programs.

Site Rehabilitation

Forest recreation areas will deteriorate with use. That is, the original character of the area will change as a result of man's presence. As his visits become more numerous, man requires more management to maintain a high quality level of recreation. Now, as often in the past, management techniques occasionally are insufficient or inadequately applied to prevent the destruction of the site. Wornout recreation areas, eroded lakeshores, gullying of bridle paths and foot trails are all too common a picture throughout the forests of the United States. Some cases of deterioration could have been prevented by good recreation management practices and administrative policies while others were inevitable because of failings in planning that did not account for problems inherent in the site or the location. A site located on a soil that is highly erosive and not suited to traffic will wear out in spite of most attempts to protect it. Some recreation areas that were designed for the casual use of twenty-five years ago are trampled under by today's heavy use. In many cases, ordinary management techniques will not raise the recreation quality to an acceptable level. A completely new program of rebuilding of the site's recreation quality must be undertaken. This rebuilding effort is aimed at rehabilitating the site for high quality use. Site rehabilitation is an expensive undertaking because it runs head-on into the basic problems that caused the site to deteriorate in the first place. The efforts required to repair the site and then to solve the problems involved might prove to be more costly than the original development costs.

Is the area worth saving? Will the improvements hold up under use? Would it be better to abandon the area and to establish another? The fact that use has worn out an area might indicate that the area was heavily used by the public; therefore, it is needed. Closure of an area without substitution could lead to serious consequences. Sometimes the construction of an alternate area simply increases the developed facilities because it becomes impossible to close the original facilities. The establishment of areas on more favorable sites followed by the closure and obliteration of the worn out areas may be the best route to take. Besides being an expensive undertaking, the obliteration of old areas is difficult to explain to users jammed into an overflow area. These are the problems that must be faced by the land managers who must make the governing decisions.

If the recreation area is worth saving and if it is located on an area where it can be saved, the problems of its original degradation must be analyzed. Certain sites might require closing and replacement in a more advantageous location. In campgrounds and picnic areas, a variety of spacings should be used to satisfy many different tastes. Some researchers believe that relocation decisions should be based heavily upon the opportunity to produce a pleasant and varied experience rather than upon the configuration of the land or type of vegetation.[11] That is, areas should be relocated in such a way as to serve the need of the users and to provide them with the most pleasure because management steps can be taken to protect or to alter the land and the vegetation. This reasoning is most sound with the more expensive developments where the demand justifies ignoring the carrying capacity of the land and the altering of its configuration. A lodge and marina might be located by its need for a large level area that is near the water and accessible by road. The fact that it will be located on an unstable terrace soil does not constitute a limiting factor. It is a problem that must be overcome by some cultural improvements. Costly jetties and stone break waters protect multi-million dollar investments along the off-shore bar resorts of the Atlantic Ocean. However, small forest recreation areas often are pressed just to support their administration and do not justify the expenditures of funds for more than normal maintenance. Because of this, the relocation of layout of many facilities is rather rigidly tied to the existing land configuration.

The next problem to face after layout is that of erosion. Most activities of man have the same effect on the movement of water. They accelerate the surface runoff and impede infiltration of water into the soil. Control of runoff is necessary to prevent damaging erosion and annoyance to users, especially campers. A storm drain system might be necessary to collect and remove the surface water. Check dams should be built in any existing erosion gullies. A grass cover should be established to stabilize the gully sides. Grasses are more effective soil stabilizers than are tree seedlings which take several years to establish themselves.

Trails located on highly erosive soils should be replaced by trails on more stable soils. If the relocation is not possible, the unstable area should be crossed in the shortest possible distance. This practice means that the steepest acceptable grade should be used if it will shorten the crossing distance. The steep grade of the trail must be accompanied by proportionally more drainage structures to prevent erosion. Culverts and water-bars will be needed at closer intervals to remove the water from the road or trail as quickly as possible. The reasoning here is to use the steep slope and drainage structures to remove the water from the highly erosive soil as quickly as possible while exposing the smallest area of that soil to erosion by using a short trail or road across it.

The closure of trails becomes a problem in rehabilation. How does a manager prevent the use of closed trails? The partial answer is to block the closed path with a barrier or a sign. Also, the trail can be obliterated by planting it with shrubbery or trees. These are good steps in closure; however, they will prove to be half measures if an alternate or more desirable trail is not provided for the user.

If an area is to be rehabilated in order to provide high quality recreation, it must be modified in such a way as to overcome the degrading effects that wore out the original site. Mechanical work such as grading with earth moving equipment might be necessary to provide the landscape configuration needed to resist erosion. Unwanted wet areas should be drained. Top soil must be hauled in to replace that worn or eroded away. Trees, grass, and shrubs must be planted to complete the site. Serious consideration should be given to the installation of a permanent irrigation system at this time.

MANAGEMENT OF EXTENSIVE RECREATION AREAS

Three out of five recreation visits to the national forests are for uses that do not require developed sites.[1] Hiking, horseback riding, fishing, hunting, and sightseeing use the forest as a setting; but their participants do not need the developed sites that camping or picnicking participants require. Extensive forest recreation use is not limited to the person who travels to the forest exclusively for that purpose. As the land managers are belatedly learning, everyone who passes through the forest feels that he has the right to enjoy the forest setting. More people are traveling more miles each year as a result of rapidly increasing mobility, leisure time, and increased income. This traveling public is very much aware of what natural beauty should be and it expects to see the epitome of natural beauty in the forested areas. As the stress on natural beauty continues to come from the White House, public opinion will have more and more influence on how the forest lands are managed. This public awareness must be anticipated by the land manager. The forester must begin to apply silvicultural practices in such a way as to increase the public enjoyment and its understanding of the uses of the forests. The engineer must consider the need for unspoiled stream fishing and the counter-pressure for water-based sports when he plans an impounding dam. Soil conservation personnel are being watched by the duck hunter whenever they plan to drain some wetlands.

The land manager must begin to think of his entire domain as a potential recreation area. He should search for ways to accommodate the public desires for recreation through management programs that reconcile timber production and watershed protection with recreation.

Silvicultural Techniques for Roadsides

Silviculture is the practice of applying knowledge of tree behavior to the production of timber. Certain timber cutting methods are premised on the expected reaction of nature. Stand quality and volumes can be improved by the proper silvicultural treatment. Just as the forester can raise the timber value of his land, so he can raise the recreation value. Simple understanding of the factors that enhance extensive recreation will aid the forester to make the silvicultural decisions that will benefit the timber economy as well as enrich the recreation quality of the area.

No-CUTTING ZONES. "No-cutting" zones along highways and streams were one of the first attempts of foresters to reconcile timber production with recreation pressures. One hundred to two hundred foot wide strips where no cutting is permitted are established along roads. This is, in a sense, a screening technique employed to hide the undesirable vista of a logged area. The establishment of this facade of trees simply underlines the arguments against even-aged cutting practices that leave large areas of the land denuded of trees and covered with slash. As even-age management techniques become more accepted in the Northeast, they run into conflict with the conservation-oriented urbanist of that heavily populated area of the country. The problem of re-educating the layman in the proper use and utilization of forests is a problem that foresters must face if they are not to lose all their powers to make professional decisions; however, the solution of that problem is out of the realm of this book.

The no-cutting strip is a good first step in that it does protect the motorist from the view of clear-cut area; however, it does not do much to integrate recreation with timber management. It is simply a wise concession to the public's wishes. The leaving of a solid wall of timber along the highway does not necessarily provide the things that mean the most to the recreationist who wants variety, vistas, and combinations of landscapes and water.[11] Also, the no-cutting strip with-

295

draws many acres from the production of timber. In spite of its many disadvantages, the technique of establishing no-cutting zones is recommended for a first step. As more positive silvicultural techniques can be incorporated into the timber management program, they can replace or supplement the no-cutting zones.

CLEAR-CUTTING DESIGN. Clear-cutting will be tolerated by the general public if it does not dominate the landscape or occur too close to the road or to their recreation area. [8] The amount of clean-up done after and during cutting should be greater on areas that are readily accessible to the public. Smaller clear-cut areas should be selected when near roads and recreation areas. A higher degree of debris clearance will be needed to improve the appearance. Planting might be needed to increase the rate of regeneration and heal the scars more quickly. Small clear-cut areas will give the landscape a multi-layer effect that will enhance the beauty of the landscape after the regeneration heals the scars caused by the logging operations.

Sequential clear-cuts can be laid out so that the standing timber or advanced reproduction of one area screens the slash of another area. This can be accomplished by orienting the cutting areas in strips that have their long axis perpendicular to the line of sight from the recreation area, vista, or road. The closest strip to the recreation area should be screened by an area not designated for cutting. After the first strip is cut, operations should jump to a strip further back or move to another location in the forest. By cutting every third or fourth strip in each cutting cycle, the forester permits the regeneration to become large enough to eventually screen the strip behind it. This technique permits the forester to harvest the allowable cut by using the best known silvicultural practice while protecting the esthetic value of the landscape.

Irregular openings formed by natural causes are considered to be desirable in providing variety to the landscape scene. [15] The terms "block selection" or "clear-cutting in blocks" denotes the forester's organized thinking. Uniform blocks are

296

easy to fit into cutting cycles and they produce the minimum amount of edge-effect, or degrade, on the neighboring hardwood trees. Irregular shaping of the clear-cut areas may help to make their appearance less objectionable.[8] They could take on shapes of burns, meadows, or slides rather than man-created blocks. This technique may be more readily adaptable in coniferous or low quality oak stands where degrading of the edge trees is not a serious problem.

SCREENING PROVIDED BY TOPOGRAPHY

SCREENING PROVIDED BY TIMBER

FIG. 14.2. Possible screening methods for use in blocking the view of clear-cut areas.

VISTAS. Driving for pleasure is the most popular form of outdoor recreation.[9] Probably it is not the driving itself that is enjoyed, but rather it is the scenery. To increase the enjoyment of the sightseer, the forester can plan vista cuttings at the places where a view is rewarding. Panoramic views, bodies of water, and agricultural patterns are favorites of the sightseers. Vista cuttings open up the world of the traveler so that he can see something besides tree trunks just outside of the window. Besides providing places for the traveler to stop and admire the scenery, the forester has harvested the timber from another clear-cut area. More cleanup of debris will be needed here than in the backwoods; however, this is a small price to pay for increasing the recreation quality of a site at the same time as the timber is harvested along the road edge.

ROADSIDE TREATMENT. Long expanses of forest-lined roads present monotonous corridors to the traveler. Instead of preserving the roadside vegetation, the silviculturist should employ techniques to utilize it and to improve the recreation scenery. Small areas can be cut at uneven intervals along the edge of the road. These open areas provide variety and contrast for the motorist. Also, they break up the straight edges of the right-of-way and give it an irregular appearance which fits into the landscape better. The reproduction on these road-edge cutting spots forms a needed transition zone between the road edge and the forest. The objective of this technique is to harvest the timber over a several years period while establishing an irregular edge effect along the road edge.

Road-edge transition. An abrupt change from open road to tall forests is considered to be less desirable than a gradual change in vegetation size and composition.[8] To obtain this transition zone, the forester should leave groups of trees, clumps of shrubbery, and ground cover to obtain the transition zone. The objective of the transition zone is to lead the viewers' sight from the road edge to the complete scene. Transition zones can be used to lead up to a view of a roadside lake, marsh, or vista. The transition zone is the ideal place to work at that extra touch of beauty by encouraging understory trees and shrubs that have showy flowers, attractive fruit, or bright fall colors. Efforts can be made to protect such species as service berry (*Amelanchier arborea*) or flowering dogwood (*Cornus florida*) when the logging is taking place.

FIG. 14.3. The seeding of grasses and legumes on abandoned logging roads stabilizes the soil and provides food for wildlife.

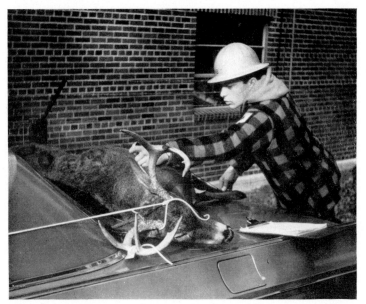

FIG. 14.4. In 1965, more than 68 million Americans engaged in hunting or sport fishing. Techniques that favor these important activities should be included in extensive forest recreation management programs.

Quite often, the trees that are of little value to the timber-man are of the greatest value to the sightseer. Acre upon acre of thrifty Douglas fir represent many important things to the trained forester; however, they are just another mountainside full of trees just like many other trees to the tourist. On the other hand, that silviculturist's nightmare of a misshapen, broken-topped, and scarred sugar pine next to the road might well be the epitome of the forest sentinels to the vacationer. Therefore, trees with unusual character should be left along roads and in recreation areas if they are sound and do not interfere with normal operations.

Open woods. Thick stands of merchantable timber often become a barrier to recreation. They are difficult to move around in and even more difficult to see into. People want to look into the forest and not at the edge of it. Around recreation areas and along roads the forest can be opened up by thinning from below or a careful selection of dominate or codominate trees. This appears to be a cross between even-age management's use of intermediate cuts and uneven-age management's use of the selective cutting system. Be that as it may, the dense stands of merchantable timber would be more appealing to the recreationist if they were thinned.

Silvicultural Techniques Favoring Fishing, Hunting, and Hiking

Streams that provide fishing for sport should be protected in every way possible by the forester. In the East, no clear-cutting should be permitted within 100 feet of a trout stream. This is to protect the stream from exposure to the heat of the sun as well as to keep logging debris and erosion from damaging the stream. The unevenage selection system should be employed along streams wherever possible. If the area in question does not lend itself to being logged by the selective logging system, it might be better left alone rather than to risk the destruction of trout fishing waters.

Research has shown that large expanses of merchantable timber are not compatible with the production of wildlife.[12]

299

Management of Forest Recreation Areas

Game animals require open areas or the edge of open areas to reproduce and rear their young or to obtain browse. The mature forest does not provide the browse required by the white-tailed deer nor the opening needed for ruffed-grouse nesting. If wildlife is to be a product of the forest, the land manager must take steps to assure that the proper environment exists for the game animals to carry out their life cycle. Turkey or squirrel will be content in the more open mature timber and black bear prefer some marshy areas for food in the spring. The land manager would do well to seek advice from a wildlife biologist prior to embarking on an extensive cutting program. A little advice from a competent wildlife expert who is familiar with local problems might greatly enhance the chances for a satisfactory wildlife population.

The logging operations create forest roads that can serve as access routes for hunters and fisherman. When timber value will permit, the roads should be built to a high enough standard to permit their being maintained as permanent roads. The construction costs of a permanent road are higher than they are for a temporary one; however, a permanent road will open an area up for returning timber operations. The roads can serve to disperse the hunters and the fishermen and thereby assist in obtaining a larger and more uniform harvest of game.

Temporary roads should be closed to vehicular traffic and protected against erosion when the logging operation is completed. Water bars should be used to drain off surface water onto the forest floor where it can infiltrate into the soil. The roadbeds can be planted with grasses or legumes that will serve as game food while they are protecting the soil from erosion. These seeded roads can be incorporated with boundary line clearings and firebreaks to form a hiking trail network. This trail network would be available for access in case of forest fires.

The land manager or forester can take some positive steps to obtain a suitable environment for game species. The even-age philosophy of timber management calls for clear-cutting of areas. This is compatable with wildlife populations for three

300

reasons. First, clear-cut areas provide browse for food and brush for cover. Second, the clear-cut area can provide the open areas that appear to be necessary for some wildlife species. Third, the valuable "edge effect" is created around the perimeter of the clear-cut block. The edge effect is described as the change in size and type of vegetation that takes place along dividing lins between open and timbered areas. Much of the wildlife can be found in this edge effect zone.

Size of the clear-cut area is the factor that limits the compatability of even-age management with wildlife management. Since wildlife prefer the edge effect, animals can make only limited use of huge clear-cuts. In most of the country, the topography and the seed source favor cutting in smaller blocks. Extensive areas of cut over land remind the general public of an unsightly era that it hopes is past. Many small areas of 4 or 5 acres can be cut over a period of many years in order to provide more benefit to the wildlife while lessening the impact upon esthetics. The irregular borders that were suggested previously would aid in producing more edge effect per clear-cut acre.

Efforts can be made to get the utility companies to improve the already beneficial edge effect along their rights-of-way. This can be done by selective herbicide application instead of broadcast spraying. A U-shaped cross-section with a central low point planted in a strip of legumes or grasses will give the greatest possible benefit to wildlife. Selective use of herbicides and seeding will cost the utility companies more than the standard broadcast treatment; therefore, cooperative agreements between landowners or government wildlife agencies and the utility companies will be needed to develop the high potential rights-of-way for their maximum benefit to wildlife.

Variety in cover types is needed to produce the best crop of game animals. Open areas are necessary for game animals to build nests, rear young, browse, graze, or just recreate in a different environment. For whatever reasons, the small clearing has proved its value in game management. Some governmental agencies have begun programs of game management that include the construction and maintenance of clusters of small agricultural plots within the forest. Small areas are scraped clean of vegetation which is roughly piled at the clearing edge. The plot soil is then physically and chemically prepared for agricultural crops. Generally, legumes are planted in the area for food and pines are planted around the edge to provide cover. These plots are very expensive to construct and to maintain; however, they are apparently successful in aiding wildlife production in areas of merchantable timber. Some of the costs to private landowners can be recouped or even avoided by leasing hunting privileges to sports clubs. In some cases, the clubs will carry out habitat improvement projects as part of a club project to improve its own hunting. Persons leasing forest land for hunting tend to become acutely aware of the dangers that threaten their hunting rights. Therefore, the clubs might undertake protective measures to safeguard their privileges. These protective and improvement efforts, if properly channeled and supervised, can provide an added bonus to the landowner.

Although wild game cannot be sold, the privilege of using the land can. Many hunters have shown willingness to pay for the privileges of hunting or camping on large tracts of private land. In some areas, the deer population can become so high that it becomes a threat to continued forest management by destroying tree reproduction. In this situation, the manager must take steps to protect the forest from an excessively large deer herd. He should take the steps necessary to encourage deer hunters to use his land and harvest the deer crop. This can be done by making the public aware of the open hunting area, by constructing and maintaining trails that permit hunters access to large blocks of timber, and by providing some services to aid the hunter.

References

1. Cliff, E. P. 1965. The Role of the Forest Service in Outdoor Recreation. *Proceedings of Society of American Foresters*, Annual Meeting. Detroit, Michigan.

2. FRISSELL, S. and DUNCAN, D. 1965. Campsite Preference and Deterioration in the Quetico—Superior Canoe Country. *Journal of Forestry*, vol.63, No. 4, pp.256–60.

3. HOPKINS, W.S. 1965. Outdoor Recreation on Small Woodlands. *Proceedings of 62nd Annual Meeting of the Association of Southern Agricultural Workers*. Dallas, Texas.

4. HUTCHISON, S.B. 1962. *Recreation Opportunities and Problems in the National Forests of the Intermountain Region*. Intermountain Forest and Range Experiment Station Research Paper No. 66. Ogden, Utah.

5. MACKIE, D.J. 1965. Site Planning to Reduce Deterioration. *Proceedings of Society of American Foresters*, Annual Meeting. Detroit, Michigan.

6. MARQUIS, R.W. 1965. *Report of Northeastern Forest Experiment Station, 1965*. U.S. Forest Service, Department of Agriculture, Upper Darby, Pennsylvania.

7. MCINTYRE, A.C. 1959. *Wood Chips for the Land*. Soil Conservation Service Leaflet No. 323. U.S. Department of Agriculture, Washington, D.C.

8. NEFF, P.E. 1965. Applied Silviculture in Managing Outdoor Recreation Sites. *Proceedings of the Society of American Foresters*, Annual Meeting. Detroit, Michigan.

9. OUTDOOR RECREATION RESOURCES REVIEW COMMISSION. 1962. *Outdoor Recreation for America*. Superintendent of Documents, Government Printing Office. 246 pages.

10. RIPLEY, T.H. 1962. *Tree and Shrub Response to Recreation Use*. Research Note 171. Southeastern Forest Experiment Station. U.S. Forest Service, Asheville, North Carolina.

11. RIPLEY, T.H. 1965. Rehabilitation of Forest Recreation Sites. *Proceedings of the Society of American Foresters*, Annual Meeting. Detroit, Michigan.

12. SHARP, W.M. 1957. *Management of a Poletimber Forest for Wildlife Food and Cover*. Agricultural Experiment Station. The Pennsylvania State University, University Park, Pennsylvania.

13. U.S. FOREST SERVICE. 1961. *Handbook on Soils*. Title 2512.5. Category 2, Handbook. U.S. Department of Agriculture, Washington, D.C.

14. U.S. FOREST SERVICE. 1963. *Recreation Management*, Handbook Title 2300. U.S. Department of Agriculture, Washington, D.C.

15. U.S. FOREST SERVICE. 1965. *The American Outdoors. Management for Beauty and Use*. U.S. Forest Service Miscellaneous Publication No. 1000. U.S. Department of Agriculture, Washington, D.C.

16. WAGAR, J.A. 1965. Cultural Treatment of Vegetation on Recreation Sites. *Proceedings of Society of American Foresters*, Annual Meeting. Detroit, Michigan.

CHAPTER 15

Operation of Developed Recreation Areas

INTRODUCTION

Operation consists of the actions and techniques employed to run the recreation area on a day-to-day basis. The actual operation of a recreation area is the heart of administration. Fee collections, user counts, signs, insurance, publicity, maintenance, and public relations are the most important parts of operation. Internal administration and business operations are not included in this book because they are governed by general principles covered in the field of business administration.

FEE COLLECTIONS

The general public is willing to pay for the use of developed recreation facilities as is witnessed by the proliferation of private enterprise establishments in this field. Private recreation areas must have efficient methods of fee collection in order to survive as a business. Public recreation areas have been open to the public without admission fees because they have been tax supported; however, this has changed in recent years. As the public demanded more elaborate facilities and as recreation management became more positive in its approach, costs rose sharply. These changes brought about a change in thinking. Now, there is a widespread belief that the cost of running tax supported recreation areas should be supplemented by those users who want the more elaborate facilities. That is, those who derive the most direct benefit from the facilities should pay the larger share. Some sound arguments against fee charging at public areas can be made; however, they are out of step with public opinion. Users have accepted the premise that they should pay a fee for the use of public facilities. The Federal Land and Water Conservation Fund Act of 1965 requires the charging of fees at certain recreation facilities.

Fees are normally charged at such developments as campgrounds, picnic areas, swimming beaches, and boating ramps. Collection usually is made manually by an attendant or mechanically by a self-service device. The manual method of collection is the most popular although not necessarily the best.

Manual Collection

The manual method has been used successfully for many years. In large areas, an attendant is usually stationed at the entrance point where he collects fees and disburses the receipts. The attendant's time would be wasted at a small recreation area if he just stood around awaiting paying customers; therefore, small picnic and camping areas often require a less formal technique of fee collection. The attendant can make regularly scheduled rounds in between other duties in order to collect the fees.

Approximately half of the attendant's fee collection time is spent in giving information to the users.[9] At large public campgrounds, the gate attendant is probably as important for the public relations value as for the fee collection receipts. Also, his presence at the gate helps to exclude intruders.

Mechanical Collection

Mechanical methods of fee collection are necessary to reduce fee collection costs. These devices must be economical to operate, reliable, and simple to operate. The two common machines used are the coin-operated gate and the automatic ticket vending machine.

COIN-OPERATED GATES. In a research study, the U.S.

305

Forest Service found that coin-operated gates were satisfactory in certain types of areas.[9] These gates are electrically powered barriers that are similar to railroad crossing barriers. They raise up and allow a two-axle vehicle to pass when a certain combination of coins is deposited in the receiving slot. Some problems of equipment maintenance arise; however, the gates generally are successful when properly installed at suitable areas.

The gates are adaptable to areas of day-use sites such as beaches and picnicgrounds but are not satisfactory in areas where the user wants to leave and return to the site. The collection costs are low and refunds are unnecessary; however, the initial costs are high in that each machine that is installed represents an investment of approximately 4000 dollars.[9] The major drawbacks to the use of coin-operated gates are the high purchase and installation costs and the need for electrical power.

TICKET VENDING MACHINES. Machines that dispense tickets when a certain amount of money is deposited provide a good mechanical method of collecting fees at recreation areas where developed sites are used. The common forms of outdoor recreation involving developed sites where ticket vending machines are used are camping, boating, and picnicking. Two types of ticket vending machines are available. The rotary type machine uses a continuous roll to supply tickets in much the same way as would a movie theater box office or "merry-go-round" ticket window. The rotary ticket vending machine's cost runs approximately 300 dollars for each installed unit. The non-rotary dispensers pay out tickets from a stack. This type of dispenser is more likely to make an error than the rotary type because it can discharge more than one ticket with one coin operation.

Since many people will arrive at a campground without the proper change to operate the vending machine, procedures must be established to permit users to proceed to the site and pay later. Usually, the attendant calls on the sites not displaying paid up tickets at some prearranged time. Some campgrounds use a card system where the user signs his name on a printed card requesting the attendant to stop at the unit for payment.

The ticket vending machines offer the least expensive way to collect user fees and they can be used at isolated or small campgrounds where the use does not warrant an attendant. One of the two major disadvantages stems from the need to provide change. This is especially true during periods of coin shortages when half dollar coins become scarce. The other disadvantage is a result the inconvenience caused to the user by not being able to pay in advance. Since the tickets dispensed are dated, they can be valid only for the day showing on the ticket. Therefore, a camper must be present each day to deposit his coins and receive a valid ticket for the coming evening.

Ticket Display Post

Regardless of whether the fee was collected by manual or mechanical means, a receipt of payment must be displayed at the camping or picnicking unit to indicate that the fee has been paid. This is especially true in campgrounds where people can stay beyond the prepaid period. Boating and other day-use areas can require that the tickets be displayed on a window of the car; however, this method does not work in campgrounds because users often drive the vehicle away for off-site trips. The receipts should have large printed numbers representing the date or else a felt tipped marker should be used to make the numbers visible from 10 or 15 feet away. The display system at each unit consists of a 3-foot tall post with some device on it to hold the ticket. Slotted metal holders, snap paper clips, or glass front display boxes are generally fastened to the post in such a way as to hold and display the ticket. The display post should be at the road edge of the camping or picnicking unit but in the back of a protective barrier. The ticket should be plainly visible to a person riding along the road. This enables an attendant to make an easy check of all the sites without getting out of his vehicle.

307

USER COUNTS

The recreation area manager needs to know how many people are using the developed facilities under his care. He is primarily interested in obtaining figures on man-hours of use, visitor numbers, and peakload use to aid him in making administration and management decisions.[4] Man-hours of use indicate the amount of wear the site is receiving. From this information the supervisor can predict depreciation rates of the facilities, establish maintenance schedules, and program the trash collection and the clean-up operations. The visitor-numbers give an indication of the total number of people who have been to the area. This reflects the number of impressions gained of the recreation development and indicates the need and the required scheduling of visitor information services.[5] Peakload data provide the basis for identifying use-trends and for planning overflow areas.

The use will be known in areas where fees are charged for a specific activity and adequate records are maintained. However, attendance at free admission or multi-opportunity recreation developments must be estimated by some technique other than actual count. The attendants at recreation areas usually have other things to do besides count users if they are in the area at all. Therefore, accurate and daily counts would require the cost of hiring additional people to stand around and count the users of various activities.

Obviously, a continuous count is uneconomical and some method of estimating the use must be employed. Three basic methods of estimating the use at recreation areas are (a) the ranger estimate, (b) the periodic attendant count, and (c) the traffic count.

Ranger Estimate

The "ranger estimate" technique of estimating use is probably the most used and the least accurate of the three choices. It consists of guesses by the recreation area supervisors as to the

308

number of users by type of activity. The ranger estimate method does have some value in that it does give a relative expression of use when compared to previous days. However, this is a weak assumption even when the estimates have been made by the same person for the same area.

Why, then, is such an inaccurate method as the ranger estimate still relied upon so often? The answer to this question probably has three parts. First, it is easy. Second, it is uncomplicated by statistics. Third, because of reason one and two, it is inexpensive to produce. Any other technique of estimating user numbers will require planning, records, and funds. In some cases, the ranger estimate has been satisfactory simply because nothing more has been needed. Other times, other available techniques do not lend themselves to the situation. On a few occasions, the ranger estimate provides some quick figures to fit into the monthly report before that report is hustled off to the next higher administrative level.

Periodic Attendant Counts

Periodic counts of users by attendants are sometimes used to get estimates of use. An attendant visits the area every day at a given time to count the participants in each activity. Research has shown that the periodic attendant counts are most accurate when they are made at twelve o'clock noon for most types of areas. [5] Although this technique is more reliable than the ranger estimate, it is significantly less accurate than the traffic counter technique.

Traffic Counter Estimate

The most reliable technique for estimating visitor numbers, man-hours of use, and peakloads is by counting the entering vehicles and equating that figure with use. Obviously, this means more than just counting the cars. Unfortunately, simple car counting is often done under the guise of traffic counter estimates; however, the only reliable information obtained that way is the number of axles that passed over the counter. Some technique of correlating entering vehicles to amounts and type of use must be worked out before traffic counting has any real value.

Ripley and Jones have devised a technique for estimating recreation visits and use by combining traffic counters and basic statistics. This technique uses a double sampling method that correlates the use of the recreation area on sample days to the traffic count for the same day. A ratio is developed between the actual use of the facilities and the traffic count. The ratio that is developed from the data gathered on the sample days is used along with daily traffic counts to estimate use for the other days. Once the ratio has been established, it will remain the same as long as the sites remain the same and no large change in fixed variables takes place. The traffic count is all that will be needed to estimate the use.

Detailed, step-by-step instructions for using the double sampling technique can be found in the U.S. Forest Service Research Paper SE-3 entitled *Instructions for Using Traffic Counters to Estimate Recreation Visits and Use.*[4]

SIGNS

The use of signs in forest recreation is a major form of communication. Signs are used to give directions, state regulations, identify areas, give warnings, and supply interpretive information. The purpose of signs is to inform the user. They are permanently implaced to give a message to the user at any season of the year or time of the day. Generally, signs can be classed as being either administrative, directional, restrictive, or interpretive.

Administrative Signs

Administrative signs identify boundaries, offices, and field headquarters. The signs identifying boundaries should be durable, easily seen, and small enough to be transported on foot.

Because of the need for a large number of boundary signs, the small size will help to keep the total costs down. Yellow, blue, or red make good background colors for boundary line signs as well as for the tree blazes along the boundary line. Office and headquarter signs should be large enough to be seen and read from a suitable distance to identify the buildings to visitors.

Directional Signs

Directional signs guide visitors to their destination whether it is within or outside of the recreation area. People in the outdoor environment are dependent upon signs to find things ranging from large parks to drinking fountains. Generally, internal direction signs are designed to be read by pedestrians while external directions are meant for motorists. There are exceptions to that generalization when the visitors drive around the interior areas or engage in extensive forms of recreation on foot or by other methods of travel.

INTERNAL DIRECTION SIGNS. The internal direction signs are the most important type of sign used. They aid the visitor in finding his way around the area. One of the most frustrating experiences for a camper is to arrive at a campground and have to drive all around the one way loop roads in order to locate the camping unit that best meets his needs and then find out that it was taken while he was driving on through the rest of the area. Strangers may not know where the water supply is located and must ask other visitors when signs are not available or else wander around looking for it and other utilities.

Utility signs. The utility signs are used to point the way to drinking water, toilets, boat landings, beaches, and other facilities. These signs should be as small as possible and should conform to the motif of the area. One or two words printed in 2-inch high letters accompanied by simple arrowheads will usually suffice for utility signs. They should be placed as low as possible without reducing their effectiveness. Certain situations force a change in this standard. Some trail signs on the Monongahela National Forest had to be raised 7-feet high on metal posts because the black bears like to chew on them.

Orientation signs. Orientation signs showing a diagrammatic sketch of the area and pointing out the readers location are very important in both intensive and extensive recreation. These signs are well received by the public and are often photographed; therefore, they should be shaded from direct sunlight but easy to photograph. Figure 15.1 shows an automobile forest tour on the Nicolet National Forest. This sort of tour should be accompanied by a handout that can be taken along on the trip. Figure 15.2 shows an orientation sign that greets campers as they enter the unattended Lac Vieux Desert campground on the Nicolet National Forest. The orientation signs brightly colored and shows the campground layout, the swimming beach, the boat landing, and other facilities located in the campground.

EXTERNAL DIRECTION SIGNS. External direction signs are needed to guide visitors into the forest recreation areas from the major highways and roads. Destination signs give the motorist an idea of the distance to his destination as he drives to a forest recreation area. Approach signs alert the driver that he is about to arrive at the turn off to his destination which is marked by an entrance sign.

Approach signs should be easily read from within the moving vehicle. The wording should be brief and in large letters on a neutral background. The distance between the approach sign and the entrance will depend upon the type of highway involved. High-speed roads will require more distance between the approach sign and the entrance sign than rural roads will require. Rougher forest roads will keep the vehicular speed low enough in some cases to eliminate the need for any approach sign. If no turn off is required, no approach sign is necessary. Entrance signs to scenic areas, public and private forests, or parks can be placed next to highways that enter them. Recreationists, as do most other people, enjoy knowing where they are; therefore, entrance signs serve the dual purposes of directing area users as well as informing passers-by of their location.

Fig. 15.2. A vacation bound family, with house trailer, stop at Camper Registration Board at entrance of June Lake public campground, Inyo National Forest, California. Here, on a diagram of the area, they can readily see which camp spaces are already occupied, and which remain available. They have found a vacant site, and will insert their own registration card, which they will remove and drop in a box on their departure. (U.S. Forest Service.)

OCONTO RIVER

Forest
Tour

ANTIGO
26 MILES

LAKEWOOD 10 MILES

AUTO
TOUR
BEGINS

AUTO
TOUR
ENDS

64

MOUNTAIN LAKES

LARGE
BOULDER

RIVER

NATURAL
RED
PINE

WILDLIFE OPENING

350 ACRES
BEAR TRAIL FIRE
5. 30. 61

SPRUCE SEED

X WHERE
FIRE STARTED

NATIONAL FORESTS · Land of many uses

Fig. 15.1. Orientation sign that shows an automobile tour of the Oconto River area of the Nicolet National Forest.

Fig. 15.4. "I Was There" is a feeling that results from the first person historical approach in interpretive signs. (U.S. Forest Service.)

Restrictive Signs

Signs are needed to post regulations, to remind people of their responsibilities, and to control visitor movements in certain situations. These signs bear messages that restrict the activities of the user to various degrees. They must be placed in a prominent place and be made so that they are easily read.

Fig. 15.3. Restrictive signs are sometimes used to cover up planning mistakes or administrative laziness.

Most forest recreationists realize the need for certain restrictions on activities within recreation areas just as there are restrictions in the general society. Administrators must be careful that they do not make up restrictive signs just be-

313

cause it seems like a good thing to do. Many restrictions that are posted around parks are just reutterances of public law. Rules that echo common legal statutes just waste space. Regulations concerning immoral conduct or stealing are favorite ones of administrators who like to make up regulations. Visitors pay very little attention to the rest of the lists of rules and regulations when they read such reutterance of public law.

Restrictive signs must be prominently placed to be effective; however, they should not overpower the entering visitor. Their message must be clear and unambiguous; however, the wording should be suggestive and the thought positive. A big sign with a long list of "Nos" might be effective, but it greatly lessens the enjoyment of the visitor. Also, it immediately sets up two warring camps. Negative signs pit the user against the manager. Granted, in some areas, strong negative action is necessary; however, the positive approach should be taken first. Figure 15.3 depicts the situation as the visitor sees it when restrictive signs take the place of proper planning.

Interpretive Signs

Signs that tell a story about the area in view are becoming very popular with the public. These signs interpret the view and highlight the outstanding attractions or they briefly tell the history of the area. Interpretive signs enrich the visitor's forest experience by adding a natural or historical interest to just where trees and landforms previously existed. Interpretive signs are recommended for such places as vistas, roadside rests, information sites, and certain forest trails. [11]

Interpretive signs should be eye appealing without distracting attention from the view. This means that they should not overpower the view with size or overshadow it with extensive use of vivid colors. Some art work and colors will help to gain and to hold interest; however, too much of these will make the sign of greater interest than the scene. Figure 15.4 gives an example of the first person historical approach by making the reader feel that he was there.

Design of Signs

All signs that are needed for one area should be designed at the same time so as to prevent duplication, conflict, and omissions. [11] The sign should fit into its environment; therefore, its site should be known before the sign is designed. It should never be so large as to be obtrusive in that its size should be determined upon its location and the distance from which it will be read. A sign does not need to be large to serve its purpose; however, small signs must be more carefully placed than large ones to be effective.

The sign serves as a frame and background for the text. Its shape should not be novel enough to go out of date or to draw too much attention to the sign at the expense of the view or the text. Wood is the generally used material for sign construction because it is strong, easily worked, and very durable when properly treated. Wood signs also fit into the environment better than do signs of other materials. All signs serving the same function should have the same shape and the same approximate size. That is, the signs along a self-guiding nature trail should be identical except for the text and illustrations. Similar signs make their identification easier.

A well designed sign has an emotional appeal, a pleasing appearance, dignity, and a purpose. [11] The signs should reflect care and talent in manufacture as well as professional skills in the composition of the text. Cheap or carelessly constructed signs will indicate that the signs are not worth reading or even taking care of. Since people want to gather information from qualified experts, they will expect to find the text presented in a professional manner. To the reader, this means that the signs have been prepared with professional care and that they contain information worth knowing. [10]

Bright colors have a place on signs as part of small illustrations but not as background for the text. The background should be a neutral shade so as to focus attention on the text. Color contrasts play an important role in making the signs legible. Usually, the letters are routed into the wood and painted white. When the signs serve a purpose at night as do

315

utility signs, the letters should be painted with a white or silver reflective paint. [12]

Text

The text is the reason for the sign's existence. [11] Any other part of the sign or the landscaping should be so designed as to make the text more effective. When composing the text, the author must make it readable, accurate, and brief. The text of interpretive signs should develop only one subject for each sign and the subjects on a directional sign should not exceed five in number. [11] Table 15.1 presents eight guides for making signs easy to read.

TABLE 15.1

GUIDES FOR MAKING SIGNS EASIER TO READ[a]

1. Do not capitalize the entire text.
2. Do not crowd the text with inadequate margins.
3. Do not set the text in a solid block form.
4. Use upper and lower case letters to make sentences and proper names more distinct.
5. Leave extra space between paragraphs.
6. Keep regular spacing between words in a sentence.
7. Spacing of words should be adequate.
8. Leave an extra space at the end of a sentence.

[a] USFS Publication No. 968.

Maintenance of Signs

Signs should be kept in good repair at all times. If the sign has served its purpose and is no longer needed, it should be removed. Damaged signs should be repaired or replaced as soon as possible. If repairs can not be made in a short period of time and no replacement signs are available, it might be better to simply remove the damaged sign than to leave it up. Common signs can be kept is stock for replacement.

Once signs begin to fall into desrepair, the public loses its respect for them. Many utility signs have ended up in fraternity houses, or similar places as souvenirs. Signs are favorite targets for misoriented marksmen. If the dangerous practice of sign shooting becomes epidemic, it makes signs impossible to keep maintained. Quick repair of the damage is probably the best defense against sign shooting in the long run.

LIABILITY INSURANCE

All recreation enterprises should be protected by liability insurance because the private operator assumes some responsibility for the welfare of his customers. He is obligated to pay for any act of negligence that results in an injury or damage. The problem of defining what constitutes negligence is difficult to answer and often must be settled in a court of law. Insurance coverage protects the operator in two ways. First, it puts the insurance company in the position of defending against the claim and saves the operator the costs of legal fees that would occur whether he won or lost the suit. Second and more obvious, the insurance company will pay the claim up to the limits of policy.

Persons should obtain professional advice from a competent insurance salesman and from a lawyer prior to opening a recreation area for profit to help assist him in determining the potential risks and liabilities. Some state laws require a minimum of 5000 dollars liability insurance for one individual claim.[3] This is a most unrealistic figure since 50,000 to 75,000 dollar awards are often allotted in death or disability claims involving liability.[13]

Liability insurance is important enough to be included as part of the operational expense budget. Many insurance companies have not had much experience with recreational enterprises and tend to charge excessive rates in order to be on the safe side.[2] By shopping around from one company to another, the operator will find that the cost of similar coverage varies widely. The Campground Association of Pennsylvania (CAP) cautions its members to be careful about which insurance category their establishment is placed into. Agents often try to place campgrounds into the 301, or general classification, category where premiums are relatively high. CAP recommends

317

that campground operators attempt to have their establishments placed in the mobile home category where premiums are lower.[7]

Many landowners have been afraid to open their land to extensive recreation pursuits such as hunting, fishing, or hiking because of the fear of their liability. Within the last couple of years, many states have enacted liability relief laws which limit the liability of landowners towards recreationists on his land. The liability relief laws have opened up many thousands of privately owned acres of forest and farm land for recreation. A suggested model draft of a liability limitation act was accepted and published by the 1965 Council of State Governments. This draft, "Public Recreation on Private Lands: Limitations on Liability", has been accepted by several states that did not have such legislation in their books.[1] Table 15.2 lists the states that had adopted liability relief laws by the end of 1965.[6]

TABLE 15.2

STATES HAVING LIABILITY RELIEF LAWS AT THE END OF 1965[a]

Arkansas	New Hampshire
California	New York
Florida	North Carolina
Georgia	North Dakota
Idaho	Ohio
Illinois	Oregon
Indiana	Pennsylvania
Louisiana	Tennessee
Maine	Utah
Michigan	Virginia
Missouri	West Virginia
Montana	Wisconsin
Nebraska	Wyoming
Nevada	

[a] Wildlife Management Institute.

These laws are based on the premise that the land owner who permits, without charge, a person to use his property for recreational purposes does not:

318

1. Extend any assurance that the premises are safe.
2. Confer the legal status of invitee upon the user.
3. Assume responsibility for any injury or loss of property caused by an act of the users.

Relief laws do not dismiss the landowner from liability for willful or malicious failure to protect the users from a dangerous situation.[14]

PUBLICITY

Private recreation areas are usually in business to make a profit and that profit depends largely upon the number of customers that the area attracts. Good facilities and locations are only part of the solution to getting users. The operator must advertise for customers to keep his area occupancy as high as possible. Some free publicity can be obtained in the local newspaper by newsreleases concerning happenings at the area.

Many sources of advertising are available. Choosing the best media for investing advertising dollars will be an important decision.

Industry-owned recreation developments are often considered as courtesies to the users and usually are not run at a profit. Publically administrated recreation developments are supplimented by tax funds. As a result, these recreation operators are not interested in gaining users and do not do any direct advertising. They are listed in campground guides when camping is offered and as such received widespread publicity. The U.S. Forest Service makes a conscious effort to avoid advertising. Forest Service destination signs list geographic points rather than developments to avoid giving direct publicity to concessions on its land.

Private enterprise must advertise to attract customers. Some of the most popular ways to advertise recreation areas are:

1. Local signs in stores and gas stations.
2. Recreation publication advertisements.
3. Distributing folders through users, mail, conventions, and organizations.

4. Membership in outdoor recreation organizations.
5. Roadside signs and bulletin boards.
6. Good public relations to get repeat customers or to spread the word to other users.

Information in the advertisement should include the facilities and the attraction of the development. The exact road directions should be given to guide the interested user to the area. Lists of nearby attractions, stores, restaurants, and entertainment activities are often included. The mailing address and telephone numbers should be given in every advertisement.

Maintenance

The maintenance or upkeep of the area and the facilities is one of the most important parts of recreation area operation. Because forest recreation consists mostly of seasonal activities, the workload of maintenance personnel must be adjusted to fit available time. Generally, a good supervisor will be able to program maintenance into two parts. The daily maintenance required to keep the recreation area operating properly during the use-season will keep the staff busy. All major repairs, construction, or rehabilitation projects should be scheduled for completion during the off-season.

By scheduling heavy maintenance during the off-season, the supervisor reduces the fluctuation in staff size between the use-season and the off-season. The staff engaged in use-season light maintenance, public relations, and traffic control can be employed at the heavy maintenance projects during the off-season when they are not needed to operate the recreation area. This use of the full time employees for operation of the park reduces the number of part time employees required.

Off-season projects do not interfere with the normal operation of the recreation area. Construction, earth moving, pipeline installation, and toilet improvements are examples of the projects that should be completed prior to the use-season. Besides physically interfering with the visitors, heavy maintenance projects create an esthetic nuisance within an area where users are searching for a picturesque forest environment.

The specific problems associated with light maintenance and the operation of forest recreation facilities are discussed within the appropriate chapters of this book that deal with each type of facility. One rule of maintenance that should not be overlooked is that dirty and run-down facilities will be treated poorly by the visitors. However, the public is inclined to cooperate in taking care of recreation facilities that it finds to be clean, well cared for, and in good repair.[8]

PUBLIC RELATIONS

Public relations are the activities undertaken to establish good rapport with a particular segment of the general population. In this case, public relations are undertaken to establish harmonious relations with the user group. The purpose of a recreation area is to provide user satisfaction. Even private enterprise recognizes that user satisfaction is necessary before the recreation area venture can become profitable.

Good public relations requires both active and passive efforts. Active public relations efforts include visitor contacts, information services, activity programs, guided tours, and other similar agressive actions by recreation personnel. Sufficient signs, proper design of area and facilities, adequate explanation of any necessary restrictions, cleanliness of the area, and appearance of personnel are some of the passive efforts in public relations that weigh heavily on the user's response to the recreation area.

Public relations consists of a two-way flow of benefits. The user benefits by having increased satisfaction in the recreation activity. Aside from the profit increases that the private operator is striving for, good public relations techniques provide the manager with information about the user which can be used to improve the recreation area. The visitor's likes and dislikes, his suggestions, his length of stay, and his reasons for visiting the recreation area will help the manager plan improvements and prepare plans to meet the public needs.

Supervisors, or their representatives, who must operate and maintain the recreation area need to ensure the proper use of the facilities and site. To do this, they frequently must enforce regulations concerning the use of the area. The use of tact in enforcing regulations can not be overemphasized. Enforcement of regulations can cause offense which is out of proportion with the regulation; therefore, every effort should be made to correct the violation without giving undue offense.

Unfortunately, it is in handling minor violations of regulations that many public servants prove inadequately orientated. Many state and local parks have so many regulations that the users are unnerved by the lists of negative expressions that greet their entry into the park. Gruff, unpleasant, or unexplained enforcement of every rule violation leaves the user disgruntled. Many public agencies have recognized the problems associated with proper methods of regulation enforcement and are taking steps to over come them. Patrolmen should be trained in the proper ways of approaching the user. Also, the new public employees must understand that they are being paid by the taxpayers and should treat them with respect.

The operation of recreation areas places personnel in close contact with the general public. Therefore, it is important that all employees be trained to meet the public in an acceptable manner. Anyone on the staff will be in the position of influencing the user's opinion of the recreation area. The wearing attire of the employees should be clean, neat, and in keeping with the work being performed.

REFERENCES

1. COUNCIL OF STATE GOVERNMENTS. 1965. Public Recreation on Private Lands: Limitations on Liability. *Suggested State Legislation*, vol XXVI, 1965. 1313 East 60th Street, Chicago, Illinois.
2. CRITES, R.S. 1965. *Handbook of Outdoor Recreation Enterprises in Rural Areas.* Farmers Home Administration. Government Printing Office, Washington, D.C. 122 pages.

3. HOLCOMB, CONKLIN and WINCH. 1963. *Opportunities for Private Campgrounds as an Alternate Use of Land.* Agriculture Extension Service Circular No. 792. Virginia Polytechnic Institute, Blacksburg, Virginia.

4. JAMES, G. and RIPLEY, T. 1963. *Instructions for Using Traffic Counters to Estimate Recreation Visits and Use.* USFS Research Paper SE-3. Southeastern Experiment Station Asheville, North Carolina.

5. OUTDOOR RECREATION RESOURCES REVIEW COMMISSION. 1962. *Sport Fishing–Today and Tomorrow.* Study Report No. 7. Superintendent of Documents. Government Printing Office, Washington, D.C. 130 pages.

6. POOLE, D. 1965. States Move on Relief Law. *Outdoor News Bulletin.* Wildlife Management Institute, 709 Wire Building, Washington, D.C.

7. SANDY, R. 1964. *Campground Owners Adopt Standards.* Campground Association of Pennsylvania Newsletter No. 6. Mercer, Pennsylvania.

8. U.S. FOREST SERVICE. 1963. *Recreation Management. Manual and Handbook* Title 2300. U.S. Department of Agriculture, Washington, D.C.

9. U.S. FOREST SERVICE. 1963. *Collecting User Fees on National Forest Recreation Sites.* Administrative Study, California Region, San Francisco, California.

10. U.S. FOREST SERVICE. 1964. *Developing the Self-guiding Trail in the National Forests.* Miscellaneous Publication No. 968. U.S. Department of Agriculture, Washington, D.C.

11. U.S. FOREST SERVICE. 1965. *The American Outdoors. Management for Beauty and Use.* Miscellaneous Publication No. 1000. U.S. Department of Agriculture, Washington, D.C.

12. U.S. FOREST SERVICE. 1966. *Sign Handbook. Forest Service Handbook,* Title 7161.4. U.S. Department of Agriculture, Washington, D.C.

13. WILLSEY, D. 1963. Outdoor Recreation Safety. *Guidelines for Developing Land for Outdoor Recreational Uses.* Cooperative Extension Services, Purdue University, W. Lafayette, Indiana.

14. WINGARD, R. and HEINEY, C. 1966. *Pond Construction and Management in Pennsylvania.* Extension Service Special Circular 78, Natural Resource Series. College of Agriculture. The Pennsylvania State University, University Park, Pennsylvania. 24 pages.

323

Appendix

A PARTIAL list of selected plants recommended for beauty, screens, windbreaks, erosion control, and wildlife food and cover as abstracted from the U.S. Forest Service Miscellaneous Publication No. 1000.

Common name	Scientific name	Hardiness zone
Trees with Attractive Flowers		
Northern catalpa	*Catalpa speciosa*	5
Southern catalpa	*Catalpa bignonioides*	5
Cherry	*Prunus* spp.	4
Crabapple	*Malus* spp.	4
Flowering dogwood	*Cornus florida*	5
Pacific dogwood	*Cornus nuttallii*	7
Fringetree	*Chionanthus virginicus*	6
Hawthorn	*Crataegus* spp.	4–5
Black locust	*Robinia pseudoacacia*	5
Southern magnolia	*Magnolia grandiflora*	7
Red maple	*Acer rubrum*	5
Yellow-poplar	*Liriodendron tulipifera*	4
Redbud	*Cercis* spp.	5
Mountain silverbell	*Halesia monticole*	5
Bigleaf snowbell	*Styrax grandifolia*	7
Sourwood	*Oxydendron arboreum*	5
Yellowwood	*Cladrastis lutea*	3
Trees with Striking Fall Coloring		
Birches	*Betula* spp.	2
Blackgum (tupelo)	*Nyssa sylvatica*	5
Flowering dogwood	*Cornus florida*	5
Pacific dogwood	*Cornus nuttallii*	8
Hickories	*Carya* spp.	5
Maples (most species)	*Acer* spp.	5

Common name	Scientific name	Hardiness zone
Black oak	*Quercus velutina*	5
Pin oak	*Quercus palustris*	5
Red oak	*Quercus rubra*	5
Scarlet oak	*Quercus coccinea*	5
White oak	*Quercus alba*	5
Sassafras	*Sassafras albidum*	5
Sweetgum	*Liquidambar styraciflua*	5

Ornamental Shrubs

Apache-plume	*Fallugia paradoxa*	5
Azaleas	*Rhododendron* spp.	3
Carpenteria	*Carpenteria californica*	8
Ceanothuses	*Ceanothus* spp.	8
Cherries, chokecherries, plums	*Prunus* spp.	2
Elders, elderberries	*Sambucus* spp.	3
Fremontias	*Fremontodendron* spp.	8
Fringetree	*Chionanthus virginicus*	4
Hawthorns	*Crataegus* spp.	4
Hollies	*Ilex* spp.	3
Hydrangeas	*Hydrangea* spp.	4
Locusts	*Robinia* spp.	3
Mescalbean	*Sophora secundiflora*	7
Mockoranges	*Philadelphus* spp.	4
Mountain-ashes	*Sorbus* spp.	2
Mountain-laurel	*Kalmia latifolia*	4
Oregon-grapes, mahonias	*Mahonia* spp.	5
Rhododendrons	*Rhododendron* spp.	3
Wild roses	*Rosa* spp.	3
Salal	*Gaultheria shallon*	5
Stewartias	*Stewartia* spp.	5
Sumacs	*Rhus* spp.	2
Viburnums	*Viburnum* spp.	2
Yellow-trumpet	*Tecoma stans*	8
Yuccas	*Yucca* spp.	4

Evergreen Trees for Screens

Atlantic white-cedar	*Chamaecyparis thyoides*	5
Incense-cedar	*Libocedrus decurrens*	5
Northern white-cedar	*Thuja occidentalis*	3

Appendix

Common name	Scientific name	Hardiness zone
Port-Orford-cedar	*Chamaecyparis lawsoniana*	5
Arizona cypress	*Cupressus arizonica*	7
Douglas-fir	*Pseudotsuga menziesii*	6–8
Eastern hemlock	*Tsuga canadensis*	4
Western hemlock	*Tsuga heterophylla*	5–8
American holly	*Illex opaca*	6
Eastern white pine	*Pinus strobus*	4
Ponderosa pine	*Pinus ponderosa*	4–8
Red pine	*Pinus resinosa*	4
Spruce pine	*Pinus glabra*	8
Sugar pine	*Pinus lambertiana*	6
Western white pine	*Pinus monticola*	5
Eastern redcedar	*Juniperus virginiana*	2
Western redcedar	*Thuja plicata*	5
Blue spruce	*Picea pungens*	3
White spruce	*Picea glauca*	2

Tall Shrubs for Screens and Windbreaks

Silver buffaloberry	*Shepherdia argentea*	2
Cherries, chokecherries, plums	*Prunus* spp.	2
Hawthorns	*Crataegus* spp.	2
Junipers	*Juniperus* spp.	4
Osage-orange	*Maclura pomifera*	5
Serviceberries	*Amelanchier* spp.	4
Sumacs	*Rhus* spp.	2
Viburnums	*Viburnum* spp.	2

Shrubs for Hedges

Hawthorns	*Crataegus* spp.	4
Hollies	*Ilex* spp.	3
Osage-orange	*Maclura pomifera*	5
Wild roses	*Rosa* spp.	3
Viburnums	*Viburnum* spp.	2

Shrubs for Erosion Control

Ceanothuses	*Ceanothus* spp.	8
Cherries, chokecherries, plums	*Prunus* spp.	2
Wild roses	*Rosa* ssp.	5
Sagebrush	*Artemisia* spp.	3

Common name	Scientific name	Hardiness zone
Snowberries, coralberries	*Symphoricarpos* spp.	2
Sumacs	*Rhus* spp.	2
Willows	*Salix* spp.	2
Yuccas	*Yucca* spp.	4

Shrubs for Ground Cover

Bearberry	*Arctostaphylos uva-ursi*	2
Bunchberry	*Cornus canadensis*	2
Creeping juniper	*Juniperus horizontalis*	2
Oregon-grape, mahonias	*Mahonia* spp.	5

Woody Vines for Screens, Banks, and Ground Cover

American or climbing bitter-sweet	*Celastrus scandens*	2
Virginia creeper	*Parthenocissus quinquefolia*	3
Crossvine	*Bignonia capreolata*	6
Wild grapes	*Vitis* spp.	2
Greenbriers	*Smilax* spp.	4
Yellow or Caroline jessamine	*Gelsemium sempervirens*	7
Common trumpet-creeper or trumpetvine	*Campsis radicans*	4

Shrubs for Wildlife Food and Cover

Crab apples	*Malus* spp.	2
Bayberries, waxmyrtles	*Myrica* spp.	2
Blueberries	*Vaccinium* spp.	2
Cherries, chokecherries, plums	*Prunus* spp.	2
Dogwoods	*Cornus* spp.	2
Elders, elderberries	*Sambucus* spp.	3
Hawthorns	*Crataegus* spp.	4
Hollies	*Ilex* spp.	3
Manzanitas	*Arctostaphylos* spp.	7
Mountain-ashes	*Sorbus* spp.	2
Wild roses	*Rosa* spp.	3
Snowberries, coralberries	*Symphoricarpos* spp.	2
Sumacs	*Rhus* spp.	2
Viburnums	*Viburnum* spp.	2

Appendix

Common name	Scientific name	Hardiness zone
Woody Vines for Wildlife Food and Cover		
Blackberries	*Rubus* spp.	3
Virginia creeper	*Parthenocissus quinquefolia*	3
Wild grapes	*Vitis* spp.	2

THE ZONES OF PLANT HARDINESS

The Plant Hardiness Zone represents the coldest zone in which a particular species might survive freezing weather. The species would be expected to be hardy in warmer (or higher numbered) zones. Other factors, such as precipitation and kind of soil, also affect how well the tree, shrub, or herb will grow.

APPROXIMATE RANGE OF
AVERAGE ANNUAL MINIMUM
TEMPERATURES FOR EACH ZONE

ZONE 1 BELOW -50°F
ZONE 2 -50° TO -40°
ZONE 3 -40° TO -30°
ZONE 4 -30° TO -20°
ZONE 5 -20° TO -10°
ZONE 6 -10° TO 0°
ZONE 7   0° TO 10°
ZONE 8 10° TO 20°
ZONE 9 20° TO 30°
ZONE 10 30° TO 40°

INDEX

Index

Index

Index

Index